## Acknowledgements

We would like to thank the HEA for its financial support for both the MESMAC project and its evaluation. All members and users of the MESMAC project collaborated in the evaluation process – our work depended on a team effort and without their support at all stages it would not have been possible. We are extremely grateful to them. Our thanks also go to partners, friends and colleagues who provided support and hospitality throughout the research process. Finally we would like to thank all those who have commented on earlier drafts of this book. All its shortcomings are of course our own responsibility.

## The Authors

Alan Prout is Senior Lecturer in the Department of Sociology and Social Anthropology at Keele University and Course Director for the Centre for Medical Social Anthropology.

Katie Deverell is the research and information officer for the HIV Project. She is also registered for a part-time PhD at Keele University, researching the construction of social boundaries in HIV work.

## Acronyms

| | |
|---|---|
| BHAF | Leicester Black HIV/AIDS Forum |
| CLASH | Central London Action on Street Health |
| GMT | Gay Men Tyneside |
| GUM | Genito-urinary medicine |
| LAA | Leeds AIDS Advice |
| MWHSWM | Men who have sex with men |
| RBA | Rent Boy Action |
| SHAKTI | South East Asian Lesbian and Gay Network |
| THT | Terrence Higgins Trust |

# Working with diversity: building communities

## Evaluating the MESMAC project

Alan Prout and Katie Deverell

© Health Education Authority, 1995
Hamilton House
Mabledon Place
London WC1H 9TX

ISBN 1 84557 921 6

Typeset from author-generated discs by BPC-Digital Data (Glasgow) Ltd
Printed in Great Britain by BPC Wheatons Ltd, Exeter

# Contents

## Appendices

# 1 MESMAC: its origin and background

## Introduction

This publication concerns an HEA-funded project called MESMAC, an acronym which stands for 'Men Who Have Sex with Men – Action in the Community'. We as project evaluators undertook three years' intensive study between 1990 and 1993, in collaboration with project members. This book is the result of both our own research and the collective reflections and practical experience of participants in the project.

As evaluators we came to our work for MESMAC both as academics (with backgrounds in social anthropology, sociology and psychology) and as people with more practical experience in HIV work and health education. We have decided to address this account of the project primarily to people involved in the practice and policy of HIV prevention, rather than to fellow social scientists. We believe MESMAC was an important innovation in HIV prevention, being (to our knowledge) the first project to apply a community development approach to men who have sex with men. As such it has garnered a great deal of valuable experience which deserves to be disseminated amongst those working in this field. Addressing this book to managers, front-line workers and others in the HIV field seems to be the quickest way of passing on the experience of MESMAC to those who can make most effective use of it.

Our chosen audience is also one reason for the comprehensive description and analysis that we have aimed at. Our account covers those different aspects of the project which may have some bearing on practice and policy. It includes the underlying rationale for MESMAC, its structure and organisation, the range of initiatives it undertook and men it made contact with, the outcomes it achieved and the methods of working which it adopted and developed. However, we recognise that not all readers will be interested in all aspects of the project and have therefore arranged the chapters so that readers can concentrate on those chapters of most concern to themselves.

Despite focusing our account around HIV policy and practice, we do not intend this book to be a practical guide to doing the kind of work MESMAC accomplished – this has been written up elsewhere (Miller, 1993) and readers will find much there that complements this book. Nor do we provide highly directive policy recommendations, believing these are better worked out by those planning or carrying out work in specific circumstances. Instead we will use our account of MESMAC to draw out and discuss some important underlying themes in the conduct of HIV prevention work with men who have sex with men. We hope these will contribute to policy and practice debate at all levels.

We have tried to avoid unnecessary social science jargon and theorising, introducing them only when we think they cast light on our subject matter in a way that will aid practice and policy development. At the centre of our discussion will be the complex exploration of community, identity and behaviour which MESMAC's work entailed. 'Men Who Have Sex with Men' (MWHSWM) proved to be an extremely diverse category: it included many men who identified as gay, some as bisexual, some who saw themselves as straight, some who felt confused about their sexuality and those who felt they did not need a sexual identity at all. Cutting across these already significant differences of sexual community and identity were other important social divisions (each of which is associated with communities with which individuals may also identify): class, race and ability, for example. We wish to stress that HIV prevention strategies must match this complexity. To achieve this they must be flexible, responsive and rooted in the diverse social contexts that give meaning to sexual behaviour.

Although we have addressed this book to the world of practice and policy, we nevertheless hope that others may draw something useful from it. Fellow social scientists may find it gives some useful examples of the complex interplay between community, identity and behaviour. Evaluation researchers may be interested in the participative and collaborative style of research that we adopted. Community development workers might find some interesting similarities and differences between MESMAC and CD projects in other fields.

## An outline of the MESMAC project

What eventually became MESMAC emerged from discussions within the HEA which started in 1988, and involved HEA officers from what was then the AIDS Division and the Professional and Community Development Division (PCD), together with a number of freelance consultants with extensive professional experience of health education and promotion, community development, and HIV and sexuality work. Central to these discussions was the proposition that HIV infection required a health promotion strategy based on collective action rather than individual behaviour change. Collective action became one of the defining features of MESMAC, although it took the particular form of 'community development' (CD).

By 1989 a proposal to set up a 'demonstration project' with the aim of exploring the value of a community development approach to HIV prevention with men who have sex with men had been developed. Before any further action was taken to fund the proposal it was decided to carry out a consultation with community-based and voluntary organisations already doing HIV prevention work. At a weekend meeting in May 1989 a range of individuals and organisations were brought together to discuss the proposal. At this stage MESMAC might well have been abandoned if the response had been negative. In fact the idea received an extremely positive reception and those at the consultation made a number of recommendations about how the proposal should be developed and implemented.

By March 1990 the core of the project had been established. It consisted of four local project sites in different parts of England, each with a general brief to undertake health needs and development work, including HIV education, with men who have sex with men, within a community development framework. Each local project (see Appendix 1 for staffing) was hosted and managed by an existing organisation; each of these had developed a more specific brief of its own and was staffed in a different way:

*Leeds MESMAC* was based within a voluntary agency, Leeds AIDS Advice (LAA), and focused on men within an urban setting. It had two full-time workers (later increased to three), one of whom was funded by the District Health Authority. It had a steering group composed mostly of LAA members but also including an HIV worker from Sheffield.

*Leicester Black MESMAC* worked with black and ethnic minority communities and was housed and supported by a voluntary agency, Leicester Black HIV/AIDS Forum (BHAF). The project was staffed by two part-time outreach workers, a full-time manager/administrator and a part-time local consultant. The steering group comprised members of BHAF and some of the black men with whom the project had been working.

*MESMAC London* was based at the Terrence Higgins Trust (THT – the UK's largest HIV voluntary organisation) and had a brief to concentrate on the needs of young men. The project was staffed by a full-time administrator and four part-time workers (six hours per week). The local steering group included the project workers and their manager. Two freelance consultants also provided supervision for the workers.

*MESMAC Tyneside* was initially briefed to work with men in an urban setting and its rural hinterland. The latter part of the brief was eventually dropped as impractical. It was hosted by a statutory sector organisation, Newcastle Social Services Department, and was initially based in its Community Support section. It later moved to its own city centre premises. This project had two full-time workers (later increased to three) and a half-time administrator. Its steering committee had members from social services and recruited members of the local gay community.

The four local projects (or 'sites' as they became known) were linked together in a national structure which provided opportunities to exchange ideas and experience, receive support and training, and liaise with the HEA. The national structure went through three different forms over the life of the project (see Chapter 3) but some of its main constituencies remained throughout the project. These were: the project workers from each local site; the managers from the different host organisations responsible for the MESMAC work; the HEA officers; a group known variously as consultants or co-ordinators (comprising the consultants who had been involved in the development and planning of the project with the HEA, later expanded to include others with specific expertise); and ourselves as the evaluation team. The co-ordinators planned and provided training for the project workers, offered support and advice to the local sites and liaised with the HEA officers. The evaluators worked with all the constituent parts of the project, collaborating with them on the development and implementation of evaluation strategies.

MESMAC as a whole set itself two key aims:

(i) To establish local community initiatives with men who have sex with men, to explore felt needs in relation to safer sex and work towards meeting these needs;

(ii) To produce a training package to equip a core team of facilitators to develop this work as a general resource for safer sex work with men who have sex with men in various localities in England.

These aims were spelt out further as a set of objectives:

(i) To recruit and train a group in the facilitation skills necessary for safer sex education as it relates to HIV;

(ii) To set up support for the facilitators in each project locality, for the above work;

(iii) Using community development methods facilitators may:
—assess felt needs in the local gay community;
—work with individuals and groups;
—enable choice and action on safer sex;
—put groups in touch with each other to develop models of good practice;
—assist in the development of individual and group action plans;

(iv) To evaluate the various methods and approaches within the projects and the project as whole;

(v) To enable men who have sex with men to bring their needs to the attention of appropriate bodies and organisations;

(vi) To inform about HIV prevention, local and national referral points and other services.

In the rest of this chapter we will explore some of the background to the project, further detailing some of the issues that were involved in setting the project up. We have divided these into five main headings:

(i)   the rationale for a collective action approach;
(ii)  the political context of the project;
(iii) what is community development and why was it the approach chosen by
MESMAC?
(iv)  are MWHSWM a community?
(v)   evaluating collective action.

# The rationale for a collective action approach

In 1988 the HEA was considering how to supplement its existing safer sex advertising. One possibility was to develop safer sex training sessions. One of the HEA officers had worked in New York and had become aware of the 'eroticising safer sex' model being used there. An outside consultant, Peter Gordon, was, therefore, asked to design and run a workshop to train trainers about safer sex. He felt that an essential first step was to review what was already happening in the UK and elsewhere at the time.

It was this review (Gordon, 1988) that set out the rationale for a collective action rather than an individual behaviour change approach. The review had two aspects. First was an empirical survey: over 70 organisations in the UK and elsewhere were contacted and asked for information about: the aims and objectives of their workshops; the content (programme) of their workshops; the number of workshops and the number of participants; the target groups and recruitment procedures; and the evaluation of their work.

The second component was theoretical: the review utilised a theoretical framework of health education models (French and Adams, 1986) as a way of interpreting and understanding the approaches being taken to current safer sex education workshops. The framework was the result of examining three fundamentally different models: behavioural change; self-empowerment; and collective action. Each of these is characterised (see Table 1) in terms of its aim, model of health, assumptions about people, society and education, characteristic methods of working and evaluation criteria.

Behaviour change was seen as the least effective model of health education and collective action as the most effective, with empowerment models in an intermediate position. This hierarchy was a grounded one, based on existing research on the effectiveness of health education, and social scientific research about the significance of social (rather than individual) determinants of health behaviour and health inequalities.

**Table 1.** From: French, J. and Adams, L. (1986) From Analysis to Synthesis Theories of Health Education, *Health Education Journal*, 1986, 45, 2.

| Model of health education | Behavioural change | Self-empowerment | Collective action |
|---|---|---|---|
| **Aim** | To improve health by changing people's behaviour. | To improve health by developing people's ability to understand and control their health status to whatever extent is possible within their environmental circumstances. | To improve health by changing environmental, social, and economic factors through community involvement and action. |
| **Model of health** | Optimum biological functioning and role performance. | Spiritual, physical, mental, environmental and social harmony. Individual feeling of active well-being. Adaptation, happiness, high self-esteem and positive self-concept. | Health is a socially defined concept related to individual and group norms. Health is a symptom of the interplay between environmental, social and economic influences on the population. |
| **Model of Humanity (Women/Men)** | Rational decision-maker. Mechanistic, knowable animal. Elitist. People are innately bad. | People are spiritual entities struggling for personal fulfilment and are innately good. | People are social animals and rational problem-solvers. People are born value-neutral. |
| **Model of society** | Positivist. Hierarchical and stratified. Ordered by consensus and conformity. Mechanistic in functioning. Operates according to universal mechanistic laws. Elitist groups guard and develop the society's high culture. Change brought about through slow evolution. | Humanist. Society is organic, plant or animal-like in nature. Society interacts with the environment and varies with time and place. Society is in a state of constant change and review and is not governed by universal laws. | Materialist. Conflict between factions and various interests is the driving force of society. Society is dynamic and ever-changing. |
| **Model of education** | Classical humanist. Education is an assimilative process and is geared to the acceptance of pre-defined knowledge values and standards. Educated people contribute to the ordered development of society. | Progressivist. Education is primarily about discovery and experience, through which growth is attained. Education should encourage people to question, reform and change their society. | Reconstructionist. Education is one of the main agents of change in society, and is concerned with the development of 'better' citizens. Education is a social process pursued through project problem-solving and discovery. Education aims to renew society. |
| **Example of methods** | Propaganda. Mass media and mass participation. Attitude modification. Behaviour modification. Self-management techniques. Administrative and legislative change. | Lifeskills training. Value clarification. Self-help groups (coping). Counselling. Pastoral care and the promotion of self-esteem. | Advocacy. Knowledge and conciousness-raising campaigns. Self-help groups (campaigning). Community action. Pressure groups. Popular legislation. Administrative change. Economic change. |
| **Examples of evaluation criteria** | Compliance rates, mortality and morbidity rates. Knowledge increase, attitude change, behavioural change. Externally assessed. | Improved self-esteem, improved lifeskills, improved understanding, improved decision-making. Improvement often self-assessed. | Morbidity and mortality rates, knowledge increase, attitude change, increased involvement in action for health. Externally assessed. |

## Individual behaviour change

In spite of some differences in style, method and expressed aims, it was clear from other data (such as the evaluation criteria used) that the ultimate goal of the majority of safer sex work was to improve health by changing individual behaviour. In fact, five years later, this remains the predominant model.

It was argued that this emphasis on behaviour change was understandable since the health crisis of the time put a premium on action rather than theoretical debate; individual behaviour change seemed obvious, tangible, desirable and demonstratively achievable. Since many, if not most, of those involved in the work had little background in health education it was not surprising that they were doing this work without a clear theoretical base.

Peter Gordon mobilised a number of powerful and well-founded arguments against a reliance on the behaviour change approach:

(i)  that individual behaviour may be of far less significance in determining health than the complex interplay of social and economic circumstances (Townsend and Davidson, 1982; French and Adams, 1986; Locker, 1991);

(ii)  that evaluation research shows that behaviour change in health education is not particularly effective (Gatherer et al, 1979);

(iii)  that studies showed that a high proportion of gay men participating in safer sex education had changed their behaviour prior to taking part in educational activities (see, for example, Quadland et al, 1987);

(iv)  that there are ethical dilemmas connected with behaviour change – for example, its assumption that what counts as desirable behaviour is obvious and agreed upon, and its tendency to focus only on the benefits of adopting the prescribed behaviour, ignoring the costs for individuals and communities (Engel, 1978; Beattie, 1991);

(vi)  that a narrow focus on individuals tends to lead to victim-blaming (Crawford, 1977);

(vii)  that there is a tendency to view sexuality in purely individualistic terms, ignoring the social, cultural and political contexts which give meaning to particular sexual behaviours within gay male and bisexual communities (Silin, 1987);

(viii)  that US research indicated that gay men engaging in high-risk behaviours were more likely to be younger, less educated, have lower incomes and be members of ethnic minority groups.

In short, the arguments used by French and Adams to place behaviour change as the lowest level of health education, were seen as having a direct corollary in relation to HIV prevention.

## Self-empowerment

The review saw self-empowerment models as a definite improvement on behaviour change. By being participant-centred, rather than 'teacher'-centred, these were seen as encouraging participants to take responsibility for their own learning. If well and authentically done, self-empowerment was seen as a useful first step which could enable people to become more confident.

Nevertheless, inadequacies in the approach were identified and applied to HIV and safer sex education. Three major problems were highlighted: self-empowerment could be misused by masking the outcomes desired by the educator, thus becoming a form of manipulation; the social causes of dis-empowerment (and ill-health) tend to be ignored in self-empowerment models and the focus remains on the individual; participation in learning, therefore, needs to be accompanied by participation in the decision-making processes that affect everyday life.

Self-empowerment approaches were, therefore, seen as only a partial step forward. Educational groups could be seen as a learning medium within which gay men might begin to break isolation and low self-esteem where it exists and take steps towards a positive gay identity, which, according to some studies (Patton, 1985) was strongly associated with the ability to respond effectively to the health crisis. Such groups could also be a way of identifying collective needs and making the step to collective action to change social conditions. Self-empowerment should, it was argued, be linked with action to address and change the social forces that shape and give meaning to individual behaviour.

## Collective action

The San Francisco STOP AIDS Project was considered (and eventually rejected) as a possible model for the collective action approach. It was recognised that the size, visibility, cohesion and political power of the San Francisco gay community made it very different from anything in the UK. Moreover, whilst any collective action model in the UK would include the kind of grassroots mobilisation methods used by STOP AIDS, it might not rely so much on individual behaviour change and give more weight to various forms of political action.

Peter Gordon's review came to some broad conclusions about future safer sex education:

(i) that it was timely to move towards a collective action model;
(ii) greater clarity of aims was needed;
(iii) consistency between aims and methods was needed;
(iv) the focus needed to be widened to include the social context of safer sex;
(v) training for safer sex workers was essential.

The MESMAC proposal drawn up in March 1989 was directly based on these recommendations. The collective action objective was itself placed in the much wider context of working with local gay communities to define their needs. The project proposal clearly ruled out prejudging what men needed, presenting instead a wide range of methods to explore with people in particular localities what their needs might be and work with them to try and meet them. It linked this work with bringing its results to the attention of relevant organisations and services. MESMAC was intended to explore the possibilities of collective action and accumulate experience of it that could be disseminated to others.

# The political context of the project

As with all other areas of HIV/AIDS work, MESMAC developed within a political context. One extremely important dimension of this context was the largely oppositional relationship between gay communities and the official institutions of government. The history of intolerance and repression experienced by gay people (especially in Britain, which compared to many societies of the industrial world has some of the least tolerant laws regulating sexual behaviour) has led to their creation of separate subcultures and organisations and a general mistrust of official interventions. When it comes to HIV prevention, these are frequently met with scepticism from many sections of the gay community, who prefer self-reliance and separateness to alliance-forming and persuasion to self-government. Others, however, are more ready to contribute to policy formation and help shape how government resources (especially those given to HIV/AIDS work) are used, despite the potential for surveillance and control that this risks.

More specifically, MESMAC was a phenomenon of what might be described as the second phase of the social reaction to the HIV epidemic in Britain. The first phase, which ended around 1987, has been well documented (for example, Weatherburn et al, 1992; and Weeks, 1989). The widespread (and continuing) fear and prejudice about AIDS which found expression in both unofficial circles (for example in media coverage) and in official indifference at a policy level was juxtaposed with the grassroots response of gay communities and other AIDS activists who began, in the face of government inaction, to build support and care systems and organise preventive education (Patton, 1985). By the mid-1980s links had been formed with sections of the health professions and influential policy advisers and this alliance was, by 1987, able to establish AIDS as an important matter for public health policy (Berridge, 1992).

MESMAC was part of this policy response. The HEA assumed its remit for AIDS public education work near the end of 1987. The years of official inaction had, however, left a legacy of mistrust especially among AIDS activists, gay communities, and HIV/AIDS voluntary organisations (as well as ethnic minority groups, which we discuss below). The contemporary government's mass media campaign was criticised for its emphasis on scare tactics, its moralising undertones and the inaccuracy of some of its messages (Watney, 1987, 1988; Carter and Watney, 1989). In particular there were many demands that the absence of a prevention programme for gay men be remedied (King, 1993a). Partly in response to these pressures the HEA set up, using the then fashionable terminology, a Men Who Have Sex With Men (MWHSWM) Programme. MESMAC was one important part of this programme.

It was recognised by the HEA officers and consultants that most of the previous HIV/AIDS work with MWHSWM had come from outside the statutory agencies. Individuals and groups, mostly within the gay community, had organised their own literature and begun to educate each other. Any HEA project had to acknowledge the value of this work and consult those already active in the field. It was agreed that MESMAC would not go ahead if existing HIV/safer sex organisations did not want it. This was not only a sign of the sensitive political environment within which the project was formed but also a measure of the seriousness with which the concept of community participation in decision-making was taken.

The result was an initial consultation (known as 'The Forum') that took place in May 1989. About 30 people from a wide range of organisations (see Appendix 2) were invited to a weekend meeting. The general opinion from the forum participants was that the project should be supported. A variety of recommendations were made, including those on: groups that should be targeted by the project; job descriptions for CD workers; recruitment procedures; a management structure for the project as a whole.

It was suggested that there be a balanced range of projects taking into account the following factors:

   (i)  geographical spread;
   (ii)  rural and urban areas;
   (iii)  unorganised as well as organised gay scenes;
   (iv)  affluent and working class areas;
   (vi)  ethnic minority populations.

It was also suggested that a London-based project should only be included if the HEA made funding available for four or more sites. If London was included it was thought it should target young men new to the gay scene as these were thought to be in a vulnerable position.

Criteria for selecting local bases were discussed in some detail and it was suggested that hosts should be able to meet a quite stringent set of requirements, including the ability to provide administrative, material and managerial support. It was particularly suggested that there should be a range of host organisations inside and outside the voluntary sector. Special care should be taken to avoid overburdening small voluntary organisations and jeopardising their established work.

Funding by the HEA was agreed in the summer of 1989. In August 1989 a further meeting was held to decide on the parts of the country and the host organisations who would be asked to develop proposals to manage a local MESMAC initiative.

One of the criteria suggested by the forum was that ethnic minority men who have sex with men should be a target group. In fact representatives from two black HIV-related organisations (the Black HIV and AIDS Network and Blackliners) were invited to the Forum. The individuals concerned, however, felt that more organisations should have been approached and that they could not be expected to represent the various ethnic minority groups. A difficult meeting, in June 1988 (see Appendix 2), underlined that the experience of racism and lack of cultural sensitivity (especially in the health services, see Dada, 1990; McNaught, 1988) meant that trust was at a minimum. Nevertheless those consulted decided to support the project with the proviso that a black sub-group was set up to advise it.

It is clear that the political environment shaped both the MESMAC project itself and the processes by which it was developed. Those who initiated MESMAC took pains to consult HIV/AIDS organisations, and gay and ethnic minority groups. The experience also hinted that really quite different contexts and processes might be involved in working with gay and ethnic minority communities (see Bardill, 1993). In fact as we will show (see especially Chapter 6) MESMAC has demonstrated that there are significant differences (as well as overlaps) between targeting black and white men who have sex with men.

## What is community development?

Early in the development of MESMAC it was decided that the form of collective action on which it would be based was that of community development. The definition of community is notoriously difficult. In the immediate post and pre-war period, for example, there was a thriving tradition of community studies which eventually foundered on (amongst other things) an inability to provide a satisfactory definition of what might be meant by community (Bell and Newby, 1971). Many social scientists reject the concept as not only too imprecise to be analytically useful but also because it can be used to hide social divisions and differences of interest. Some community development practitioners have made the same criticism (Lees and Smith, 1975; Green and Chapman, 1992).

Nevertheless, the term continues to be used widely – perhaps because it has such flexibility of meaning. A common way of dealing with these problems has been to adopt a 'working' definition of community such as that proposed by Smithies and Adams, 1990:

> *People with a basis of common interest and network of personal interaction, grouped either on the basis of locality or a specific shared concern or both.*

From the point of view of community development workers it has the advantage of allowing practical work to happen without waiting for theoretical questions to be solved completely. It also suggests that a sense of community need not only be based on geographical location and opens the way to work with interest-based groups such as women and gay men.

There are several different definitions of community development (for example: Martin, 1990; Smithies, 1991; Sheffield Health Authority, 1993). Rather than something that can be given a water-tight definition, CD is perhaps best seen as a way of working, informed by certain principles, which encourages people to identify common concerns and supports them in taking action related to them. When MESMAC was established the HEA's own definition included the following principles of working (Smithies and Adams, 1990):

(i)   with groups rather than individuals;
(ii)  prioritising disadvantaged and marginalised groups;
(iii) encouraging a positive holistic view of health;
(iv)  aiming to increase self-confidence;
(vi)  aiming to improve relationships between professionals and voluntary and statutory groups, although it may also challenge statutory organisations to meet needs;
(vii) the community defining its own needs rather than receiving a professionally presented list of needs;
(viii) the process of work is seen as important in its own right;
(ix)  valuing people whatever their background, starting from where they are, and challenging discriminatory or oppressive behaviour from individuals or bureaucracies;
(x)   promoting access to information and resources.

It is important at this point to distinguish community development from community-based work, of which there are many varieties. Community-based outreach, for example, has been increasingly used in relation to HIV, especially when particular groups (for example drug users) are seen as vulnerable but hard to reach. Work is initiated which aims to reach individuals outside the formal setting of an agency (a clinic, for example) by contacting people in the settings of their everyday life, on the streets, or in pubs and cafes, or a housing estate, or in prisons, hostels or youth clubs. Contact might be followed up by providing individuals with health information or other resources (such as condoms or syringe cleansing equipment) and trying to attract them into the services that are available.

One key difference between this sort of work and community development is that CD aims to work collectively rather than with individuals. CD may start with individuals but it aims at helping individuals to group together to take collective action. Another difference is that CD is prepared to take on changing social conditions and services if that is what is seen by groups and communities to be appropriate.

As we shall show (see Chapter 7), coming to terms with these principles and translating them into practice took some time. A milestone in the process, however, was the introduction into the project of a somewhat sharper and more clearly stated CD strategy (Sheffield Health Authority, 1992).

> *Grassroots work* Resourcing grassroots work and local action was seen as a central element of CD work, often being the work that starts first. In the case of MESMAC it involved building on the shared experiences of local MWHSWM and working with them to find solutions to their problems as they defined them themselves. A great deal of MESMAC work (see Chapter 4) could be seen as fitting into this heading.

> *Organisational development* If project work remained at grassroots level, the strategy suggested, then it would be inadequate to bring about social change (for example, the type of health services provided or the way they were provided). A CD project therefore had to find ways of articulating needs (as they came out of grassroots and other work) and stimulate organisations to change in response. This might be done by winning participation in decision-making processes, lobbying and campaigning, and giving training.

> *Community infrastructure* All the above activities could be carried out in ways that established networks of individuals and groups which could collectivise experience and act together. A key aim here is to establish some durable resource and organisation which might continue to be effective even if the project itself ends.

> *Participation* Important to each of these was the notion that MWHSWM should become involved in the MESMAC project itself, being part of its structure and taking part in its decision-making processes.

Because this strategic formulation played a very important role in what was accomplished by the project, we will return to each of these elements when we look in detail at the development of MESMAC, its methods of working and the outcomes of the project.

## Why community development?

As we indicated earlier, MESMAC was one of the first attempts to bridge the gap between governmental institutions and community-based gay and AIDS/HIV organisations. The tension between these, which we discussed earlier, can be seen throughout the history of CD as a whole. As Webster (1989: 1-2) has pointed out:

> *The history of Community Development in this country is a dynamic one, involving initiatives from outside of particular communities and initiatives that have developed from within them...the practical and theoretical development of Community Development can be seen as a spectrum embodying contradictory elements: the push for change within communities themselves, including social movements, and the pressure from outside those communities, notably from central or local government, to control dissent and shape the future.*

One way of looking at this would be to see contemporary CD theory as a specific professional ideology (Johnson, 1972). In the post-war period community development has grown as a service sector occupation with a clear professionalising dimension. As such it occupies, and has constructed ways of handling, exactly this space between 'bottom-up', autonomous, grassroots activities and 'top-down' initiatives from both government and voluntary organisations. To the grassroots CD promises a way of influencing official attitudes and policies and access to public resources; to officialdom it presents ways of relating more effectively and realistically with difficult client groups and hitherto intractable social problems, as well as a route to 'public participation' and meeting 'consumer need', which emerged as powerful themes in the social policy of the 1980s.

CD is not the only form of collective action (Homans and Aggleton, 1988). Overtly political groups in the HIV field such as ACT-UP are also based in the grassroots and take collective action. Such groups are, however, entirely oppositional to government and other official institutions such as the pharmaceuticals industry. They have been able to collectivise action in the form of radical political protest and calls for sweeping social changes. Because CD occupies a more ambiguous position, somewhere between government and communities, it offers a different way of working, with social change achieved through more domesticated means. It does not, for example, eschew campaigns to change service provision but tends to advocate less dramatic forms of protest (such as lobbying or winning representation in the decision-making of statutory organisations). This point should not be seen as criticising either form of collective action, but recognising their different positions. Because MESMAC brought together a range of different people and organisations (a government agency, freelance professionals, statutory and voluntary sector organisations, front-line workers who identified with gay and black communities, and academic researchers) CD was an appropriate way of working to adopt.

## Are MWHSWM a community?

The term 'men who have sex with men' was a product of attempts in the mid-1980s to break down the misleading stereotype of AIDS as a 'gay plague'. One of the main advantages of the term MWHSWM was that it recognised that sexual self-identity is not a good guide to actual sexual practice. It encompasses a wide range of individuals who may have in common some sexual behaviours which place them at risk without sharing an identity. But this very advantage creates a problem: individuals who may have common sexual practices do not necessarily share a sense of belonging to a community. The concept of MWHSWM put together at least two possibly quite distinct groups: men who identified as gay, some (perhaps most) of whom might not take an active part in gay communities, but for whom those communities were important points of reference and/or sources of identity; men who had sex with men but who did not identify as gay (for example, seeing themselves as bisexual or heterosexual, or not having a distinct sexual identity at all).

Whilst it was clear that CD was at least feasible as a way of working with gay men (and much community-based HIV prevention had already been done by grassroots organisations), it was not at all clear whether or how community development might work with behaviourally-defined MWHSWM.

To say this is not a criticism of the project's rationale. The concept of MWHSWM was the current orthodoxy at the time the project was started (although circumstances changed later – see Davies, 1992; Scott, 1993) and it was quite reasonable to adopt this perspective. It was recognised that working with gay men was likely to be different from working with men who did not identify as gay. In any case MESMAC was set up to explore whether, how and with what outcomes CD approaches could be adopted for work with the different groups of men falling under the general behavioural term of MWHSWM.

From the outset therefore MESMAC was working with a fundamental tension – as a CD project it was rooted in the idea of working within the context of community and yet it incorporated terminology based around sexual practice, rather than identity. The 'community' to which it referred in its title (MWHSWM), and towards whom the project was targeted, was not defined in community terms at all.

These issues were particularly important given that MESMAC was an HIV project. Much organising in the West around HIV/AIDS has arisen from within, and continues to be resourced and supported by, lesbian and gay communities. This has led some to argue that the response to HIV/AIDS has strengthened the lesbian and gay community, providing it with a powerful motivating and organising force (Altman, 1986:102 and Plummer, 1988). Such community responses were necessary because official institutions were unconcerned. However, in addition to this mobilising tendency the impact of HIV can be seen to have had a more fragmenting effect, as the realities of the epidemic have highlighted the boundaries of, and diversity within, communities (Murray, 1992). This has refocused debates about identity and practice and raised questions about the inclusiveness of community. As Patton notes:

*Activists and educators, too, find themselves confronted with the disparity between notions of communities and the realities of sex and drug practices. The notion of 'community' required adherence to identity categories; yet AIDS activists were increasingly concerned to delink practices and identity, so that for example men-having-sex-with-men could recognize the risks involved without having to reorganize their identity and claim to be gay. (1990:8)*

The inclusiveness of lesbian and gay communities has also been challenged with regard to race and gender in relation to support, prevention and service provision (Patton, 1990; Altman, 1986:94; Dada, 1990), for example through the neglect of the needs of black MWHSWM by gay community-based groups. The social response to HIV has therefore served to highlight differences and brought into focus the multiplicity of identity. Working within the context of HIV and being a CD project for MWHSWM, MESMAC was clearly enmeshed in debates concerning identity, practice, community and diversity, and the work continually engaged with these issues. Many discussions within MESMAC (especially at the site level) grappled with them as different ways of working were tried out. As time went by these debates also started to take place in other organisations and countries (see, for example: Bartos et al, 1993; Prestage and Hood, 1993) and began to emerge as important issues for HIV prevention in the 1990s.

Clearly there was an important question for the evaluation of MESMAC: to what extent would a CD approach prove appropriate to HIV prevention with the different categories of men included in the term MWHSWM? It is one to which we will return throughout the book as we unfold the evidence we have gathered, and forms an important part of our concluding discussion (see Chapter 10). We will argue that MESMAC uncovered a great deal of diversity both within gay communities and between gay-identifying and non gay-identifying men. Its great strength was that the CD strategy allowed it the flexibility to work with this diversity.

# Evaluation

Finally we turn to the problem of evaluating MESMAC. The details of our methodology and our role in the project will be described in Chapters 2 and 3. At this point we will limit ourselves to explaining why our approach was different from that used in much health education, including much HIV prevention.

The fundamental point is that MESMAC was a distinctively collective action project and therefore required an appropriate evaluation. As we suggested earlier, despite the availability of alternative approaches most HIV prevention (and much health education more generally) takes an individual behaviour change approach. The mode of evaluation characteristically linked to such work also focuses on individual behaviour change. Often using quasi-experimental designs (involving pre- and post-testing, and experimental and control groups) such research is concerned to establish how much individual behaviour change can be attributed to what type of health education intervention. In fact such research designs are notoriously difficult to achieve and are fraught with methodological difficulties (Fitzpatrick et al, 1989; Kotarba and Lang, 1986). It was, however, not so much these difficulties as the straightforward *inapplicability* of individual behaviour change questions which determined the development of our approach (see also Harris, 1992). MESMAC did not aim at directly bringing about individual behaviour change and we did not, therefore, evaluate it in those terms.

Instead we asked a series of questions which taken together form a full (if not strictly comprehensive) account of MESMAC's outcomes (what the project achieved) and its processes (how it achieved them). When it came to outcomes of the project we put the emphasis on the collective dimension – especially building community infrastructures and bringing about organisational development. We also asked users of the project what they felt their involvement had given them. Occasionally this included individual behavioural change but, as we shall show, much more important were outcomes such as knowledge, access to resources, increased self-confidence and a sense of working together with others.

The questions that we set out to answer can be grouped as follows, and in fact map out the contents of this book:

- how MESMAC was structured and organised at local and national level. In particular, we were concerned to see how the project might bring together its different constituencies and show what could be learnt from this experience. Chapter 3 deals with these issues.

- the methods of working that the project workers used and developed. Although the CD approach has a history, MESMAC was an innovative application to HIV and MWHSWM. How would the general perspective be translated into practical working methods? Which methods would prove useful and which less so? Chapter 4 covers these points and Chapter 7 discusses some of the issues that arose in developing work at a local level.

- determining whom MESMAC made contact with and what the patterns of contact were. If possible we wanted to compare MESMAC as a CD project with other approaches. This is dealt with in Chapter 5.

- the needs of MWHSWM. What would be the character and range of the needs that users of the project identified? Chapter 6 discusses these in detail.

- the impact of the project on the individual men contacted by MESMAC and the impact at a collective level. Chapters 8 and 9 cover these questions.

# Summary

In this chapter we have:

*defined the aim of this book as addressing the practice and policy implications of the MESMAC project's experience and work;

*given a brief sketch of MESMAC;

*set out the rationale for a collective action approach to work with men who have sex with men;

*analysed the political context within which the project was formed;

*set out the basics of community development and suggested its appropriateness as a form of collective action for the MESMAC project;

*pointed to an interesting tension in MESMAC's work between a behaviourally-defined target group (MWHSWM) and community development;

*set out some of the questions asked in the evaluation research and explained the particular focus of our evaluation on collective work.

# 2 Evaluating the MESMAC project

## Introduction

Evaluation was an integral part of the project and took place at all levels. We matched the evaluation methodology to the CD principles of MESMAC itself, taking a basically collaborative approach. Rather than treating evaluation as something imposed from the outside we saw it as a task that every member of the project could play some role in.

This chapter discusses the principles and practice of our methodology. It begins with a discussion of the theoretical principles, describing how these were incorporated into an evaluation strategy tailored to the needs of the project. We then discuss how this strategy was implemented through: building relationships with project participants; training and facilitating project workers in evaluation procedures; collaborating on project records and information-keeping; and balancing this with our need to take an independent view of the project. We go on to describe how the strategy was reviewed, developed and modified as the work progressed. In the second part of the chapter we discuss some of the issues and problems that arose in the course of our work.

## Designing an evaluation strategy

The evaluation strategy was closely tailored to the specific character of the MESMAC project and reflected many of the project's guiding principles. It was argued that the approach had to be consistent with the overall philosophy of the project and responsive to its developmental way of working (see Prout, 1992). The nature of the project impacted on the evaluation design in several ways:

(i) Evaluation was seen to play an important role in drawing out the lessons of the project and it should therefore be as comprehensive and as rigorous as possible.

(ii) Given that MESMAC was such a challenging project, it was thought that the evaluation should not add to the difficulties. This did not imply an unwillingness to criticise MESMAC, rather it entailed that evaluation should be *formative* as well as *summative*, supplying constructive criticism throughout the project as well as making overall judgements at the end.

(iii) A comprehensive evaluation meant that several, distinct but not separate, evaluations needed to be bundled together: the national one, focusing mainly on strategic decisions made when setting up and maintaining the project; and the local projects and their different areas of work. Combining these levels into a coherent whole was clearly a complex task.

(iv) The evaluation was required to be one of process as well as outcome. We recognised that the most telling weakness of outcome-only evaluation is that it assesses without explaining. The lessons that can be drawn from it are therefore very limited (Stenhouse, 1975; Hamilton, 1977). In the case of MESMAC a description of processes and practices was vital – at all levels of the project but especially so in the case of the local work. This meant taking account of the 'how' and 'why' of practice: why the project was conducted the way it was, what obstacles were met and how they were overcome, and what resources were needed for success.

(v) Two types of outcome were needed. On the one hand some basic, pre-given and standard information was required in relation to all the different areas of work we expected the project to generate; for example, information was collected about the number of clients/users who became involved in a particular initiative. On the other hand the diversity of work that the project was expected to produce meant that we had to leave room for outcomes which were unplanned and emergent, or simply specific to the type of work.

# Illuminative evaluation

The evaluation design was firmly based in what is sometimes referred to as the 'illuminative tradition' of evaluation research. As Aggleton and Moody write:

> *This alternative approach...tries to identify how the various elements of a health education programme were perceived and understood by those involved. It thereby aims to interpret and illuminate how and why particular outcomes were brought about. Ethnographic research methods are the ones most often used in order to do this. (1992:16)*

As well as drawing on our own previous research experience and matching our preferences in terms of research style, there were some underlying political reasons for constructing the evaluation within an illuminative framework. In 1989, as officialdom became interested in HIV prevention, evaluation had moved further up the agenda of HIV/AIDS work. The process had, however, not been without resistance, suspicion or, at the very least, ambiguity. Broadly speaking the further up the (formal or informal) hierarchies of organisations that one went, the greater was the enthusiasm for 'evaluation'. Conversely, among front-line workers anxiety about 'evaluation' was at its highest, especially in relation to concerns about surveillance and control.

Such responses were entirely understandable given the purposes and ethos of much evaluation research, which has been severely criticised (Prior, 1989). However, evaluation researchers (especially in the field of education) have made a powerful critique of the dominant paradigm and, going beyond mere critique, have developed alternatives to it. These alternatives are far from having resolved the many dilemmas which evaluation poses but they do at least engage with dominant approaches, contesting the terrain it seeks to monopolise. They do so by suggesting methods of evaluation more subtle (and therefore more adequate to complex fields of activity such as health care and education) and more open to the many different viewpoints and interests that are represented there. Their promise is to allow other perspectives, especially those of grassroots workers, to have a voice in evaluation. They pay far more attention to contextual and 'political' factors, such as the adequacy of resources, pressures from competing demands on workers' time, and needs around professional development. Their general strategy is to examine processes (how and why work is done) as well as outcomes of work.

In the health services these alternatives have not found much expression (but see Smith and Cantley, 1985), while in social work (Lishman, 1984) and, most markedly, in education, oppositional approaches have a considerable history and tradition (Stenhouse, 1975; Hamilton et al, 1977).

The evaluation of MESMAC was informed by the fieldwork (or ethnographic) tradition of social research (see Burgess, 1984 and Hammersley and Atkinson, 1983). At the centre of this methodology is a great deal of direct contact with the participants in a social situation – in this case the four local MESMAC sites and the various aspects of the national organisation. However, ethnography is a multi-method approach combining participant observation with the whole range of data production methods (including, for example, document analysis, formal and informal interviewing, and questionnaires). The fieldwork approach gave us the flexibility we needed in a project as open-ended as MESMAC.

The strategy adopted had several consequences for our own role as evaluators. We were committed to working in ways that were collaborative and participative. We clearly had a role in supporting the evaluation activity of the project participants but in addition we were to act as independent moderators, taking a more detached and critical point of view. However, this detachment did not mean that we claimed to have a superhuman 'objective' or 'neutral' viewpoint. We were clearly participants with a distinct role in the project as a whole and were enmeshed in its network of relationships.

Since MESMAC was set up as a multi-level, diverse and complex project it was important to avoid planning too rigid an evaluation strategy. This was particularly the case because, as both a demonstration and a CD project, many outcomes and plans for work were emergent rather than predefined. The aim was therefore to be flexible and responsive to the actual work done by the project. This meant that the detailed implementation and elaboration of the strategy was done as the project unfolded. However, the development of evaluation was guided by the principles and methods outlined above.

# Implementing and developing the evaluation

Because of various delays within the project the evaluation began later than planned. Initially the work was carried out by Alan Prout until the appointment of Katie Deverell as evaluation fieldworker in May 1990. From then on Katie Deverell carried out the great bulk of the work and Alan Prout supervised, helped to plan and occasionally took part in fieldwork. This basic pattern changed from October 1992 to April 1993 when we both worked full-time on the evaluation.

Throughout the project we worked collaboratively, albeit with different roles. We planned and discussed the progression of the work, the different views and experiences of those in the project, contemporary gay and HIV politics and their impact on the project, and various themes and ideas emerging from the data. In addition to these more reflective and analytical discussions a lot of time was spent on practical and administrative tasks, such as planning and organising data collection and discussing the best methods to use. A variety of methods was needed, both qualitative and quantitative. We maintained a flexible and responsive approach using the methods that seemed most appropriate for the task involved, providing that they:

—produced appropriate data;
—made reasonably efficient use of resources;
—dovetailed with ongoing evaluation by project workers;
—provided reasonably quick feedback;
—did not harm project work.

We have split our account of the practicalities of evaluation work into various phases: a first implementation stage; a review period; a second implementation phase; and the final writing up of the project. These are shown schematically in Table 2.

# MESMAC evaluation – phase 1

The main tasks in this phase were establishing relationships with project members, training, and establishing mechanisms for recording the work of the project, collecting data and beginning to decide where to focus the evaluation.

**Table 2.** Phases of the MESMAC Evaluation.

| PHASE | MAIN ACTIVITIES | MAIN OUTCOMES |
|---|---|---|
| **Design** | Deciding basic approach<br>Discussions with HEA,<br>co-ordinators and managers | Evaluation proposal |
| **One** | Building relationships<br>Evaluation training | Evaluation guidelines |
| | Site visits<br>Recording local work<br>Evaluating specific<br>initiatives | Initiation report<br>Feedback<br>Local project<br>Records |
| | Report writing | Working papers |
| **Review** | Consulting project members<br>Reflecting on experience | Clarifying relationships<br>More emphasis on outcomes<br>Self-evaluation projects |
| **Two** | As Phase One, plus Impact<br>studies | Working papers |
| | Self-evaluation | Condom distribution report |
| | | Section in DIY Guide |
| **Final** | Writing up<br>Consultation on drafts | This book |

## Building up relationships

The importance of evaluation was established from the start of the project and everyone in the project had a commitment and responsibility to undertake evaluation in their own work while also participating in the overall evaluation. One of our first tasks was to explain the evaluation to project members and ensure that they understood the purpose and nature of our approach.

It was clear that fruitful relationships between ourselves and the different participants in the project depended upon openness and negotiation at all stages and levels of the project. It was proposed, therefore, that all aspects of the evaluation (including criteria used, methods and processes, provisional conclusions etc.) be made public to all project participants. We gave regular reports on our work, sent out our work plans and invited discussion of them.

As different participants had different needs in relation to the evaluation, methods of working, goals and interpretations must be negotiated. For example, we found that the project workers were keen to have detailed evaluations of the work they had done, covering both successes and failures. The HEA officers and co-ordinators, on the other hand, wanted shorter reports that stressed successful work.

In addition we emphasised the importance of confidentiality and informed consent; mechanisms for feedback and reporting within the project as a whole were discussed early on. It was agreed that information would not be disseminated outside the project without the prior consent of those involved, giving project participants the opportunity to negotiate the way that information was reported. This book is itself a result of such a process.

The majority of project members saw the importance of evaluation and were pleased that it was going to be integrated from the start. By the end of the project most were positive about the evaluation, with several members citing it as one of the project's strengths. Initially, however, there was some suspicion as to the purpose of evaluation and many were concerned that it would be merely tokenistic, with no impact on the HEA. The workers were particularly concerned that evaluation would be used as a form of surveillance by the HEA and this was frequently mentioned in our initial discussions with them.

It was, therefore, important for us to establish our independence and to reassure all project members that our aim was for an evaluation that was as honest, comprehensive and useful as possible. This also meant establishing our commitment to reporting the work and views of the HEA officers, managers and co-ordinators as well as the workers.

## Drawing up working guidelines with workers

As one of the main principles of the evaluation strategy was that the formal evaluation should be integrated with the evaluation activities carried out by the local project workers, it was crucial for us to build up good relationships and trust with them. Much of this happened through the course of the project as we worked together and got to know each other. However, we also put a lot of work into explaining our role and negotiating guidelines for working together at the start. In addition to talking with the workers at training weekends and in site visits we decided to draw up a document outlining our mutual roles and responsibilities. This process resulted in a set of guidelines which covered the following areas:

(i) commitment to the importance of evaluation within the project;
(ii) incorporating evaluation into the work of local projects;

(iii) procedures for regular communication between evaluators and local projects and the joint planning of evaluation activities;

(iv) procedures for feedback from the evaluators and for the incorporation of the workers' views in evaluation reports;

(v) procedures for obtaining informed consent, access and permission to use data from the project;

(vi) procedures for confidentiality and the security of evaluation material;

(vii) procedures for the negotiation and discussion of evaluation reports;

(viii) commitment to the fullest possible reporting of the project.

In retrospect what was important was not adherence to the letter of the procedures agreed but rather that time and effort was put into the discussion of guidelines. This established a level of trust which, with some inevitable ups and downs, was sustained throughout the project. This process also helped the workers to feel reassured about our approach and understand the value of evaluation in developing their own work.

Establishing the importance of evaluation did not always mean that it was in fact consistently undertaken by the workers (see below), but we did enjoy friendly and co-operative relations with them throughout the project. The guidelines were also very useful to us since they helped to establish clear practical mechanisms through which to carry out our work.

## Evaluation training

We recognised early on that in order for project workers to undertake evaluation they would need appropriate practical skills and support. In July 1990 the evaluators ran a training weekend for the workers, giving a basic introduction to evaluation concepts and technique. The sessions were a mixture of talks, discussions and activities and covered: definitions and types of evaluation; skills needed in evaluation; methods of collecting evaluation material (especially project records, diaries and designing questionnaires); and planning evaluation.

Projects were provided with a reading list on evaluation and a checklist of issues to think about when planning it. The weekend helped to demystify evaluation and encourage workers to see how it could be of benefit to their work.

This training was followed up at various points throughout the next year and in November 1991, about halfway through the project, a further half-day review of evaluation was done and some specific training in self-evaluation methods was given.

In some ways more important, however, were the ongoing discussions between the evaluators (especially the evaluation fieldworker) and the local projects, which provided a kind of on-the-job training (see overleaf).

# Recording local work

One of the first tasks in building relationships with the local workers was to find ways to keep in touch with developments in their work and to record what they were doing. This involved deciding with the workers where to focus the evaluation, tracking the progress of the work and providing assistance in designing evaluation sheets, monitoring forms and other project records.

We were particularly concerned to share the records that were being kept, where possible. This meant, for example, that we would use the results of the workers' own evaluation (with participants' consent) and workers would use our records and information to write reports on their own work, or to prepare funding bids. The first step for us, however, was to establish record-keeping and find ways to keep it updated.

## Site visits

The evaluation fieldworker regularly visited the sites and held in-depth discussions with the workers about their work and the issues involved. The content of these interviews varied according to what was happening locally and nationally at the time but the topics covered included such things as: initiatives undertaken and the issues, successes and difficulties involved; the successes and difficulties of using a CD approach; the men who had been met and their needs; the national structure and co-ordination; training; relationships with managers and the host organisation; evaluation; relationships with the HEA and the impact of local and national structures and politics. The interviews were semi-structured and audio-recorded. Each interview was transcribed and sent back to those involved to alter or add to if appropriate. Sometimes this feedback was used to highlight areas which projects could usefully think about or develop, or sought further information. This feedback was also used as a basis for further interviews, for example by following up pertinent issues.

In the first phase of the project sites were visited on average every two months since it was important to have regular contact with the project workers and keep up to date with the way that the work was developing (see Appendix 3). This process helped maintain relationships and enabled us to gain a good understanding of the context of the work.

Site visits also enabled us to look at the records being kept and discuss any issues arising. It was important to ensure that the records were meaningful and being used to develop the work. This meant that record-keeping was regularly reviewed with the workers to ensure that it was meeting its purpose. Through the site visits the evaluators also established mechanisms for access to records, for example minutes of meetings, evaluation sheets and project records. We did not ask to see personal work diaries or confidential client records but were never denied access to any records we did ask to see. Indeed, as time went on the workers became increasingly relaxed.

## Project diary

At the start of the project it was suggested that each site keep a project diary as a way of recording overall developments in the work and to keep a record of what they had done. This was also enshrined as a requirement in the workers' code of practice. Guidelines for diary keeping were drawn up at the evaluation training weekend.

In fact the diaries were not as successful as we had hoped. When they were kept they proved a useful record of the work, often containing great insight and detail. However, as work took off the sites found that the diaries were too time-consuming and impractical. They found other ways to record the work, for example by taking minutes of meetings and keeping monitoring forms for outreach work, and instead of receiving diary updates we began to use steering group minutes and records from specific initiatives in order to keep in touch. Some of the sites also 'phoned us regularly.

## Evaluation of specific initiatives

Separate records would need to be kept of the various initiatives undertaken. We gave each site a list of headings which outlined the minimum information that we would need to know for each initiative. This included:

—the numbers of those involved in each initiative;
—the type and range of those involved;
—the effectiveness of the activities gauged according to appropriate criteria (for example, self-reported increments in knowledge, agency referral, understanding, empathy, skill, and actual and intended changes in conduct).

Records for each initiative had to be tailored to the aim and character of the initiative itself. This meant taking into account what would be useful to know and balancing this against what was appropriate and practical to collect. The main issue in relation to monitoring and evaluation was finding ways to keep it practical and integrated into the work. Finding time to write, read and record often seems hard when there is a lot of pressing direct work (an experience reported by other HIV workers – see McKevitt, 1993). The experience of the project was that the workers preferred methods that were simple and not too time intensive. Over time the workers began to see the usefulness of evaluation: it was a good way of getting feedback and useful to develop their work; it helped when lobbying or seeking funding; it was a good way of publicising the project; it enabled others to learn from the work; and it helped workers to validate their own work.

In order to support the evaluation activity of the sites we made it clear that we were willing to offer advice and support. We were often sent draft evaluation sheets or monitoring forms and asked for advice in improving or developing these. Debate on this contributed to our understanding of the process of the work. It was also important to us that we shared our skills as a way of contributing to the development of the project, supporting the workers whilst they gained the confidence to use the evaluation and research skills which they were developing. (Of course some workers already had excellent writing and research skills.)

## Evaluators' detailed work

Early on an important problem was beginning to emerge: so much work was going on that it could not (within the resources available) all be evaluated in the same detail. Our solution to this problem was to ask each project to nominate one strand of their work and develop (in collaboration with the evaluators) a programme of evaluation activities around it. The following areas were prioritised:

(i) In Leeds: a theatre group presenting a safer sex review. Interviews with participants were carried out by a project worker and the material gathered, together with some kept in the Leeds project diary, was written up with the help of the evaluation fieldworker, who also interviewed the worker. In a separate initiative, the project workers were helped in devising a questionnaire which was used as a way of assessing the type of work that might be done on the gay pub and club scene. This was evaluated as a strategy for initiating work on the scene.

(ii) In Leicester: outreach work in saunas was identified as a key area and discussions about its evaluation took place. Methods of record-keeping were devised and access to the worker's own reports negotiated. The project workers who did the outreach were also interviewed in depth about the process of doing the work.

(iii) In London: the evaluators worked with the local project workers on evaluating their meetings with youth groups, particularly through designing evaluating sheets and discussing the purpose of the visits. Workers were also interviewed in depth about the process of doing the work. There were also discussions on debriefing methods for club outreach work.

(iv) In Newcastle: project workers designed an evaluation questionnaire on the self-defence workshops they had organised. The evaluation also focused on work with an estate-based group of gay men using material from the worker's project diary and interviews with the MESMAC worker and group members.

Most of these areas of work were eventually written up as Evaluation Working Papers (Deverell, 1992; Deverell and Doyle, 1992; Deverell and Prout 1992a, 1992b and 1992c) and have contributed to this book.

## National record-keeping

As well as working with the local sites it was also vital that we kept in touch with other project members. The work of the project at a national level was expected to have a bearing on how the sites were able to work towards their aims and objectives. Therefore we had to collect data and make interpretations about the role of the HEA, the Project Advisory Group (later the Project Network Meetings, see Chapter 3), the managers and co-ordinators as facilitators of the work. Recording the insights and experiences of these project members also helped us to build up a detailed account of the different views in the project.

This involved attending co-ordinators' meetings, steering group meetings, national project meetings and training weekends. Here we would observe and take notes and where appropriate take part. Throughout this work we collated and collected a large number of national documents.

We also interviewed members of the black sub-group, the co-ordinators, HEA officers, managers and steering group members. This helped us to build up a much more sophisticated picture of the different viewpoints in the project and brought a national perspective to the work. The interviews covered similar areas to those with the workers and were also transcribed and sent back to participants as feedback.

## Feedback

One of the main aims of the evaluation was to be responsive and to give feedback to project participants. As mentioned above after each interview we gave feedback to allow people to amend and add to their accounts. This process also gave people a chance to put their own concerns on the evaluation agenda.

As a way of providing feedback to the project as a whole we also wrote reports on the project as well as individual initiatives. The most important of these during the first phase of the project was the initiation report, which documented the project's origins and the first few months of the local project workers' experiences. They were all interviewed, and an initial report circulated for feedback. HEA officers, co-ordinators, some managers and black sub-group members were also interviewed. The ensuing Initiation Report was circulated to all project members, who were invited to comment. While the workers found the report useful and informative, the co-ordinators and the HEA felt there was too much focus on the national project, at the expense of the local project work. It did, however, raise a number of issues for discussion, and contribute to an important change in the national structure of MESMAC.

In addition to the report, papers were written on local sites' work and a similar process of incorporating members' own knowledge and insights was adopted.

This way of working often took some time but ultimately enriched the evaluation through incorporating members' own knowledge and insights, and building in their responses to our own reflections. This collaborative style also ensured that participants felt some sense of ownership in relation to the evaluation.

## Reviewing the evaluation

The evaluation strategy in Phase 1, then, consisted of both *intensive* and *extensive* components: an attempt to keep a record of all the work undertaken nationally and by each project (extensive evaluation) and a rolling programme of more in-depth (intensive) evaluations done with each local project.

Individually and as a team we reviewed our work regularly in order to plan work and update and amend the evaluation strategy. There was regular discussion about the process of the evaluation itself as well as more formal work reviews. In autumn 1991 we decided to have a major review of the evaluation so far. Discussions were held with the HEA, the co-ordinators and the local project workers to identify strengths and weaknesses in the evaluation.

The review showed that on the whole the work had been successful. All the local projects were keeping records of their work (though not always consistently) and relations with the evaluation team were co-operative and open. A great deal of high quality, detailed information on the work of MESMAC had been collected and some of this had been written up as working papers: a sound base for the writing of final evaluation reports.

From the review it emerged that most of the evaluation work so far dealt with processual aspects of the project. There were two main reasons for this, the first being that the evaluation was in fact meant in large part actually to be concerned with process, in particular the ways of working that the local projects developed. From this point of view the emphasis on process was not a problem. The second reason was contingent – that it took time (about 18 months) before significant outcomes to the local project's work began to emerge. It was difficult to focus on outcomes when they were as yet unclear.

In practice the balance between process and outcome in the evaluation was bound to be a matter of judgement. It had always been planned to collect information on outcomes; the question concerned when it should become a major part of the work. In mid-1991 the HEA and some of the co-ordinators felt that more emphasis should be placed on outcomes and began to discuss this with the evaluation team. As evaluators we were independently coming to the same view and the evaluation was refocused accordingly.

Another conclusion of the review was that we had not so far developed a really effective way of integrating evaluation into the work of the local projects. This judgement was a relative one. Compared to many (perhaps most) projects, the MESMAC workers spent a great deal of time monitoring their work and reflecting on what they were doing. Nevertheless, recording the work of the project and planning how to develop the work tended to be rather distinct activities. Instead of informing future work, evaluation could still appear to be a chore that got in the way or took time away from 'real work'. Our solution was to adopt the model of 'self-evaluation' described below.

A third need related to our relationship with the co-ordinators and the HEA. It was clear that we needed to establish a better understanding of our respective roles and responsibilities. We were also keen to improve communication in order to build up a better understanding of their views on the project. Furthermore, to maintain the integration of the evaluation at both a local and national level, we felt we needed more support and clearer links with the HEA.

Overall, our response to the three main issues identified by the review was to shift the emphasis of the evaluation. This was not a wholesale shift in our style of work, which remained essentially collaborative, but it did place the stress differently. The components of our revised approach played a large part in the second phase of the evaluation. These are described below, following an outline of the other work undertaken at this time.

# MESMAC evaluation – phase 2

The work in this phase built on that described in Phase 1. We continued the work of collecting information on the overall work of the projects, and project workers, co-ordinators, managers and HEA officers continued to be interviewed and the course of the project monitored. We attended co-ordinators' meetings and arranged site visits to coincide with local steering group meetings, ensuring that both a co-ordinator and an evaluator were present.

Our own role shifted slightly more towards writing and less to site visits. During these visits, though, we began to collect more detailed information on specific initiatives. This often involved working with particular project workers and negotiating with the workers to interview project users, and led to several group interviews.

We continued to help the workers with record-keeping and offered help and support to those writing up their work. We were also asked to participate in events to promote the sites' work and asked for information that might help the workers prepare for funding bids.

In addition to these tasks we undertook several new initiatives which developed from the review. These are discussed below.

## Local self-evaluation work

In order to help the workers incorporate the information they were collecting into their work review and planning cycle we introduced a model of self-evaluation. This model was based on Stufflebeam's (1985) Improvement Oriented Evaluation approach. It started with the needs of the practical work and stressed the link between evaluation and improving work (see Fig. 1). Training was given to the project workers and each project was given a set of practical guidelines (see Appendix 4) for carrying out self-evaluation. Each project was asked to:

—review its overall work;
—to select one area (or more if appropriate) which could be developed or improved;
—prepare a plan (with aims and objectives) for developing or improving the work;
—plan how to monitor the extent to which the aims were being met;
—review and evaluate the work;
—write a report.

Project workers were asked to find local support in doing this and project managers and the co-ordinators were briefed by the evaluators on their support role. The self-evaluation work was the responsibility of local projects rather than the evaluators.

A major advantage of this approach was that it suggested a way to integrate evaluation work directly into project priorities. It started with the work itself (rather than the pious belief that evaluation should be done) and concentrated on areas of work that project workers themselves identified as ones which could be improved or developed. It drew on and developed the skills and insights of local project members who were asked to be active evaluators and it fitted evaluation into a systematic cycle of planning, implementing, monitoring and reviewing work. We also hoped that it would facilitate a sense of ownership of the evaluation by local projects.

By the start of 1992 each site had decided on the area in which they would carry out self-evaluation. These were:

**Figure 1.** From: *The Mesmac guide – a practical resource for community-based HIV prevention with gay and bisexual men and other men who have sex with men*, Health Education Authority, 1994, p. 44.

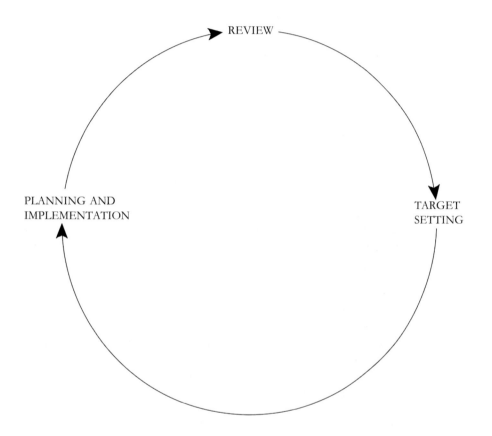

In Leeds: their street-based outreach;
In Leicester: the personal projects of each worker;
In London: the small grants scheme;
In Newcastle: their club/pub condom distribution scheme.

It was also suggested to the co-ordinators, the black sub-group and HEA officers that they carry out a similar self-evaluation of their role (or aspects of it).

At the time of writing MESMAC Tyneside had produced a valuable and comprehensive report on their condom distribution scheme (see Miller (ed), 1993a). The London and Leeds sites were in the process of writing up their work. Unfortunately the Leicester workers were all appointed to other jobs before their writing up was completed.

## The impact reviews

By the end of 1991 it was appropriate to begin drawing together the information we had about the outcomes of the project. This was done under the heading of the impact review. In the course of routine monitoring of the project a great deal of information had already been collected about the impact of the projects in their localities. The idea of the impact review was to draw together all the local information and present an overall picture. The sources of information drawn on were:

(i)  each project's own records and evaluation activities;

(ii)  interviews with project members (including workers, co-ordinators and HEA officers) about the work;

(iii)  the views of project users (i.e. men who have sex with men, for whom the project had been set up) collected, sometimes by the project workers and sometimes independently in interviews with the evaluators and/or through questionnaires.

Data from all these sources were used in writing up the impact review. The material was collected in two phases, the first between March and April 1992 and covering all outcomes of the projects from their setting up until December 1991. This material was collated and published as a working paper (Prout and Deverell, 1992). The first phase also acted as a trial run for the second, which took place in early 1993 and brought the information as up-to-date as possible.

The data on outcomes was collected using a specially-devised framework. In order to make data collection and interpretation more manageable, project work was divided into four different types: work with individuals and outreach; work with existing groups and organisations; work with newly-created groups and organisations; and other work.

The next stage was to collate information on the impact of each initiative (i.e. each separate area of work) for each of the local projects. We divided impacts into four types:

(i)  Impacts on individuals: the number of people (both users and other relevant workers/professionals in the field) who had contact with the projects and the degree of their involvement (ranging from one-off contact to prolonged involvement in the project); the social characteristics (e.g. sexual self-identity, ethnicity etc.) of those worked with; estimates of the impact of the project on various factors such as their awareness of HIV/AIDS, the acquisition of specific information and/or skills, growth in confidence, and changes in social/personal situation.

(ii)  Impacts on groups and organisations: the HEA; the host organisations; other MESMAC projects; other organisations with whom they may have collaborated. Under this heading we also registered any new groups or organisations initiated through MESMAC work.

(iii) Impacts on understanding HIV/AIDS and CD work: under this heading we drew together the main insights from project workers on methods of working – both in specifically CD ways and in relation to HIV/AIDS generally. We also collected information about how this experience had been disseminated.

(iv) Other impacts: collecting information about resources used and/or produced by the projects.

These headings were conceptualised to fit the specifically CD character of the project, the emphasis being on collective action. As evaluators we have acknowledged the need, therefore, to look at the impact of the project at several different levels – especially collective and organisational ones – as well as the more usual health education focus on individuals.

Although a laborious process for the evaluators and workers involved, this proved a useful and comprehensive way of collecting information. Much of Chapters 5, 8 and 9 are based on this information.

## Further intensive studies

In order to widen the scope of work that could be reported upon in more detail we also selected a further aspect of each project's work for in-depth evaluation. These were decided upon in collaboration with local projects and were different from those self-evaluated by project members. The initiatives covered were:

> In Leeds: the formation of Fit Together, a gay men's health group;
> In Leicester: workshops on health and beauty;
> In London: the formation of the Black Aids Action Project, a networking group for black people working in the HIV/AIDS field;
> In Newcastle: the formation of a gay youth group.

Information gathered from the evaluation of these initiatives has been used throughout the book, but particularly in Chapters 8 and 9.

# Final phase

The final phase of our work involved a last round of data collection and the planning and writing of the final report. As in the rest of the work the plan for the report was circulated and drafts sent to members for comments.

The final project meeting held in February 1993 served as an end to our fieldwork and here we were able to gather information from the project as a whole about the main lessons learnt, successes and failures, as well as have project discussion on certain key issues. Although we kept in touch with the sites after this period there were no further site visits.

# Advantages and disadvantages of our methodology

In this section we highlight some of the main issues that arose whilst carrying out the evaluation. Overall our experiences were positive, rewarding and productive. We believe that the collaborative approach resulted in a more rounded picture of the project, and produced evaluation material which could be used by other projects and over which project members could feel some ownership. It is an approach we would recommend to others. However, we also stumbled over problems and learnt some lessons. We discuss these below so that others might learn from our mistakes.

## The stresses of fieldwork

As evaluators we had to find ways of balancing the many different needs and demands of various project members whilst maintaining our own viewpoint and ideas. The innovative character of the project, together with its own internal disagreements, at times added to the difficulties of doing research. As one of the workers said:

> *Having to evaluate an innovative project is like doing an experiment on an experiment. (24/7/91)*

A further dynamic which related to our role and relationships was our unique position as evaluators in being able to relate to all the members of the project. When there were tensions between different members of the project, this could put us in a particularly difficult position. Our strict rules about confidentiality meant that we would not reveal what one person had said to us in confidence – but this did not stop us being asked.

Striking the balance between participating in the project and observing it proved difficult. Although independent of particular constituencies within the project, we were clearly participants with a commitment to the work. This commitment was very important to some members and our involvement in building up relationships reassured people about our role. As one worker said:

> *There is a level of trust between us and I feel comfortable talking about anything...all the consultation has been very important, not only to build up trust but to make us feel more comfortable about telling the truth, so the evaluation is accurate, true. (24/6/91)*

However, we were also criticised for being over-involved and too close to the workers. Finding a balance is difficult, but regular discussion with and reassurance from each other helped us to validate what we were doing. This was particularly valuable at times when we felt under pressure. About a year into the project the evaluation fieldworker started receiving external supervision which also helped and should be considered for anyone doing fieldwork-based evaluation.

## Defining our role and its tensions

Overall our relationships with the project members were good and comments about the evaluation were mainly positive, although it is important to note that people may not have felt able to say otherwise in a face-to-face interview. Our relationships were particularly good at local level, reflecting perhaps the effort put into this right at the start of the project. There was a high degree of trust on both sides and, with a few hiccups, the procedures for working together ran smoothly. This aspect of the evaluation is something mentioned by many members of the project. For example, an HEA officer noted:

> *What has been impressive in many ways is the negotiation with the project sites and their general contentment with the evaluation, and finding it helpful. (22/10/90)*

In comparison, our relationships with the HEA officers and co-ordinators had their ups and downs. At various points we felt under pressure to keep surveillance on the project and to play a 'public relations' role. We sometimes felt that we were being encouraged to keep the focus narrowly on the local projects and not comment about the national framework. From our point of view, these pressures seemed to reflect the shifting concerns arising in the management of the project rather than a dialogue about the purpose of evaluation. It therefore seemed particularly important for us to stick with the priorities we had planned and not be swayed by a particular interpretation of our role in vogue at any one time.

By the end of the project we all felt that more time spent talking about the process and nature of the evaluation would have helped. This underlines the importance of doing preparatory work (such as drawing up evaluation guidelines) with *all* the different constituencies that make up a project. In addition project evaluators need to have a forum for receiving support, raising issues and having joint discussion with representatives from different groups and interests with a project.

## Collaborative writing

We did find it difficult to get people to respond to the documentation that we sent them. It was disheartening on the occasions when we received little or no feedback, when recommendations were not discussed or when our role in bringing about changes in the project was not acknowledged.

Despite these difficulties we were pleased with the style of work we maintained. We felt that the opportunity to negotiate accounts was not abused or used to hide aspects of work. On the contrary it was used productively. For example, in a report on outreach work in saunas (see Deverell, 1992) we were keen not to identify the saunas as this might have had negative impacts on the work or the men who used them. A collaborative approach to writing meant that we could discuss this with the workers and find the best way of handling the information.

The collaborative nature of much of the writing and the process of feedback and negotiation may have slowed the dissemination a little but this was compensated for by the depth and detail of the information we were able to collect.

## Writing style

A related issue was the style of evaluation documents. Our intention was to provide the most honest and accurate account possible through negotiation with project members. This was particularly supported by the workers who were keen that others should learn from their mistakes, and encouraged us to give a 'warts and all' picture of their work.

The workers were prepared to be extremely honest. As one woman member of the project said:

> When I read in the report that there are gender issues for me being involved in the project at first I felt a bit uneasy seeing it there, I thought 'Everyone else will be reading that as well (and) it would be a lot safer for me if I could just get that scrubbed off.' Then I thought 'that is not being honest enough, there are issues there so why shouldn't everyone else know about it?' You have to take responsibility. Overall I think it's great. I get sick of reading reports that are really glossy and cover up all the problems for the sake of publicity. (27/2/91)

Feedback from practitioners, which we received in relation to the working papers, stressed the importance of honesty and detail in the discussion of work practices.

However, other members of the project often felt that our reports concentrated too much on tensions or difficulties in the work, with too much detail about the process of the work. In fact no single style of writing will suit all purposes. Deciding what is appropriate in different circumstances is an issue that needs input from different constituencies – underlining again the need for evaluation support structures and a discussion forum.

## Integrating evaluation

As researchers we might inevitably have been somewhat marginal to a project with a sense of urgency about practical work. At times, however, we felt overlooked at both national and local level. To some extent, and despite everyone's best intentions, the evaluation of MESMAC had been 'bolted on' to the national organisation of the project. We lacked a clear support mechanism and, for example, had no place where we could discuss the different demands placed on us.

It was also sometimes difficult to keep evaluation to the fore in local project work. A symptom of this (and one that may be familiar to other projects) was that it almost always came as the last item on project meeting agendas. It is not difficult to see that for practitioners ongoing work has a dynamic which is more compelling than monitoring and evaluation. As one worker said:

> *I know the argument would go evaluation is important and you need to make time to do it but you try it...you are working every minute of the day you haven't got time to sit down with paper, whatever and make notes...I feel like hyper-busy and anything which doesn't seem immediate gets left. Evaluation falls into that category, unfortunately, because in the short term it seems expendable. (13/12/91)*

In the early part of the project our agreement that records be kept was adhered to but as time went on it was increasingly seen as a chore, or records would be kept but not used. It would have been much easier to integrate evaluation with practical work if we had been based in the same localities as the projects themselves.

The model of self-evaluation followed in the last part of the project was an attempt to integrate work and evaluation. The self-evaluation work done by local sites is an important outcome of the project and other projects might find the model useful.

## Gender, sexuality, age and race

Like other researchers we found the work at times personally difficult and challenging. Although we were very committed to the project, at times we both questioned whether it was appropriate that we should be evaluating a MWHSWM project when we were not MWHSWM. This was a continual dilemma, sometimes keenly felt, at others less of an issue, and as such parallels the experiences of some others in the project, particularly the women (see Deverell and Bell, 1993). Overall, however, our genders and sexualities did not seem to have obstructed the evaluation and we managed to establish a rapport with both project members and users. As one worker said:

> *It would not have made much difference if the evaluators had been gay men. (It) may have added something but it's not been a problem because of the evaluators' attitudes...(It) would have been*

*an issue if we had felt you were just involved for research purposes, but because it seems you are committed to the project it's OK. You seem to have been sensitive to a lot of the issues and understood and empathised with things that have been said. (I) know lots of gay men who could have made a mess of it. (24/7/91)*

There is never a one-dimensional or clear relationship between researchers and those that they are working with. At times our age or race seemed just as important as our gender or sexuality. In the final analysis what was probably most important was that we recognised the impact of these factors, tried to be sensitive to the issues they might raise and where appropriate discussed them with project members.

## Shortage of time

A major problem we faced was the spiralling amount of work which the project generated. This was a project-wide phenomenon and seemed to affect everyone – there was simply much more to do than anyone had envisaged. In part this was because the local projects were extremely productive, generating a large number of initiatives, any of which could have been evaluated in depth. But it was also rooted in our own style of work: collaboration, networking and consultation all take time. So does arranging meetings and trying to articulate together the timetables and efforts of over 25 people. This was particularly the case as many project members only worked part-time and the project itself was geographically spread.

As a way of coping with the immense amount of evaluation that could be done, extensive and intensive studies had to be balanced. Towards the end of the study the amount of material was so great that two full-time workers were necessary. Throughout the work there was a continual need to effect a balance between reflection, writing and collecting data as well as updating each other on what was happening and making future plans.

## Talking to clients

We were particularly keen to get information from clients/users of the project but we faced several problems in collecting this data. As we did not live in any of the areas where MESMAC projects were based, collecting information from users had to be fitted into site visits. This usually restricted data collection to group interviews and the use of evaluation sheets and questionnaires, rather than participant observation, for example, which would have required longer visits in order to build up trust and relationships. Thus on the whole our data come from those who have been more directly involved with the project over a period of time.

A further difficulty relates to the CD nature of the project itself. Because of the diversity of initiatives and since each initiative was locally tailored and developed with men themselves, the impact varied considerably. This was particularly the case since the impact that the project had was wide-ranging and not just focused around HIV and safer sex. For example, it was impossible to produce a standardised monitoring form which could be used for all types of work and which may have made it easier to collect larger amounts of information.

However, despite the difficulties, we have been able to collect a substantial amount of information through interviews and questionnaires. Combined with the workers' own evaluation sheets, records and interviews and some groups' evaluation questionnaires we have been able to build up a good picture of individual impact. We feel it is particularly important that we have obtained information from the men themselves because, after all, they have the best information as to what they have got out of the project.

## Dissemination

Compared with many projects MESMAC members spent a great deal of time on recording, monitoring, reviewing and evaluating their own work. The stress placed on evaluation at the start of the project, not withstanding its inadequate integration, created an atmosphere of critical reflection and constant development. The process created a body of high quality, honest and accurate information about both the process and outcomes of the work (see Appendix 3). By being closely involved with the detail of project work and being able to discuss our ideas with project members we gained detailed insights into its character, its problems and its very great strengths. In subsequent chapters we draw on these data in analysing the processes and outcomes of MESMAC's work.

From the beginning we had been keen to disseminate the experience of MESMAC in a way that was useful and that others could learn from. This aim was shared with other project members who were keen that the findings of the project should be disseminated as widely as possible. However, from the beginning there was a concern that this ideal would not be fulfilled: people had to be reassured that the collection of evaluation data was worthwhile and that it would be used.

In the event dissemination took much longer than we wished. Requests for evaluation reports to be published were dealt with very slowly. Although most were eventually published as working papers, it took up to 18 months after they were first produced and happened only when the project's general lack of national profile was addressed. Perhaps it has to be accepted that working in collaborative ways will slow down publication.

By the end of the project, however, a great deal of information had been made available. The documentation of the project (in the evaluation working papers, the MESMAC DIY guide and the annual reports edited by the co-ordinators) is exceptionally large. Project members felt that these publications helped to validate their work.

## Summary

In this chapter we have:

*shown how we designed an evaluation to fit the needs of a community development approach;

*stressed that it was a collaborative approach in which all members of the project could play a part;

*described how we collaborated by giving training, negotiating procedures and developing a self-evaluation model;

*outlined the different stages that the evaluation went through and emphasised the importance of flexibility and review;

*described the methods and sources by which we produced data;

*outlined some of the lessons we learnt in the process.

# 3 The national and local organisation of the project

## Introduction

MESMAC brought together a number of different constituencies at both national and local level: the HEA; the freelance professionals acting as co-ordinators; the evaluators; the managers of the local voluntary and statutory organisations which hosted the projects; the project workers; and project users. In addition, at various points in MESMAC's development, representatives from existing AIDS/HIV organisations, from the HEA's own advisory group on work with men who have sex with men, and from various black and ethnic minority organisations also took part. Given the variety of organisational and professional backgrounds from which all these different people came and the political context of the project (see Chapter 1), finding an organisational structure in which people could work together was bound to take some time. In this chapter we will describe and analyse the organisation of MESMAC at national and local level. We will show that MESMAC was organisationally dynamic and changed its structure in response to the views of participants as the project evolved. Although the process of change was sometimes difficult, we see the ability and willingness to change as a positive feature of the project.

## The national organisation

There were three main stages in the development of the national structure:

> *Structure one* lasted from the HEA decision to fund the project until the choice of sites had been made (July 1989 until February 1990);

> *Structure two* came into being as a result of the involvement of the project managers from the host organisations, through the recruitment of the project workers and the first period of their work (March 1990 until July 1991);

> *Structure three* arose from the demand from project workers that they participate in the national structure and remained in place until the end of the project (July 1991 until March 1993).

These various structures were formed at each stage in consultation and negotiation with those involved in the project. As such the structure of MESMAC was the result of participation in the project – something which flowed from the CD strategy itself.

Two main dynamics can be seen in the way that the project structures changed. The first came from the ever-widening circle of people involved. As they came into the project they began to look for ways to express their point of view and be represented in the structures of the project. This necessarily meant negotiating a structure which all the different participants, with their different perspectives, could share.

The second dynamic expressed the multiple lines of accountability involved in the project, an issue frequently found in community development projects. As Baker and Craig (1990:1) have commented:

> ...complex funding and management arrangements are...repeated throughout the UK. The expectations, policies and requirements of the various funding agencies have to be balanced with the principles of the community health movement: there are inevitable conflicts of interest.

On the one hand MESMAC was funded by the HEA, which required some accountability. On the other, the CD approach and the innovative character of the proposed work required a high degree of freedom for the local projects as well as the participation (in, for example, project steering groups) of local communities. For these reasons MESMAC had an organisational form somewhat unusual for an HEA project. It was not directly a part of the HEA, and therefore within its management structure; nor was it contracted out to another organisation. It occupied a shifting middle ground in which the tension between distance and control was played out in various ways.

In the next section these themes will be illustrated by our account of the changing organisational forms that MESMAC underwent at a national level.

## Structure one

The May forum in 1989 (see Chapter 1) made two key suggestions which shaped the subsequent organisation of MESMAC. The first was that there should be three project sites with a geographical spread across England. The number of sites was later increased to four when the HEA decided that they wanted a London-based project at the Terrence Higgins Trust. It was felt that London had an existing network of gay and HIV organisations with which a MESMAC project could link. Additionally the Forum, whilst noting that resources were urgently needed in the provinces, had recognised the needs of the large number of young gay men moving to live in the capital city.

The second suggestion of the forum was that a project advisory group (PAG) be set up, to include representatives of existing HIV/AIDS organisations, HEA staff, the evaluators and the consultants to the project. It was also envisaged that eventually,

**Figure 2**

**MESMAC STRUCTURE ONE**

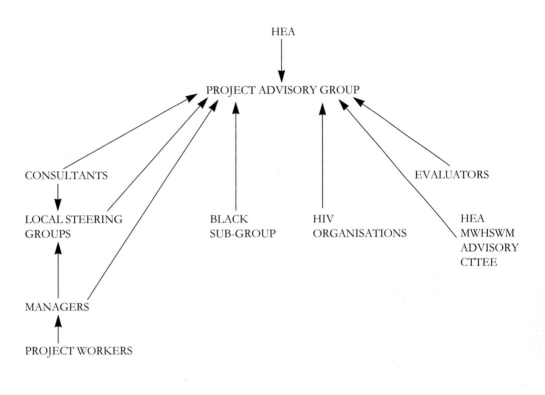

= attending meetings or being represented

when they were established, each of the local projects would have a steering group and that a representative from each would attend the PAG. After the decision was taken to set up a black sub-group, it was clear that they too would have a representative on the PAG. The function of the PAG would be to monitor the work of the project and give advice on its development.

Figure 2 shows the relationship between the various parts of the structure.

Within this structure the HEA was represented by two officers (a project officer and a project supervisor). The project officer had day-to-day responsibility for administering the project as a whole and the project supervisor liaised with those working on the AIDS programme, of which MESMAC was a part. An existing HEA consultative group (the Men Who Have Sex with Men advisory group) also sent a representative to the PAG.

The consultants' role was two-fold: they would set up and deliver the training programme for MESMAC workers; and they would act as consultants to the local projects when they were established, bringing particular expertise in sexuality, health promotion and community development.

Representatives of HIV organisations were there as a mechanism of on-going consultation and would help maintain MESMAC links with other work. Invitations were accepted by the Network Association of HIV/AIDS Workers (NAHAW) and the Network of Voluntary Organisations in HIV/AIDS (NOVOAH).

The black sub-group comprised black members of the project and other black HIV/AIDS workers. A representative of the group attended the PAG. Their role was to contribute to project discussions generally but with a special brief on black perspectives.

In August 1989 the project advisory group (PAG) met for the first time. The main work of the meeting was to decide, using the criteria suggested by the forum, which host organisations would be asked to develop proposals for hosting a MESMAC project. Drawing up proposals took longer than expected and encountered a number of problems. One of these was that it was difficult to establish rough parity between the salaries and grades of appointment of workers who would be based in such diverse host organisations. Another was that it took time for some of the host organisations to digest the full meaning of a CD project.

## Structure two

During the discussion of the problems which arose in setting up the local sites, a number of concerns about the structure of the project came to a head at PAG meetings. Although the PAG played a useful role, it was becoming clear that several different constituencies of the project were beginning to find it unsatisfactory and there was growing pressure to revise it. This pressure eventually resulted in the structure shown in Figure 3.

Site managers, most of whom started to attend the PAG at the end of 1988, were in the forefront of the push for change. In particular they felt unsure about whom in the existing structure they were supposed to be responsible to – the consultants (with whom they had been working on the development of proposals and the appointment of staff) or the HEA officers? Underlying this problem was a more fundamental concern about their relationship to the HEA. The tension between HIV voluntary organisations and government institutions was reflected in PAG discussions. For

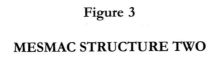

**Figure 3**

**MESMAC STRUCTURE TWO**

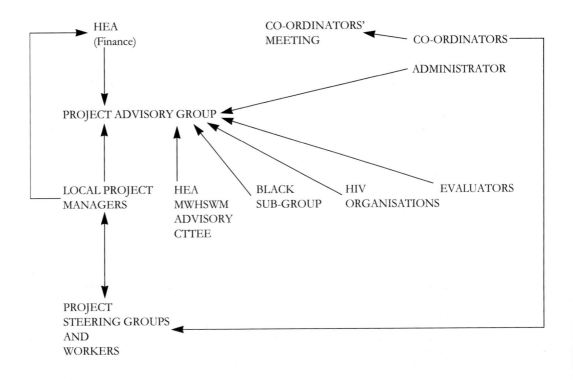

= attending meetings or being represented

example, a suggestion from the HEA that local projects should use HEA leaflets and videos met with opposition – with managers arguing that they did not want to be part of a national mechanism through which the HEA disseminated literature and information to local bases. They stressed that each project should develop in response to local needs and should be free to use whatever resources and materials it thought appropriate.

Questions were also raised by HEA officers about the practicalities of managing the project. The amount of work involved was greater than envisaged and the project officer was finding it increasingly difficult to co-ordinate MESMAC while doing his other work. A counterpart to this was that the consultants felt that they were increasingly having to make decisions essential to the development of the project; they felt responsible for them but had no formal power in the existing structure.

At a PAG meeting in February 1990 both the consultants and three of the project managers requested a change in the consultants' roles. The managers felt the lines of communication and responsibility needed clarification. Within this they wanted the local projects to have more autonomy from the HEA. As a result the consultants' roles were renegotiated and a new name, 'co-ordinators', adopted. As such they became responsible for co-ordinating *national* aspects of the project (for example, the training programme, future Forum meetings, and extensions to HEA funding). They met together to do this work and also met regularly with the HEA officers. A part-time administrative worker was employed to work with them. They retained their role as advisors to the local projects which continued to be managed locally, and advised the HEA on the progress of work in the local projects.

It was also agreed that the HEA project officer would have less day-to-day involvement. The exception to this concerned financial matters, which would remain the responsibility of the HEA. In this area managers dealt directly with the HEA but in all other respects they worked through the co-ordinators. The HEA continued to attend the PAG meetings and MESMAC continued to be identified as an HEA project.

(During the discussion it was suggested that the MESMAC project be contracted out to the co-ordinators, who would take responsibility for managing it as a whole. This was rejected by the HEA, who wanted to keep the possibility of a more direct element of control should they deem it necessary. MESMAC was also seen as a 'flagship' of the HEA's MWHSWM work and there was a high degree of personal commitment to it from the HEA officers.)

It can be seen, then, that although the HEA as funder kept ultimate control of the project, the second structure gave greater autonomy to the local project managers and created a 'buffer' between them and the HEA.

## Structure three

Although setting up the local projects had taken much longer than expected, by March 1990 the majority of staff for the local projects had been appointed and were starting work. Almost immediately the recruitment of this new layer of participants in the project began to create strains in the project structure.

The main source of strain was the lack of representation of project workers on the PAG. Project workers were to be represented by project managers – this decision was based on sound reasons (PAGs becoming too unwieldy, and the project workers' need to focus on their local work), but left project workers feeling isolated. They were being urged to incorporate community participation methods into the local projects, while their own participation in MESMAC structures was missing. In addition, the

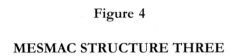

# Figure 4

## MESMAC STRUCTURE THREE

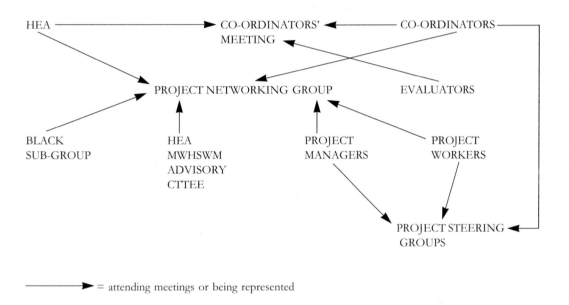

———————▶ = attending meetings or being represented

workers' only opportunity to meet as a whole group was at training events, where discussions of other issues tended to disrupt the training process.

Other drawbacks to this structure were that discussion at PAG meetings of local site issues was restricted because of the absence of the workers, and the HEA felt it had distanced them too far from the actual work of the projects.

On occasion the site visit was combined with holding the PAG meeting at one of the local sites. Although this helped communication with the HEA, it also underlined the fact that project workers were not invited to PAG meetings – even when held on their own premises.

These problems came to a head in March 1991, when two meetings for all the members of the project were organised; the outcome was a radically new structure that created opportunities for all project members to meet together. The main lines of this are shown in Figure 4.

The main difference between the second and third structures was the abolition of the project advisory group and the creation of the project networking meeting (PNM).

The notion of the PNM was that all members of the project should be able to meet, discuss current issues, give reports of the work in the localities and exchange experience and ideas. From September 1991 until the end of the project PNMs were held every three months. The meetings often took place over a weekend, with the first day used for business and whole project discussions, and the second for particular groups (such as the project workers or managers) to meet and discuss matters of common concern. The local projects took it in turn to host and organise the meetings. In all other respects the structure remained the same.

The decision to revise the structure helped to defuse many of the tensions which the non-representation of the project workers had created. In retrospect, perhaps the most important outcome of the change was its symbolic one: project workers no longer felt formally excluded from discussions and decisions. At the same time they saw more clearly (and were prepared to accept) the managerial hierarchies of the project. The workers had direct communication with the HEA officers for the first time, which helped them to feel that the HEA officers were involved and interested in their work. The new structure allowed HEA officers to find out and discuss what was happening at local level and to deal with administrative issues at one time and place. At the same time the new structure kept separate meetings with the co-ordinators, at which other administrative and managerial matters could be dealt with efficiently.

In retrospect the single greatest loss which the new structure caused was the contribution from other HIV organisations. It is interesting that at the time when the structure was changed no one at all highlighted this problem. In later months MESMAC was to suffer from too little dissemination of its work amongst other HIV projects and workers. Although the continued presence of HIV organisations at PNMs might not have overcome this entirely, they might have been able to remind the project that keeping links and communications with others outside the project was very important.

Another issue was how to integrate effectively representatives from the black sub-group BSG and MWHSWM advisory group. Although valuable contributions were made by individuals, guidelines and mechanisms for consultation were not sufficiently clear. For example, some of the local sites who wanted advice on working with black communities were unclear about how they could consult the BSG. By the end of the project the MWHSWM Advisory Group had dissolved and the BSG had stopped meeting.

This third, most participative national structure, came relatively late in the development of the project. By the time it had been set up there was a considerable backlog of problems to overcome and, at the same time, the projects had created strong local identities. The habit and culture of national discussions, therefore, took some time to establish. Nevertheless, a structure had been found which could bring all the main constituencies together; towards the end of the project some useful discussions were held and PNMs began to facilitate the kind of discussion envisaged at the initial forum meetings.

# Local organisation

In this section we will describe the local organisation of the projects and some of the issues concerned with its development. We will also look at the links between these structures and the national elements, especially the relationship between the local projects and the co-ordinators and HEA.

As a preliminary to this we will describe the process of appointing the project workers.

## Appointing the project workers

It was originally planned that the workers would be in post by October 1989 but due to various delays this was not the case. Because the project proposals were accepted at different rates workers in different sites (and even within sites) were appointed at different times. In London, for example, workers began in March 1990 but in Newcastle they did not start until May 1990. The latest of the initial appointments was in Leicester, where the administrator did not start until August 1990.

The May Forum, working on the basis of equal opportunities, had suggested that the local posts should be open to anyone – irrespective of gender, sexual orientation, ethnicity or disability. In retrospect this was a generous and open-minded view but not one grounded in the realities of the work. In later chapters (especially Chapter 7) we will discuss the implications of MESMAC's experience for the complex issue of who is best able to do MWHSWM work. We shall argue that it is a complex issue around which no automatic or simple assumptions should be made; circumstances do alter cases. Nevertheless, there is a strong a priori case that gay men should be recruited if a project is aimed mainly at gay men.

In fact, no standard procedure was used to implement equal opportunities in the initial recruitment of workers, although those involved were sensitive and aware of the issues raised. There were no national guidelines and local project managers were left to decide on their own practice, although some of the host organisations did have equal opportunities policies and procedures. This meant, for example, that some project posts were advertised in the ethnic minority press whilst others were not; some were advertised locally and others both locally and nationally; some used interview procedures based on equal opportunity principles and others did not. At this point the HEA was still developing its equal opportunities policy; had it been available at the time, it might have played a useful role in ironing out discrepancies between the sites, and as a comparison point for discussing local practices.

In the event, all the initial workers recruited were men, all of whom had a self-identity as gay. The exception was in Tyneside, where a woman was appointed as project

**Figure 5**

**ORGANISATION OF LOCAL MESMAC PROJECTS**

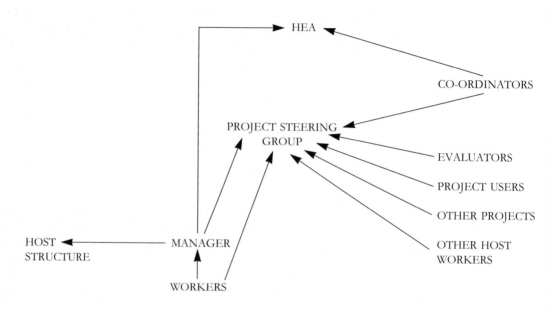

administrator. Half (six out of 12) of the workers defined as black or as from an ethnic minority.

The previous experience and backgrounds of the workers was very diverse but only a few of the workers had any experience of working in CD projects or a good working knowledge of all the issues it raises. This had implications for training, support and translating the idea of MESMAC into practice, which we will explore in Chapter 7.

## Local structures

The different projects worked out their structure and organisation for themselves, with the advice of a co-ordinator. All had some form of steering group, and their composition and role varied. All were variants on the structure shown in Figure 5.

The diversity of structures underlined the autonomy of the projects, although initially this led to some discontent when workers from different sites compared their situations.

Two major issues underlay the setting up and functioning of the steering groups. The first concerned whether or not project workers should be involved in and attend their steering group. In all cases project workers eventually attended meetings and they became useful forums in which the work could be discussed.

The second issue, closely related to the first, was whether or not steering groups were advisory or had the power to take decisions about the character and direction of work. This took somewhat longer to resolve but eventually all the projects saw steering groups as advisory. In practice this was inevitable since the projects had two other lines of accountability which were more powerful than the steering groups: firstly, the project managers were responsible to their host organisations and to the HEA on financial matters; secondly the co-ordinators were accountable to the HEA for the quality of work in the projects. Although the relationships between managers and co-ordinators were generally good, in theory the co-ordinator could have advised the HEA to stop funding the projects. In these circumstances, however valuable the discussion taking place in and advice coming from steering groups, such essentially ad hoc bodies did not carry this responsibility.

Despite the clarification of steering group roles there were still some potential ambiguities about the lines of accountability for each project. Essentially these remained unresolved since they never became major issues, but in theory there were four different groups to whom the project workers might be asked to account for their work: the communities with whom they worked; the manager and, through her/him, the structures of the host organisation; the project manager as the point of contact for the HEA on financial matters; the co-ordinator and, through him/her, the HEA on the work being done. In addition, project workers were expected to work with us as evaluators.

Creating a space in which the different constituencies of a CD project can come together was complex. Nevertheless, MESMAC has shown that such a collaboration is possible and the organisational problems it entails can find a practical solution.

## Relationship with the HEA

As we have shown, the local projects' desire to distance themselves from HEA control created a problem for HEA officers who at one point felt out of touch. For them it was a matter of balancing their need to know enough about the local work (to be able to account for it inside the HEA) whilst respecting the relatively high degree of autonomy given to the projects. This was difficult and often stressful for the HEA officers, especially when they also felt that their personal and professional commitment to MESMAC was not properly recognised by many of the project workers. As one of the HEA officers said:

> *At all stages through the project there has been too little time spent in supporting each other and too little time spent in terms of actually sitting down and saying to each other: 'Look what we*

*are involved in here is a very difficult concept.' ...I was never in a situation where people really expected to be able to do that with me because again of being in this position of the person at the HEA. I felt that, and I still feel...at that time I was in a difficult position of being this person, the scapegoat in the HEA, but [I was] still left with all these feelings about the work I was doing and how important it was and how close it is to me as a gay man who knows a lot of people with HIV, who may potentially have HIV, who knows a lot of people who've died of AIDS and AIDS-related complexes and all those other things which are part of this field of work. (18/9/90)*

Communication was improved by HEA site visits and the establishment of PNM meetings (see above). The HEA officers also played a very useful role in protecting and legitimising local projects when, in the early stages of the work, one of them was subject to hostile political comment (see Chapter 7 and Appendix 6).

In retrospect it is plain that projects bringing together local organisations and government agencies require team-building and partnership. Emphasis needs to be placed on this throughout the project, and especially at the outset. Each partner in the collaboration needs to explore the perspective of the other and understand the organisational context from which each is working. Local projects need to acknowledge the important role of bodies such as the HEA in funding innovative work such as MESMAC and appreciate the administrative work that entails. At the same time agencies such as the HEA need to be seen to be responsive to and have effective mechanisms for drawing on the experience of the projects they fund.

## Role of the co-ordinators at local level

MESMAC also brought together the HEA and a group of freelance professionals. This collaboration was essential to setting up the project and establishing the groundwork for its success. The co-ordinators continued to work at the national level and played an important role, for example in representing the project within the HEA, negotiating an extension of funding for a third year and organising training events. They also took up issues coming from the local projects with the HEA, insisting for example that local projects should be able to produce their own safer sex leaflets (see Chapter 7).

The co-ordinators also had a role within the local projects. They visited the projects and attended the steering group meetings. One of the co-ordinators had a brief to work with all the sites on the theory and practice of community development. Although there was some unevenness in the extent to which co-ordinators were utilised by the local sites, their advice could be extremely useful. They played an important part in reviewing work and developing plans and were valuable in legitimising and validating the work done at local level. They also helped to formulate plans for winning further local funding after the end of the HEA funding period.

The co-ordinators' role in the project was a complex one. Acting as a liaison and buffer between the sites and the HEA, they were sometimes seen by project workers as being part of the HEA; in fact their role was wider and more independent. They had to be sensitive about how they deployed their extensive professional experience, especially at the start of the project when the majority of the workers were relatively inexperienced. They also had to judge the importance of their collective professional experience against more political considerations such as their gender and sexual identity. Initially the co-ordinators comprised one gay man and two heterosexual women. As the project unfolded (and after discussions both at the local sites and at the PNM) the number of co-ordinators was increased to include more professionally experienced gay men and black people.

## Role of the local managers

Although the roles of managers developed differently at each site, they all centred around supervising and supporting the work, giving advice, planning, and acting as the accountable person to the HEA on finances. In most sites the managerial role in reviewing and planning work with the project workers was very important. At its most systematic this involved regular meetings for supervision, support and the review of work. Managers also provided individual supervision for workers and in some cases had an important input into local training. Some of the managers also had an extremely important role in developing proposals for further local funding to take MESMAC work forwards in the period after the end of HEA support.

The amount of contact managers had with workers varied. The least direct contact was with the Newcastle project, where the manager was not only based in a different division of social services but also in a different building, geographically remote from the MESMAC office. In the other sites shared premises meant direct contact was easier and more frequent. In London, for example, contact tended to be more with the full-time project administrator than the part-time project workers. After some experimentation London adopted a system of three-monthly reviews, which all project workers attended together with the manager and a co-ordinator, and monthly meetings with the manager. More frequent meetings were thought to take too many of the already limited part-time hours of the workers (see Chapter 7).

In London MESMAC gradually became a more central part of their manager's work. As she said:

> They (the workers) recognised that I saw MESMAC as a full-time piece of work, not a part-time one. I think until that was clearly said they had the feeling that I was always seeing their

*work as an extra, which I think maybe a bit at the beginning I was... Whereas as its settled down I've recognised its not an extra bit of my work, its an important part of my work. (2/10/91)*

In Newcastle this issue of managerial time being devoted to MESMAC was never satisfactorily resolved. The project manager was under pressure from other work (the majority of it unconnected to HIV) and was from time to time asked by his own managers to cut down even further the limited time he could devote to MESMAC.

For a long period managers had little or no support from within the project. There was some from co-ordinators, but sometimes they had to put pressure on the managers, and these two functions did not fit easily together. Until the setting-up of the PNMs it was difficult for managers from different projects to meet together, although this contact was felt to be useful when it did happen. Although MESMAC was unusual in being a geographically spread national project, it did highlight the importance of thinking through their role and needs at the start of the work.

## Relationship to host organisation

The host organisations were very different from each other and each presented a different combination of benefits and problems in their relationship with the MESMAC project they hosted. This relationship seemed to vary according to:

  *the size and complexity of the host organisation;

  *the character of the host's main work and its history and experience of HIV work;

  *whether the host was in the voluntary or statutory sector.

The interweaving of these factors had a strong bearing on the different degrees to which each MESMAC project became autonomous from the host. Although it was important for each project to have as clear an organisational structure as possible, it was these substantive and contextual factors which were ultimately more important in determining the relationship between the projects and their hosts.

Leeds AIDS Advice, for example, had some history of HIV prevention work (especially its Hot'n'Healthy campaign) but its main focus was and remains on support and care. As a voluntary organisation it receives the bulk of its funding from statutory organisations. Additionally, its client base is diverse and it does not want to be identified as a solely 'gay organisation'. In these circumstances, and despite MESMAC initially sharing office space with LAA workers, MESMAC Leeds developed a distinct and autonomous identity. This was strengthened when LAA moved to new premises, leaving MESMAC in the old offices.

In contrast Leicester Black MESMAC and Leicester Black HIV/AIDS Forum (BHAF) had an extremely close relationship, at times being almost entirely merged together. BHAF is a small voluntary organisation with very limited resources. BHAF and MESMAC workers shared administrative systems and office space and this gave a great deal of scope for dovetailing their work. The aims of BHAF (which focus on HIV prevention with black communities) overlapped with MESMAC to a high degree. As MESMAC gained more experience it became clearer that reaching black MWHSWM might best be accomplished within the context of broader approaches to black communities as a whole. This led to a very close relationship, shared perspectives and much joint work. This was very fruitful but in some respects it confirms the warnings given at the initial forum consultation: small voluntary organisations can be put under pressure when they receive funding from the statutory sector and the implications need to be well thought out at the beginning (see also Chapter 9).

Whilst also a voluntary organisation, the Terrence Higgins Trust (THT) is large, complex and does a wide variety of work. Its size and complexity impacted on MESMAC in quite practical ways. For example, it took some time for its switchboard to be aware that the part-time MESMAC workers were based at THT. The history and development of THT's work also had a bearing on the relationship and MESMAC workers felt that for some purposes they had to establish a separate identity. For example, they felt a THT identity would not help them in relation to working with black MWHSWM, many of whom saw THT as a white organisation. Similarly, MESMAC joined THT at a time when it was (despite its strong roots in gay AIDS activism) under criticism for turning away from work with gay men. MESMAC, therefore, created their own logo and produced separate posters and leaflets. At the same time they could both draw on and contribute to THT's experience. In addition, two experienced youth workers joined their steering group, sometimes contributed to the planning of their work and gave individual supervision to MESMAC workers. Becoming more integrated into the THT took longer, although it never became fully integrated into the formal structure. As the project manager said:

> With time everyone in the Trust has recognised that MESMAC is a major part of our work and the Trust probably owns MESMAC a bit more. I think at the beginning it was seen as an extra project, it was housed here and nothing more. Now we are saying more about it like in the Annual Report. Also people (in the Trust) are learning to use the resources that they (MESMAC) have. (2/10/91)

MESMAC Tyneside was based in Newcastle Social Services Department which, like THT, is a large and complex organisation, although this time in the statutory sector. When the project started HIV work was only a small part of social services' overall responsibilities. The established administrative procedures were quite rigid and the division of labour complex. This created problems when it came to MESMAC integrating into the structure.

An added difficulty was that the Social Services Department was not used to dealing with externally funded projects. Gradually, however, both MESMAC and NSS developed a working relationship which was more administratively flexible.

Unlike the other host organisations, the environment was experienced by the workers as a homophobic one, although this gradually improved:

> *The authority as a whole seemed so against us... 'poofs over at MESMAC'. They were very stand-offish and scared, lots of gossip about a gay men's project. It seems to be changing for the better and they seem to have realised we are a bona fide project and are human not radical and weird. (11/2/93)*

As the project developed it managed to utilise the networks offered by a statutory organisation. For example, MESMAC made important contributions to the development of a city HIV prevention policy. However, in comparison with, for example, Leicester BHAF's relationship to its MESMAC project, there was relatively little overlap or collaboration in practical work.

At the same time as it utilised statutory sector networks MESMAC Tyneside developed a distinct identity of its own, to a large degree as a resource centre for gay communities in the area. This tendency towards an autonomous identity was strengthened when MESMAC moved to its own city-centre premises.

## Participation of MESMAC users

A key part of the CD strategy was to encourage the participation of MWHSWM in project decision-making. This certainly occurred but the forms it took were somewhat less formal than anticipated by many members of the project. Participation was initially seen to be about the involvement of project users in the formal structures (for example in the local steering groups). In two of the projects (Leicester and Tyneside) this happened: six project users in Tyneside and three in Leicester joined the project steering committees for periods of time.

The reasons for their absence in Leeds and London are interesting. Because the London project was staffed by part-time workers with only six hours per week each, one of its main administrative problems was organising meetings of the workers themselves.

A more important point, however, concerns the perspective of the men who became involved in the project. Many did not necessarily want to participate in formal structures. In London, for example, a group of young men became involved in a peer education training initiative and were invited to attend MESMAC business meetings alongside the workers. Very few attended; they were clearly happy to give their ideas and views more informally or through evaluation and in any case were primarily motivated to do direct peer education rather than take part in formal decision-making about MESMAC.

This experience coincided with that of Leeds MESMAC. They decided they would, as they put it (perhaps with some overstatement) 'redefine participation'. Instead of organising representation on their steering committee (or in the LAA structure), they saw each of the groups they set up as an arena within which participation could take place. They coined the term 'self-defining, autonomous groups' to describe their work in helping to set up groups for men who have sex with men (for example, a self-help group for sex workers called Rent Boy Action, a gay men's health group called Fit Together and a theatre group known as Latex Productions). Each of these groups involved participation from the start and the workers aimed at the groups becoming autonomous and self-running.

A similar approach was also taken in Tyneside where the groups which MESMAC helped to initiate, but which later became independent, had an agreement to meet a MESMAC worker once a month to discuss group activities for feedback into the MESMAC project.

It may be that setting up more formal systems of participation and representation is difficult to achieve and has to build on substantial work. To that extent they may come relatively late in the process of CD work. On the other hand, it may be that there are better, more imaginative alternatives to formal participation structures. MESMAC has not been established long enough to generate clear conclusions on this point.

All the projects put needs assessment, including consultation with communities, groups and individuals, at the centre of their work. Apart from participation in the groups MESMAC established, this involved consultation with project users on their needs, regular work reviews and evaluation, and participating in other organisations. These will be discussed more fully in later chapters.

Finally it is interesting to note that towards the end of the project we began to hear the first demands from local project users that they be allowed to come to PNMs, and we expect these would have grown if MESMAC as a national project had continued.

# Summary

*MESMAC brought together a number of constituencies with different organisational, professional and political backgrounds;

*at both national and local level project organisation was flexible and changing, eventually finding structures which could balance the various lines of accountability involved;

*the structures eventually adopted allowed the greatest participation of the different constituencies and the most interaction between them;

*bringing together these constituencies underlined the importance of team-building, for the commitment of HEA officers to be recognised and of the funding body having mechanisms for drawing on the experience of the project;

*co-ordinators and managers played important roles;

*the MESMAC sites each developed different relationships with their host organisation;

*the participation of project users was achieved through the needs assessment, setting up independent groups and to a lesser extent by formal representation.

# 4 Areas of work

# Introduction

In this chapter we discuss the different areas of work developed by the MESMAC project. We have chosen to discuss areas rather than methods of work because this allows us to put the methods in their context. For example, working on the gay scene may involve many different methods: carrying out questionnaire surveys; doing outreach; setting up condom distribution schemes; one-to-one discussions; and working with managers, all of which can be discussed under scene work.

MESMAC work involved an eclectic mixture of methods. The important point was that they were used within the guiding theoretical framework of the CD strategy. Rather than sticking to one particular method the workers used their skills and imagination, adapting to any given initiative. This enabled them to tailor their work to their locality and the needs and experiences of the men they worked with.

MESMAC has undertaken too much work for it all to be described in detail. This chapter provides a general account in order to give readers an idea of the range of work undertaken and a description of what each area involved. As such it draws on the combined sites' experience. We have, however, pointed out differences between the sites where appropriate.

This chapter is not intended as a practical guide. More detailed information can be found in the MESMAC DIY Guide (Miller, ed, 1993) and various MESMAC evaluation working papers. A discussion of some of the issues involved in doing the work can be found in Chapter 7.

In order to describe the work undertaken we have divided it into nine areas:

(i) One-to-one work
(ii) Scene work
(iii) Outreach
(iv) Forming new groups
(v) Workshops
(vi) Work with existing organisations
(vii) Sharing learning
(viii) Materials production
(ix) Lobbying and funding.

It should be noted that monitoring, evaluating and keeping a record of the work was emphasised as important at the beginning of the project and the workers had responsibilities to do this. (See Chapter 2 for details on evaluation.) Examples of some of the evaluation and monitoring methods as the workers developed can be found in Miller (1993). The approach within MESMAC was to integrate evaluation into work itself rather than seeing it as an extra. Here we have included comments about evaluation where appropriate in each area of work.

# One-to-one work

As the term suggests this involved working with individuals. It most closely resembled advice or counselling work: discussing problems, giving advice and referring people to MESMAC or other groups or organisations. Across the project this work ranged from one-off discussions to more in-depth counselling covering several sessions. Some one-to-one work also took place in the context of outreach.

Although in a CD project the focus is on working with groups rather than individuals, the project workers found that this did not rule out one-to-one work. To those unfamiliar with CD work this may seem at odds with the CD philosophy of collective rather than individual work, but one-to-one work proved to be a good way of finding out needs and was incorporated into other elements of the CD strategy. In addition the fact that so little provision exists for the health, welfare and support needs of gay men/MWHSWM inevitably meant that some individual work was necessary.

## Why do one-to-one work?

All the sites found that one-to-one work was generated as a result of advertising and raising the project's profile. For example, people often contacted the project as a first step towards becoming involved in a group or other MESMAC initiative. However, advertising also generated a lot of contact with men who simply wanted to talk about issues such as sexuality, HIV or relationship difficulties. Often the project's association with gay men or MWHSWM was the reason for the contact here. For example, in Newcastle an advert for the MESMAC youth group in the local free press unexpectedly generated many calls from married men, most of whom were too old for the youth group but saw the contact number as a chance to talk about their own sexuality. All the sites received letters and phone calls from men who wanted information and support in relation to: sexuality, relationship difficulties, finding ways to meet men for sex, sexual problems, sexual abuse and information about MESMAC including MESMAC groups. It should be noted that as well as these more positive contacts the project's profile also led to abusive and 'wank' calls.

On a related theme, one-to-one work arose as sites were seen by local communities as a resource. The projects were contacted for information on a huge range of topics, including where to buy gay porn, information about legal rights, how to contact transvestite/transsexual support groups or even where to find a good black hairdresser.

Getting people into groups was another reason for doing one-to-one work. Some men were not ready for, or were afraid of, going to a group, and one-to-one work built up their confidence. It helped men to understand what they could expect from the group and enabled the workers to find out if the men had any special needs.

By being available for discussions outside the group's meeting time and building up relationships, workers also helped men to stay in groups. For example, some of the men in the Newcastle youth group emphasised the importance of the workers being available to discuss issues and deal with crises as they occurred, rather than having to wait for a group meeting (see Chapter 8). As the work progressed many of the sites found that individuals would pop in for a chat, to pick up condoms or to use the photocopier, and the workers saw this as a good way of building up relationships and keeping themselves informed of local issues.

Despite their best efforts at encouraging and involving men in groups the workers found that many did not want to join. Some were scared of being identified as gay or as a man who has sex with men, while others did not like groups or did not feel a need to meet other men, or indeed felt there was not an appropriate group for them. As such one-to-one work was a good way of reaching these men and exploring their issues, giving advice and information and even building up skills, for example by demonstrating how to use condoms.

## Doing one-to-one work

One of the main issues for the workers in relation to one-to-one work was deciding how long-term it should be. In some cases the contact would only be one-off, while sometimes workers tried to make the contact long enough to be useful (for example, by encouraging people not to put the phone down). In still other cases there was a need to make decisions about how many times to see someone, as well as how much work to take on. The workers were keenly aware that they were not counsellors, and so although they tried to develop basic listening and problem solving skills the main emphasis of this work was placed on referral. The workers had to be flexible in this respect since there was not always a suitable place or person to refer to. For example, there are very few services outside London for men who have been sexually abused or raped, and in such situations the workers found it hard not to give support.

A related dilemma arose in deciding which issues could be addressed. Although CD validates working with needs wider than just HIV or sexuality the workers found they still needed some boundaries, and had to remind themselves that they could not meet every felt need. It was therefore important to set limits and refer people to other organisations. It was also crucial for the workers to have good supervision and support to help make such decisions.

Because the workers could not do long-term individual work, one of the anxieties they found was feeling that they may be encouraging people to deal with issues and then abandoning them. For example, supporting married men to acknowledge their sexuality may eventually lead to their decision to come out and leave their wives. Setting limits and offering referral helped here. Indeed in some cases this work encouraged other organisations to do work with MWHSWM or to change their services and as such fed into organisational development. A further way of supporting men was by setting up new groups related to their specific concerns and developing these as supportive environments e.g. a married men's group. In this way individual work often led to more collective action and developing community infrastructure.

A final consideration was thinking about how to record the work. Workers developed phone diaries and monitoring forms as a way of keeping track of the work. Information from these could be useful for funding purposes as well as lobbying and dissemination to other groups.

One-to-one work could be very time consuming and needed to be balanced against other work. However, it was a way of: finding out needs; generating information for lobbying; suggesting ideas for developing new groups; helping to maintain groups; encouraging organisations to change; and developing infrastructures through building good referral systems. As such workers found ways to integrate the work into the CD framework. In any case, the workers felt the work was necessary and valuable in itself.

# Scene work

This area of work relates to initiatives carried out in pubs and clubs on the commercial gay scene. The actual work done was diverse, ranging from informal discussions, needs assessment and outreach to high impact safer sex promotion nights. Leicester and London mainly carried out outreach and needs assessment, whilst Newcastle and Leeds did more safer sex promotion events. All the sites used the scene as a place to advertise MESMAC groups and to give out information. MESMAC Tyneside also established a very successful condom distribution scheme on the local scene (see Chapter 5 and Miller, ed, 1993).

## Why do scene work?

All the sites considered it important to spend some of their time working on the local gay scene. One of the main reasons for this was the large number of gay men who could be accessed there directly. The scene was seen as a good place to get people to identify with the project and to encourage them to get involved, as well as a way for the workers to get to know men. Although many of the men using the scene could be reached elsewhere, the workers found it politically important to have a visible presence on the scene and to use it as a place to raise the project's profile.

## Doing scene work

Although the workers recognised the importance of working on the scene, it was not quite so obvious what they should do. Initially many of the workers found the prospect of scene work daunting. As the Newcastle workers wrote in the report on their condom distribution scheme:

> The scene was perceived as an occasionally hostile environment for health promotion work, a noisy place unsuited to meaningful interventions. It was felt that the argument that work should happen on the scene might be simplistic, based merely on the fact that this was the place where one could encounter the largest number of gay men in one fell swoop. Workers were concerned that there was an element of intruding on men's space, of foisting an HIV agenda onto them when they were out to enjoy themselves, and that the last thing anybody wanted to hear about on the scene during a relaxing night out was AIDS and its negative corollaries. (Miller, ed 1993a:11)

### Establishing need

The first step for all sites was to establish whether there was a need for scene work, rather than assuming it would be a good place to work. General observation and needs assessment concluded that the scene was a good place to work (BMRB 1992; Deverell and Prout 1992a; Eades 1993). This was confirmed in other MESMAC work; for example, London's consultation work with youth groups revealed that young men who only socialised on the scene may be particularly vulnerable since they were not getting safer sex information or peer support. Additionally the fact that little or no scene work with MWHSWM was taking place in any of the localities when the projects began encouraged the workers to plan some initiatives.

### Targeting venues

A further part of planning scene work was to decide which venues to target. For sites like Leicester, where there is only one gay club, this was relatively simple. In London, however, where there are more gay venues than in the rest of England as a whole, this was more problematic. A further consideration was whether to target clubs in other towns since men often travel to socialise, either so as not to be recognised or just for more variety.

## Making contact with men

The next stage was to decide what to do. The main aims across the sites were: to try and contact people; to give out safer sex information and condoms; to raise awareness of MESMAC and HIV. One of the key issues in clubwork was finding suitable ways to approach people. As in other outreach it took time for the workers to build up their own confidence. Initially some workers felt the work was unsuccessful because they only spoke to people they felt safe with. Approaching individuals was usually easier than going up to groups, although often getting to know one member of a group would lead to introductions to others. Going as a team also helped give workers the confidence to approach people, and meant they could give each other feedback and share strategies.

Workers found that a short, basic introduction to the project was best as people were generally amenable if contact was kept brief. As the workers became known they found that people would come up and talk for longer; such conversations could be quite fruitful as the scene was a place where men felt able to discuss sex frankly.

Sometimes making contact was difficult. It was hard to do health education work with people who were drunk. In addition there was often a lot of sexual harassment which workers could find wearing, especially when they were trying to be approachable and friendly. It was a difficult role since there was a need to fit in with the general club atmosphere, and to reassure other men that they were not there to police their behaviour, whilst also making it clear that they were working. As one worker explained:

> ...if you are not careful (you) can come across as this person who's a boring straight guy, who's not having a lot to drink, maybe not smoking and you are not tapping off with anybody...You are there as this Health Education (person), you are a sensible, responsible, fully informed person but you are also friendly, not stand off-ish and you are a kind of normal guy who would have a pint. Bloody hell it's not easy. (13/12/91)

Having something to offer was helpful, especially as the venues were usually dark, busy and noisy, making conversation difficult. Business-type cards helped in explaining who the workers were and made them look official and genuine. Projects also gave out condoms, although several of the sites talked a lot about whether this was making assumptions about needs and might put people off. Workers found that as they became known they were often asked for condoms, being referred to as 'the condom man'. Some sites developed safer sex packs containing safer sex information, lubricant and condoms which were given to everyone in the club. Generally it was found that people liked 'freebies', so it was important to make it clear that these were free to encourage people to take them. It was also important to think about having materials for women when working in mixed venues.

Newcastle and Leeds found it best to be upbeat and sexy and to use well-produced materials. Often there were no suitable resources available and so sites had to make their own. MESMAC resources produced for scene work include T-shirts, badges, leaflets, business cards, safer sex packs, mugs and beer mats. It was felt important to have these since they helped with contact. Interesting posters or T-shirts, for example, often led to someone coming up and initiating a conversation. Wearing MESMAC T-shirts also helped identify the workers. Producing such materials meant that scene work could be expensive, particularly as it was felt that to maintain interest there was a need to introduce new materials regularly.

London and Leicester found that a low key approach was more successful when working with black men on the scene. Trying to contact black men raised several issues in itself: there were often few black men on the scene, which meant that large road-show type events were not suitable. This was particularly the case in Leicester, where early on in the project no other scene work was taking place locally. As a black project they sometimes felt that their doing scene work reinforced ideas about Africa being the origin of AIDS and suggested that HIV was only an issue for black men. In the final year of the project a men's sexual health worker was appointed in the city and the workers were able to work with him to develop more road-show type events. This enabled them to integrate their work with black men into a wider initiative for work with gay men generally. Interestingly this initiative showed that some black men preferred to talk to white workers. The workers suggested this was because some black men feel that white gay men are more accepting of their sexuality. Additionally as there are so few black men on the scene many black gay men are used to seeking support around their sexuality from white men. The fact that in the prevailing culture white men are often seen as the most desirable (see Chapter 6) also meant that black men would often see other black men in terms of competition rather than support.

A further issue in the Leicester work related to their brief as a black project: although they were set up to work with black MWHSWM, they found that 90% of black men on the scene were having sex with white partners. This meant that it was vital for them to work with white men in order to meet the needs of black men, and to be careful not to alienate men's white partners. As a worker wrote:

> One of the main reasons we face hostility is that they may be with their white partners who feel that either we are cruising the black partner, or that somehow our reason for talking to them is excluding the white partner, and so to them a threat to their relationship as we are a black MESMAC project. Many times I have spoken to a black and white couple. The black partner

*has been welcoming and interested but the white partner has been hostile and unfriendly, and soon distracts the black partner onto another subject or encourages him to move away. (1/10/90)*

The situation was made more difficult since the workers found that by concentrating their efforts on targeting black men many men assumed that the project was political, rather than there to provide a service. As a worker explained:

*Because you have black in your title you become a pressure group rather than a service provider. (24/6/91)*

This meant that the work attained an additional political dynamic. The workers felt that black men sometimes shied away from contact with the project because of this, and therefore the Leicester project began to widen its client group and work with white men.

A very important finding in the London and Leicester work was that many of the black men using the scene had female partners. Leicester estimated that about 75% of the men that they worked with were married or had relationships with female partners. Gay-identified material was therefore often inappropriate, or seen as offensive, and only met some of the needs these men had (see Chapters 6, 7 and 10 for further discussion).

## Working with managers/staff

Another key issue was deciding whether to work with managers or other club/pub staff. Several of the projects did their observation, and some initial outreach work 'undercover'. However, they all moved to a position where they decided to tell managers that they were working. Some of the owners were very amenable and helpful, others let the workers in but were indifferent, and some were not very keen. Managers were usually concerned about making a profit and so their priorities often did not coincide with those of the project. The workers felt they had little bargaining power as they had to keep on good terms with the managers to maintain access to the clubs. However, personal contact and having a clear strategy to present to managers helped somewhat.

Building relationships with bar staff was also tried by some of the sites, for example, getting them to give out cards or condoms with change. In MESMAC Tyneside a stripper wore a MESMAC T-shirt and waved a condom. Newcastle found the condom racks which they placed in each gay club in Newcastle helped build relationships as the bar staff had responsibility for maintaining these and would talk to the workers when they were restocked. In addition, several of the workers reported that links were built up indirectly when socialising in their own time.

## Impact on personal life

Scene work often impacted on the workers' own personal and social lives. For those who lived in a place where there was only one gay club, this impact could be major. Being known as a worker made it hard for the workers to socialise as they would be approached by men seeking advice or support. Workers would worry about how their image would be affected if a session went badly. Working in a community they were part of made this inevitable. Some tried to work in venues which they did not socialise in and others would visit other towns in order to lessen the impact (see Chapter 7).

## Who was being reached?

A crucial issue in all the sites was the difficulty in reaching black men through scene work. In Leeds, Newcastle and Leicester there were very few black men on the scene: many experience the scene as unwelcoming and racist and choose other places to meet men. London is slightly different in that there is a black gay scene. Nevertheless, in many gay clubs most of the men are white. Given their small numbers, the Leicester workers found having black men as a target group made scene work difficult (see above). The other sites had difficulties finding black men to help do scene work. In London there was initially only one Afro-Caribbean worker and he did some joint outreach with other London-based black projects until another Afro-Caribbean outreach worker was appointed. Newcastle involved black volunteers, which they felt was an important public statement. However, it did not solve the fact that very few black men used the scene. This raises important questions about who is reached through doing scene work and points to the need to find other ways in particular of reaching black men.

Scene work also raised issues around finding ways to contact deaf men, as well as men who cannot afford to go to clubs, or who do not like or use the scene. Although many men can be reached on the scene, workers were also aware of the need to work elsewhere.

## Recording the work

Finding suitable ways to record and evaluate scene work proved challenging. Debriefing seemed the most appropriate method, but workers reported that finding the energy to do this at 2 am was not easy. Leicester kept monitoring sheets on the number and type of contacts they had made, which helped to build up a picture of the work. Other sites chose to count the number of packs given out or simply to evaluate particular initiatives.

Many of the workers were worried that doing scene work was not really community development, but as no one else was doing it they felt a responsibility. In any case it was a good way to get information to a large number of men quickly, and could lead to people joining groups and to the development of ideas for further initiatives. For example a questionnaire in Leeds used for Leeds assessment led to the development of at least three new groups. It was also a useful way of obtaining feedback on MESMAC work. In some sites there was a concerted move to train others to do scene work, thereby having a MESMAC presence on the scene but freeing workers up to do more CD-based work. London did this through training a group of black men to work with their peers, and Newcastle secured local funding for two outreach workers to work on the scene.

Scene work required a lot of preparation and could be demanding. However, it was good for advertising, raising the project profile and keeping HIV/safer sex in people's minds. The workers all felt it was very important to do, although what could be achieved was limited.

# Outreach

This was a major area of MESMAC work. All the sites undertook some outreach, whether as a long-term initiative, a short-term project or preparation for other work. It involved working in public cruising areas, toilets, saunas, gyms and clubs. Outreach in pubs and clubs is described in the scene work section above and does share many similarities.

Within MESMAC outreach mainly took the form of what Rhodes et al (1991: 3) define as detached HIV-related outreach. That is:

> ...*work undertaken outside any agency setting, for example, on the streets, station concourses, in pubs and cafes. This may aim either to effect risk reduction change 'directly' (in situ) in the community, or to facilitate change 'indirectly' by attracting individuals into existing treatment and helping services.*

Workers gave out condoms, cards and information and tried to get men involved in MESMAC. Within a CD framework the ideal outcome of outreach is seen as moving from individual outreach to more collective action. In some cases this process worked quite well, but at other times it seemed inappropriate or virtually impossible and led to some questioning of the CD model (see Chapters 7 and 10 for a further discussion).

## Why do outreach?

Outreach proved to be an important area of work for several reasons:

(i) as a form of needs assessment;
(ii) to reach people who do not want to join groups, and may have little or no contact with existing groups or organisations;
(iii) as a way of advertising and encouraging people to join groups;
(iv) to get feedback on MESMAC work and ideas for new work.

## Doing outreach

Generally there seemed to be several stages to the way outreach developed in MESMAC. These did not unfold in a linear fashion, and sometimes not all stages were reached. However there was a basic pattern which is described below.

### Preparation

Although it was felt that there was no such thing as safe outreach, only safer, there was much that could be done to make this work less risky, and a period of preparation was vital therefore. Projects needed to be clear about the legal situation and secure ID and insurance (see Miller (ed), 1993; van Reyk, 1990). Guidelines around the work were also drawn up, many drawing on Streetwise (a London-based outreach project) guidelines, which included: going in pairs; informing other staff of where and when you were working; not having sex with users whilst working. Some workers also underwent self-defence training.

Another practical issue to consider was whether to tell the police about the work. Some sites chose not to; Leicester in particular felt that the police would not be sympathetic to their work. There was also a concern that if the workers were identified by the police as MWHSWM workers it may increase the risk of the men they worked with being arrested; a kind of guilt by association. Therefore, those sites which did tell the police used their managers, or a representative, to liaise. It was felt important not to ask the police for permission, but to be firm and state that the work was happening.

For those working in indoor venues a further decision was whether or not to tell the owners. Leicester initially decided not to tell the managers of the saunas where they worked, fearing that this would make an issue of the fact that sex might be occurring there, and may breach the confidentiality of the men using the venue. Later a relationship was built with some of the sauna managers, which enabled the workers to seek information about the men using the venues; in one case workers showed a safer sex video in a sauna.

In addition to sorting out practicalities the workers also had to build up their own confidence. Therefore, it was important to talk issues through as a team and work out common stances on issues such as safer sex.

## Observation and familiarisation

This was crucial in terms of getting to know areas and understanding how they worked. In outdoor venues it was important to do this in daylight first of all for safety reasons. Most observation periods lasted about a month, during which workers would find the best venues or cruising areas and consider where within these to work. For example, Newcastle found in their chosen public cruising area that some areas were like a 'meat rack' (similar to the 'hot areas' described by Henriksson and Mansson, 1992), and they were likely to be felt up there, so they positioned themselves in more social places. Overall MESMAC workers found it was best to work away from where most sexual activity was taking place.

Discovering when to visit was also important. Places could be very different at different times of day (see also van Reyk, 1990). For example, in the Newcastle cruising area 'picking up' was a major concern in the evenings, whereas in the afternoon and very early morning it was more social. Often busy times were not the best times for working as people were less willing to talk. Not all public sex environments were suitable to work in – they might be popular but too dangerous, or there might not be enough people there to make work worthwhile. Working out the appropriate length of a session was also necessary.

## Finding a role

One of the most important aspects of outreach is developing a suitable role (see Broadhead and Fox, 1990; Deverell, 1993a). Workers had to find a way to fit into the environment and get trusted while keeping their separate identity. It was important that they were not seen by the men as a 'safer sex bore', 'gay do-gooder' or 'undercover policeman', as this would discourage contact. Indeed, part of the familiarisation stage was about enabling the men using these various places to familiarise themselves with the workers.

## Making contact

Through hanging around and getting known workers gradually built up trust. This was a slow process, requiring sensitive judgments and good interpersonal skills. Often it was a case of relying on gut feeling. The next step was to make contact. A key issue here was deciding who it was appropriate to contact. Although there were various signs that the workers could pick up on, attempting to identify which men it would be appropriate to talk to was often very complicated:

*...it is really difficult 'cos one week you might think 'Hmm, he's straight'. The next week you might think 'Oh, he must be gay'. It goes backwards and forwards. It's really quite strange. It's quite nice to see actually, because it tells you a lot about people and the way people act, but it's confusing as well and it's hard to actually go up to someone and say 'Oh I actually work for MESMAC' 'cos you don't know how safe you are. (12/12/90)*

Similar experiences to those of the MESMAC workers have also been reported for outreach work with (behaviourally) bisexual men in Australia, as Davis et al. (1991: 7-8) write:

*Often a worker's supposition about the type of man he is approaching is wrong. For example, the worker initially decided to approach men with wedding rings and who looked straight, in an effort to talk to bisexually active men. However, many of these men said they were gay and had no sexual relationships with women. At other times a man assumed to be gay and with very typical patterns of social interaction in the gay community was also having sex with women. These apparent contradictions are reflected in other research findings and alerted us to the non-fixed nature of sexual identity and the difficulties of conducting outreach to bisexually active men.*

Workers learnt to observe very closely and to keep an open mind. They all spoke of the need to err on the side of caution when approaching people, with some suggesting that this led them to target certain men, as one worker said:

*Maybe we choose our targets consciously to go for men who have more 'gay personality'...there was a businessman standing around, about 55 I suppose, with a briefcase, around outside the toilet obviously cottaging, but if we'd have gone over to talk to him, he'd either have thought we were renting and leave the area very quickly...or he'd just have buggered off immediately and, I may be wrong, but I have this little scene in my head before I turn round to someone and start talking. (17/12/92)*

As well as considering who they were approaching there was also an issue about whether projects could, or should, work with people under 16.

Workers used a variety of strategies to get men to approach them or to achieve contact. These varied according to the individual worker, the environment and the men involved, and often developed through a process of trial and error. Overall it seemed that having an open, friendly approach worked best. Cruising strategies were used, although the workers stressed the need to manage these carefully, and to establish their role as a worker as soon as possible.

Generally workers found approaching individuals easiest. There was a need to be subtle; for example, when in public cruising areas not rushing up to men or crashing about in bushes, but perhaps standing under a lamppost. Workers would take cues from people as to how long to keep conversation going – sometimes men did not want to talk at all. In addition workers had to be prepared to talk generally about absolutely anything.

Talking to some men proved almost impossible, as one worker described:

> *I don't know, maybe you're confronting them with something that maybe they don't want to admit to, their actual sexual practices that they'd rather not talk about. What they do is cottage in silence. They just get off with someone and that's it, they don't go off afterwards and have a chat. They can't talk to anyone about it. As soon as you start talking about it they're out of the door. (29/7/92)*

Where possible, workers tried to build on the contacts they had formed already. This was important as being seen with someone who was known helped to build up trust and workers could be introduced to other men. Some men found it hard to talk about sex with strangers, so finding someone they could identify with and getting them to disseminate information instead also worked well. The downside to using known contacts was that contact with other men could be restrained or limited, particularly if there were long-standing feuds or allegiances.

A key issue in relation to outreach was the identity of the workers. Many felt that only gay men could do the work since other men had not developed the necessary cruising skills. However, some of the workers felt that they had had to learn to cruise themselves and it was not something that all gay men knew about, or were skilled at. There was also an issue that being identified as an out gay man would prevent contact with more closeted men (see Chapter 7 for a further discussion, also Davis et al, 1991).

For Leicester a similar situation arose in their sauna outreach as in their clubwork: many black men did not feel comfortable talking to another black man. Many of the men met through outreach did not identify as gay and were having sex with men in secret. This meant that they were wary of being recognised by, or talking to anyone from the same community. As one of the workers reported:

> *Asian men will come to the door and ask if other Asian men are there. If there are they don't come in. (3/11/92)*

This meant that a lot of work was needed to build up trust and reassure men that they would not be approached outside the sauna environment.

Workers found that they needed to have a regular presence in order to build up their own skills and confidence, and to build up relationships with users. Building relationships could be difficult as there was often a different group of people each time the workers went. The slow pace and sensitivity that the work required meant that workers would often feel demoralised, and disappointed if they made no contact. It was therefore important for workers to debrief and get support, particularly early on in the work, when they felt under pressure to produce results.

## Introducing MESMAC

Sometimes the work never got beyond talking about the weather, but wherever possible workers would introduce the topic of HIV/safer sex. Occasionally the workers would tell men about the project and answer any questions, at other times they would try and steer the general conversation to HIV. On some occasions HIV or safer sex were major news stories and so the workers would be able to join in general discussions that would be taking place concerning these, for example pointing out any information that was incorrect.

As with clubwork, having something to offer such as cigarettes, condoms and KY helped as a way of striking up conversation (see also van Reyk, 1990). Flavoured condoms or more novelty items were particularly useful. Printed information had to be appropriate and frequently non gay-identifying, so that men could take it home. It was also important to have clear, concise messages and to use appropriate language. Trying to find out people's preferred terms worked best. The Leicester project found that speaking to Asian men in their own languages also helped build trust quicker and led to more candid discussions.

## Moving work on

Generally it was difficult moving the work from outreach to more collective action as people wanted information, condoms and the space to talk, but did not want to come to groups. Workers felt that for most men using public sex environments there was not enough in common to build a group around. The only groups that developed from outreach were those with something more specific in common, for example rent boys, who organised around issues related to their work.

This area of work was also the one where workers were most likely to reach non-identifying MWHSWM. Often men were married and did not live nearby, could not risk going to a group, or had no time because of family responsibilities. Many of the men were having sex with men in secret and feared being found out. Others did not identify as gay and felt they had little in common with other men they had sex with. Although there was often a collection of men using a place regularly they did not constitute a community, and certainly they did not define themselves as being part of one (for a similar discussion see Davis et al, 1991; van Reyk, 1990; and Bartos et al,

1993). Trying to develop a new group with men in an outreach setting was thus inappropriate; instead workers would encourage individual men to join other groups, for example a theatre or youth group. If the men were not interested in groups, workers tried to involve them in other ways (for example, asking their advice when producing materials). In this way they managed to tie their outreach work into the participation aspect of the CD strategy.

## Record-keeping

Here confidentiality was particularly important. Workers thought long and hard about keeping any outreach records. There was also a dilemma as to whether to tell men that records were being kept. As one worker wrote:

> *Do we tell that we are monitoring our meeting with them? If we do will that either put them off talking to us (we have to remember that their activities are criminalised by the law and marginalised by their communities) by engendering a sense of mistrust? However, what right do we have to collect this information without telling the men how it will be used? (4/12/91)*

All the sites kept records of their outreach, but developed systems of anonymity and confidentiality (see Miller (ed), 1993).

Outreach work proved a good way to find needs and contact men who may not be reached elsewhere. However, it was one of the hardest areas to move into collective action, although some individual men were attracted to existing MESMAC groups. It did prove possible to link into organisational development, however, with information from outreach work being used successfully to lobby for changes in services. In Newcastle funding from social services was also obtained for two new outreach workers.

# Forming new groups

Because MESMAC was a CD project this area of work was one of the main priorities. It involved establishing needs for groups, planning and setting them up, facilitating them and in some cases acquiring funding and enabling groups to become independent. Overall 23 new groups were set up through MESMAC work (see Table 3). Some of these were joint initiatives with existing organisations but most were set up by MESMAC alone. In this section we look at the groups MESMAC had sole or major responsibility for setting up and running.

## Table 3

### MESMAC Groups 1990-1993

Twenty-three new groups were set up (either by MESMAC alone or in collaboration with others). For example:

— Latex Productions (a lesbian and gay theatre group);

— Rent Boy Action (a self-help group for male prostitutes);

— a Police Monitoring Group;

— gay men's health groups;

— a Young Gay Men's Peer Training Group;

— young gay men's groups;

— black gay groups (for young and older men);

— a Black Peer Training Project;

— Gay Men Tyneside (providing social alternatives to the commercial scene and other activities, including safer sex education;

— Pink Ink (a group producing a gay and lesbian newspaper);

— a Gay Men's Photography Group;

— a Survivors' Group (for men who have been sexually assaulted);

— a Married Men's Group;

— Cruddas Park Group (a gay group for men on a local council estate);

— a self-defence group;

— Black HIV/Gay Workers' network.

## Why the work?

Setting up new groups was important as a way of encouraging men to share experiences and get support, while building up their skills. For many it provided a forum for meeting other men and became a valued alternative to the scene. As a youth group member said:

*(I) wanted something more than a 'phone line, didn't just want to talk, didn't want to go on the scene. (15/9/92)*

As such establishing new groups was a way of providing new resources and helped towards building up community infrastructure.

## Doing the work

A great deal was learnt about setting up and working with groups (see Miller (ed), 1993). Below we summarise some of the main points.

## Establishing needs

New groups arose from the basis of established need. This occurred in a number of ways: through the workers' observations and experiences; through a more formal needs assessment such as a questionnaire; or through men directly asking for a group. Frequently it was a combination of these developing over time. For example, the black youth group in London grew out of the project's aim to prioritise work with young black men, the fact that they had met very few black men through their work with existing youth groups, and the findings of a questionnaire survey carried out with 50 black men on the scene. The idea of a group was then developed through discussions with existing black workers.

## Advertising the group

One of the first steps in establishing a group was to advertise it. Often this took several stages: announcing the group was setting up and encouraging people to get involved; advertising the group itself and later advertising to attract more members. Workers tried to use men's input in this wherever possible.

Advertising included using cards, fliers, posters, radio adverts, local and gay press, word of mouth, outreach, telling men in other MESMAC groups, and using other organisations, contacts and referrals. Personal contact and word of mouth seemed to be most successful, particularly in places where posters could not be used for fear of increasing harassment and abuse (see Deverell and Prout, 1992a) and in relation to deaf men, where using existing friendship networks was often most fruitful in attracting other deaf men. However, adverts in general papers helped attract those not on the scene, and advertising local groups in the national gay press often gave them greater credibility.

Another important consideration was to think about how groups were advertised, for example, whether they were specifically for gay men or all MWHSWM, ethnically mixed or for black men only. Details about signers, childcare and travel expenses also needed to be included to encourage people to come. It was also important to have follow-up information if people rang about a group. The CD aspect of the project often made this difficult since the workers were keen that men set the agenda of groups and therefore had only a rough framework when establishing a group. As a worker explained:

> Because the group was so new and we didn't have a major agenda for it, or a clear agenda, when people were ringing up for more information we didn't have it. [We said] 'Well, it's going to be around health but it's very much up to you what you'd like to do inside that.' (29/7/92)

The workers felt that this was not helpful as people expected to get a clear idea about what a group would involve when they rang. They learnt to suggest some of the things a group may involve, which helped.

It took people a while to get the confidence to go to a group so the results of an advert could take weeks to materialise. This was particularly true in the case of deaf men, who told both the London and Leeds workers that it took a long time for information to reach the deaf community. Several ways were tried to encourage men to become involved; for example, meeting new members before the group and having clear equal opportunities statements. Lesbian and gay venues were not appropriate for those not out, or not identifying as gay, and confidentiality was also a major concern. Many black men also wanted to meet in venues away from their communities. For others, there was also a worry about using a venue associated with HIV or drug use. Finding good, central, fully accessible venues, however, often proved a major headache.

## Establishing the group

Having established a need for a group the workers had to decide upon the format. Although this process was always developmental and consultative it varied from holding open meetings where people decided together the focus and aims of groups, to workers being more directive about the aims and structures of groups.

It became clear that to get a group running there was a need for a clear structure, achievable and practical aims and regular, planned events. Although at first workers had shied away from pre-arranged agendas, seeing this as against CD philosophy, they found that having some structure was important, as long as it was flexible and participative. It was also important to have quick rewards such as free food and travel expenses to gel the group and encourage people to stay involved.

The need to establish a common shared aim and decide on the focus of the group involved considering whether the group was primarily social or task-centred; open or closed; for gay men only or MWHSWM; for men and women. There was also a need to set guidelines for the group and build in equal opportunities statements. The latter were crucial for running a group since it meant people could be challenged in a way that was not too personal.

## The workers' role

It was important for the workers to establish their role from the start. If the aim was to withdraw, this had to be stated.

There was also a need to think about their relationship with participants. Usually the workers would have a facilitating role, but they would encourage group members to plan and run group sessions in an attempt to build ownership and skills. Occasionally outside facilitators were used and here it was important to be clear as to their role and what was expected of them.

Often work was needed to give men the confidence and skills to run or facilitate groups. Workers would also help plan and prepare sessions and be available to advise men if they ran into difficulties whilst facilitating. Often this method worked particularly well and was a good way of integrating men's needs into the group. For example, in the Newcastle youth group one of the members ran a session on 'outing' after being picked up by the police for cottaging. His family discovered he was gay when a neighbour pointed out to them the ensuing article in the local paper. The group responded to the session in a very positive way and the discussions ranged from the unfairness of the police/paper/parents to the implied immorality of picking up sexual partners in public places as opposed to meeting them on the scene. The group were very supportive and suggested ways in which the facilitator could solve some of his present difficulties, including offers of accommodation and suggestions about how to deal with his parents' situation.

Running groups took time. There was a need to plan sessions, service the group and carry out evaluation. Although workers tried to encourage people in the groups to take on these tasks, frequently they found themselves doing them. Group members often did not have the necessary time to commit to such work.

## Maintaining involvement

In order to have a successful group there was a need to encourage people to stay involved. One of the main ways to keep people interested was to ensure that there was a social side to meetings and a variety of activities. Although many people referred to meeting new people as one of the things they liked most about groups, for some men going to a group for the first time could be daunting. Thus there was a need for sensitivity and support and it was important that the group was welcoming and friendly. Workers tried to find ways of encouraging old members to befriend new ones and would talk to members about the best ways to integrate new men. In Newcastle this led to the youth group developing a scheme whereby new members were met by old members before the group started and taken to the meeting room before others arrived.

It was important to develop a sense of ownership of the group, so having a clear goal and aims to stick to was crucial. The most successful groups seemed to be those with a very specific remit. However, it was important to reassess the aims periodically and check that the group was meeting needs.

The group had to be interesting since the people most likely to join were often those who were already active and had other commitments. Workers found that building the group around men's needs and encouraging them to plan group activities maintained involvement. Another way of keeping people involved was through encouraging them to get involved with other MESMAC work, for example helping with scene outreach.

One of the main reasons for people dropping out of groups was because of other commitments. In addition for some men MESMAC was the first initiative they had joined in relation to HIV and gay men, and often they moved on to other things once they had experience or skills. Other people dropped out because they had commitments such as exams, they became ill, got bored or could not attend regularly (particularly if their parents or wives began to ask too many questions).

## Who goes?

The workers found that the men most likely to go to groups were those who were out, or beginning a process of coming out. There was some success in attracting MWHSWM, for example, in a Married Men's Group in Newcastle, where they used an inconspicuous venue and ensured that no one else was around when the group met. However, most of the time workers found it hard to get men to organise around something that was secret. This was also true of black men. Only a small number were prepared to be out and identify as gay and for these often being black was a more pressing issue (see Chapters 6 and 10 for further discussion).

## Becoming independent

It was felt that it was not appropriate for some groups to become independent because the members did not have the time, skills, experience, confidence or willingness to run them. For example, members of the Married Men's Group in Newcastle felt that it was hard enough getting to the group let alone taking responsibility for running it. With other groups independence was always the goal and from the start of the group workers tried to build in mechanisms to achieve this.

The workers had to consider when they should leave the group. It was important to be flexible in relation to this as some groups needed more support than others. Rather than withdrawing completely, workers learnt that it was best to maintain some contact with the group, perhaps by reducing their involvement. It helped if some structure was agreed and left in place before the workers withdrew so that there was something solid for people to work around. Having resources to offer seed funding was also crucial in enabling groups to become independent. For example, when setting up Pink

Ink (a lesbian and gay free-sheet) Leeds MESMAC resourced the group so that it would not be dependent on advertising revenue for the first two issues.

Giving advice and allowing new groups access to MESMAC resources enabled them to build themselves up before becoming completely independent. Usually the projects developed contracts with new groups which specified responsibilities on both sides (see Appendix 5). This was also a way of integrating the MESMAC philosophy into new groups, for example, the importance of equal opportunities. Through experience it was found that having a dedicated core of people to take on the responsibility of running the group was crucial if it was to survive. Having regular reviews with the MESMAC workers to discuss progress also helped.

Setting up new groups was a direct way of meeting the support needs of men and enabling them to develop their own projects. In addition it provided workers with information on needs with which to lobby organisations and policy makers. In this way the work fed into both the participation and organisational development aspects of the CD strategy. For example, MESMAC groups were often used for consultation purposes by other organisations, and they also lobbied organisations to change their services. As well as providing new resources for MWHSWM in each locality, new groups added to the development of community infrastructure, particularly when different new groups started to work together and use each other as a resource. However, there were still a lot of men who did not join groups, and workers were keen to ensure that the groups did not become a buffer between themselves and the community.

## Workshops

Workshops usually took the form of a facilitated session involving discussion and group work exercises. Within MESMAC these were mainly in relation to safer sex, HIV and sexuality. Workshops were carried out by MESMAC projects for several reasons:

   *as a way of getting people involved in MESMAC;

   *to find needs;

   *as one-offs for other groups or organisations;

   *as one-off sessions or as part of a series for men in MESMAC groups;

   *as training;

*as a way of providing a collective experience for men who do not wish to join groups.

The sites felt that workshops were a good way to get people together to share information and experience and to discuss issues; as such they were both a first step towards a group and a complement to groups.

## Doing the work

Many of the considerations were similar to those of running groups (see above and Miller (ed), 1993) with thought required on the venue, day and time, publicity and the size of the group. Workshops were usually facilitated by MESMAC workers, although sometimes outside facilitators with particular skills were employed, for example, for drugs training or a health and beauty workshop. Sometimes the facilitators chosen were well known within the community, which helped to attract more people.

Workers tried to make workshops fun as well as informative, often producing their own resources or adapting existing ones to MWHSWM. Workshops were usually set up as a result of specific requests and tailored to the needs of men in the group. Centering the workshop around men's self-defined interests proved crucial in attracting people.

Some sites had greater success with more social events which had a workshop base but were not focused around HIV. For example, the Leicester health and beauty evening where men learnt about basic skin care and discussed the use of various cosmetic products was found to attract many more people than a safer sex workshop. In fact making events more informal-sounding than a workshop often helped. However, getting men to attend a workshop, like a group, proved hard.

As a resource for other organisations workshops proved a good way of raising issues and building up skills and thus contributed to organisational development. In addition several of the MESMAC groups which became independent asked the MESMAC workers to carry out safer sex workshops. This helped to integrate different groups and contributed to developing community infrastructure as well as building individuals' skills.

All the sites found that those people attending workshops got a lot out of them. They were a good way of training individuals and giving out information as well as providing collective support. However, they tended to attract only small numbers of men, even when there was a lot of publicity.

# Working with existing organisations

This was a diverse area of work, ranging from one-off contacts for resource or referral purposes to more intensive pieces of joint work. Workers also had a networking role trying to bring individuals and organisations together. As such there was contact with a diverse range of statutory and voluntary groups (see Chapters 5 and 9).

Work with existing organisations was important in order not to duplicate services and to build on the skills and support of other organisations, as well as to support other organisations doing similar or related work. Where possible workers tried to feed back their findings and encourage organisations to change or develop new services. Sometimes this involved informal lobbying, and was part of an overall cycle of work; at others it was a more formal piece of work in its own right and as such is discussed below. Existing organisations also proved a useful way to meet MWHSWM.

## Doing the work

In this section we discuss three main areas of work with existing organisations, including targeting MWHSWM, doing joint work and networking. Other work has included being a resource and lobbying, which is described in relevant sections below.

### Targeting MWHSWM

At the beginning of the project, workers in each site liaised with existing groups and organisations as a way of getting to know people and discovering what work was already taking place. This was also used as a form of needs assessment and in some cases led on to future work and the setting up of new initiatives (see Deverell and Prout, 1992a, 1992c), thus taking the work from grassroots to building community infrastructure.

Workers found it was important to be clear what they wanted and what they could offer when working with existing groups. A particular dilemma was how to meet their own needs without taking over the group's agenda. Another was that existing groups often had a target group different from MESMAC. For example, they might include older men or women and the workers had to fit around these.

Workers found that encouraging interested individuals to become involved in MESMAC initiatives was often more fruitful than trying to get the whole of an existing group involved. They were also keen to help existing organisations to develop as well as create new ones, and as such MESMAC often played a resourcing role. For example London MESMAC set up a small grants scheme to resource and support existing groups (see Chapter 9). In addition workers worked with people in other organisations to get information about MESMAC incorporated into their leaflets.

## Joint work

Several of the sites set up new initiatives by working jointly with other organisations. This included setting up new groups as well as one-off events. Joint work had the advantage of forging links which could help in building community infrastructure and enabled workers to build on the reputation, contacts and experience of other organisations. When this worked well it often led to lasting involvement.

When working jointly, workers found that there was a need to establish common aims and objectives and to define roles and responsibilities. Being paid workers and having resources, the MESMAC workers sometimes found themselves doing the bulk of the work, especially if those in other organisations were volunteers. However, they tried to ensure that the work was shared out, though working collaboratively often meant that things took longer.

## Networking

All the sites were involved in setting up forums to bring statutory and voluntary workers together. This involved meetings around specific issues – for example Tyneside's forum on sexuality work with people with learning difficulties – as well as developing ongoing networks for lesbian and gay HIV workers and black workers (see Chapter 9).

It was important to liaise with other workers to share ideas and support and develop common strategies. However, at times the workers found that networking turned into training and they had to educate other workers, for example through heterosexism awareness, before they could get support themselves.

As a well-funded project MESMAC often took a lead role in developing networks, being able to resource groups by providing a venue or administration. Ultimately the workers hoped that some of the networks set up would become more established and statutorily funded.

Working with existing organisations was a good way to find needs, target MWHSWM and develop MESMAC initiatives. It enabled the workers to build on existing work and skills, build alliances and feed back information. As such it was a useful way of understanding how organisations work and in some cases helped them to develop. In this way work with existing organisations often enabled grassroots work to be knitted together with strengthening community infrastructure and organisational development.

# Sharing learning

This area of work involved advertising and promoting the work of the project and sharing the MESMAC experience with others. Dissemination of the project's learning took place at both local and national level and included: writing up the work in the form of papers and reports; doing presentations, talks, workshops and training; reviews of work in the local media and adverts in the press; radio interviews; and through workers and group members using their MESMAC experience in other jobs. Dissemination was often a two-way process and as such this work enabled workers to keep in touch and learn from others in the field.

## Doing the work

The two main strands involved disseminating information formally, through talks, conferences and reports, and more informally, through workshops and answering telephone and letter enquiries.

As the project developed and became known, the MESMAC workers were increasingly used as a resource by other organisations, not just around HIV and MWHSWM issues, but in relation to black, and lesbian and gay work too. The sites were contacted by local, national and international organisations, as well as their host organisations and other MESMAC sites who wanted advice, information, training or support. Workers sat on interview panels, helped draw up job descriptions and carried out needs assessments for other projects.

The increase in British MWHSWM projects in the last year and a half of the MESMAC project had a big impact, with many requests for advice and information. This meant that the MESMAC workers began to be seen more as experienced workers than pioneers, and it increased the pool of other workers to share support and ideas with. Both the workers and the co-ordinators played a role in supporting the new MWHSWM projects which were setting up. The workers were particularly keen that other people undertaking the work should not have to start from scratch as they considered they had done, and felt a responsibility to share information. They also felt it important that they disseminated what they had learnt. As one worker said:

*We need to take a lead somewhere along the line and I think we should not be scared of that.*

*We have learnt a lot and we do have a major role and wealth of knowledge and experience and stuff that we need to let go of and document. (15/1/92)*

A key issue in relation to this was work time. As the workers took on more consultancy work, they began to worry that their own work would not get done.

Most time was put into dissemination at a local level since this is where the work was taking place and the workers were known and integrated into local networks. Outside London most of the sites found that they were initially the only ones doing MWHSWM work. This helped them to create a greater local profile which helped in dissemination.

Nationally most dissemination was achieved in the final year. It was felt by the co-ordinators and workers that this was because it had not been made clear who was responsible for disseminating the learning from the project nationally. The workers felt that the lack of dissemination nationally had led to their work being marginalised and overlooked at this level; this was particularly the case in London:

*Another thing is that I feel there is a lot of pressure from elements in the gay community saying 'Why are you doing this and why are you doing that? Why aren't you more like this?'...and that's quite difficult...A lot of this criticism has come from London-based groups who are actually very ignorant about what is happening in Leicester, Leeds and Newcastle...they don't even know what we are doing because there hasn't been the dissemination of information. (15/1/92)*

Workers found dissemination work useful as they were able to learn about other people's work as well as disseminate their own learning and experience. As part of networking and building community infrastructure such contacts often proved very useful. This work also helped to build the projects' profile and gave validity and legitimacy to the work.

# Materials production

This involved the production of materials such as leaflets, posters, cards, beer mats, condom packs and mugs, either for specific MESMAC campaigns or general project profile raising. Projects also undertook joint work with other organisations or were involved in host ventures. For example, the London team was approached to contribute to the development of the THT video for gay men. All the projects also worked with MESMAC-initiated groups to enable them to develop their own materials. For example, Leeds resourced the production of a leaflet for rent boys designed by members of Rent Boy Action.

## Doing the work

Like other MESMAC work materials production began from a basis of needs assessment. This took into account needs related to both the form and content of materials, as well as ideas for new materials. For example, the production of a pack containing legal advice was suggested by men in public sex environments.

As part of the CD way of working men were consulted about the style, images and language used in materials, and where possible were involved in their design and production. The workers found that using local references and appropriate imagery was particularly important.

The centrality of equal opportunities to the CD approach meant that the workers strove to incorporate positive images in their materials and tried to meet the needs of more marginalised men. Both London and Leicester felt a responsibility to use some of their funding to produce resource material which could be used by other black projects. They were also keen to produce materials that black men could relate to. For example, many black men feel the few posters which do feature black men portray them only as the partners of white men or use exoticised and sexualised stereotypes of black men. Leicester also began to develop resources for working with men with learning difficulties and developed material for conducting safer sex workshops in Asian languages. The Leeds project funded a local bisexual group to produce a leaflet and the London project resourced the production of materials for use with Chinese men, Jewish men and deaf men through their small grants scheme.

An issue which arose in relation to materials production concerned what could actually be depicted. Although all the sites worked within the existing law, several found that printers refused to print their materials (for example, pictures of men kissing), arguing that they found it personally offensive. Producing materials often pointed to the need for heterosexism awareness training in other organisations.

As well as the production of materials, sites also found it important to think about their distribution. Making information as accessible as possible was vital, for example by asking other organisations to stock MESMAC leaflets.

The huge diversity of MWHSWM and their different needs underlined the importance of having a corresponding diversity of material. For example some men liked more sexually explicit images than others; and both gay and non gay-identified materials were needed for MWHSWM. Involving men in the design and production of materials was an effective way of enabling their participation in a direct way.

## Lobbying and funding

This area of work grew in importance as MESMAC developed and the projects gained experience. It involved lobbying organisations to take on MWHSWM work or to change specific aspects of policy as well as seeking funding for further MWHSWM work. Some of the sites began the process of seeking funding early on by obtaining money for particular initiatives or other workers. However, most of this work began in the final year, when the sites all sought refunding to continue their work once the HEA contract ended.

This whole area of work was important in enabling the needs of MWHSWM to be heard at an organisational level and to secure recognition and resources for meeting these needs, thus playing a vital role in organisational development. (More details on what was actually achieved at this level can be found in Chapter 9.)

## Doing the work

To be successful in this area workers found that they needed good documentation and evaluation. For example, it was much better to be able to say '70% of the men we have spoken to said', than 'a few men I know said'. To some extent it involved learning how organisations work and fitting into that culture. This meant preparing well for meetings, getting known, and finding out what was being planned at a local and regional level. It was also important to have clear policies and ideas about what MESMAC could do.

Workers felt that it was important to get training on presentation and communication as well as being well-briefed on issues such as NHS internal market procedures, which had to be taken into account when submitting appropriate funding bids. It was important to tailor their proposals closely to what was required to increase their chance of being selected.

In relation to the statutory sector it was crucial to find out what committees and planning groups existed and to get invited onto these where possible. Once here workers found that through attending regularly, staying for the whole meeting and offering to write things they could have quite an impact. Often as the only gay representative on committees workers played a role in putting sexuality on the agenda of other workers, as well as HIV. As one said:

> It's the first time in Newcastle that you've ever had committees, groups – whatever – that have out gay representation, who are there because they are out gay men and are pushing the issues of gay men in general, not just HIV, and making people listen to that sort of stuff and...make it part of their agenda. You forget that at times, but its actually very important. (16/9/92)

This meant that in Newcastle, for example, the workers had the needs of young gay men specifically written into the HIV prevention strategy concerning young people. Through organisational development work such as this workers were able to air issues related to gay men's health and other needs and thus feed their experience and knowledge directly into policy-making. This was felt to be very important.

Although lobbying and funding could be time-consuming and took time away from more direct work it was essential to ensure that the work had maximum impact and effect. Several of the workers commented that such organisational work was also a way of creating lasting change.

## Summary

In this chapter we have shown that:

*the MESMAC project undertook a huge diversity of work at individual, collective and organisational levels;

*the work was both flexible and creative, with workers using methods appropriate to their locality and the men they were working with;

*the CD strategy enabled the workers to draw on a wide range of methods and techniques whilst still maintaining a clear aim and direction to their work;

*the CD strategy ensured that the work at many different levels was knitted together to achieve maximum impact.

# 5 Patterns of contact with project users

## Introduction

In the previous chapter we examined the areas of work undertaken by the local projects. In this chapter we turn our attention to the men (and women) whom the project contacted, providing an analysis of some of the numerical and quantitative data which has been collected in collaboration with the project workers. We have chosen the term 'project user' to describe those who were contacted by MESMAC. This is not entirely satisfactory because, as we shall show, there were many levels of contact. Nevertheless, we feel 'project user' is preferable to 'client' because the latter implies a traditional (often one-to-one) professional-client relationship that does not really fit MESMAC's style of work.

This chapter covers the following topics:

(i)  the sexual identities of project users;
(ii)  numbers of users directly contacted;
(iii)  levels of contact;
(iv)  the rate of making new contacts;
(v)  contact with other workers;
(vi)  a comparison of the first and second phases of the project.

The most basic information collected was the number of individual users directly contacted during the course of the project. Whilst we do not accept that 'more is (necessarily) better', it is clearly important to know what scale of impact (in this case in terms of individuals) MESMAC has had. The numbers of people contacted was recorded through various forms of monitoring (and where necessary estimation) by project workers. We distinguished between direct and indirect contact. By direct contact we meant any face-to-face interaction and/or exchange between project workers and users. We also counted some telephone contacts such as those involved in helplines or telephone advice giving.

Also important was the level of contact between individual users and MESMAC workers. We measured this by asking workers to monitor the number of times an individual was in direct contact with them. In later analysis this data was grouped according to the following categories (used in Tables 4 and 5 on page 97):

- observation only – when an individual was observed but not spoken to, in settings such as clubs, public sex environments and saunas;

- one-off – when an individual was contacted only once;

- occasional – when two to four direct contacts were made on separate occasions;

- regular – when five or more contacts were made on separate occasions;

- involved in project – when an individual acted as a volunteer, was very intensively involved in a MESMAC-initiated group (for example, acting as a group facilitator or attending very regularly) or joined a steering group;

- employed – when an individual did paid work for a project.

We were particularly concerned to be able to show any differences between the collective action aspect of CD approaches and more individualistic ways of working such as that used by many outreach projects. The main limit on this way of categorising data was that it did not refer to the duration of contacts. Thus, for example, brief one-off contacts (for example, giving out a leaflet during a safer sex promotion) were put in the same category as more intensive one-off counselling. This is clearly unsatisfactory but the alternatives, for example asking project workers to time encounters, were impractical given the diversity and complex character of their work.

An advantage of collecting data on number and level of contact, however, is that it allowed us to record not only the number of individuals contacted by MESMAC workers but also the total number of direct encounters they had with users.

The project also attempted to monitor the proportion of people of different sexual identity (as well as some other characteristics) which it contacted. Apart, however, from some conceptual difficulties with the notion of identity (discussed later in this chapter) there were some practical obstacles to collecting this information. Where workers had regular contact with individuals it usually became apparent (through MESMAC work itself) how people thought of their sexual identity, but with one-off contact (for example whilst doing safer sex outreach in clubs) it was not practical to ask every (or even most) individuals contacted. In making our estimates we have, therefore, drawn on other research such as the HEA Gay Bar Survey (BMRB, 1992).

We were also aware that the project may have indirect contact with individuals in many different ways. For example: men directly contacted might pass on information to others; condoms and leaflets might be taken by people the workers never actually met; and mass media work might reach others. Keeping an accurate account of these indirect contacts was impossible but we did ask project workers for any examples or indications they might have. In one instance (the Tyneside MESMAC Condom Distribution Scheme) the project workers were able to monitor indirect contacts more effectively (see Miller (ed), 1993a).

Workers were also asked to monitor their contacts with other workers in the HIV and related fields. This material was categorised in the same way as that for project users. The distinction between users and other workers is, however, not a completely exclusive one. Some other workers (especially those in the HIV field), for example, did join MESMAC initiated groups. We have done our best to avoid double counting these. The data on other workers has the same mixture of advantages and disadvantages discussed above in relation to users.

Across all the types of information the most reliable data were collected through the monitoring forms, meeting minutes, phone logs and other project records kept by the workers in relation to their work. Nevertheless, such records tend to be incomplete and therefore to underestimate numbers of users contacted.

In addition, there were a number of difficulties in collecting numerical information. First, no single monitoring form could have covered the diversity of work accomplished by project workers. Sometimes, indeed, the work was exploratory and until it became an established part of project work detailed records were not kept. Even then, record-keeping was rarely the first priority for project workers. Where necessary the evaluators asked project workers to make their best estimate (using relevant records and other material). We are confident that these estimates are within appropriate ranges and tend to be under-estimates. Nevertheless, the figures in the tables derive from varying sources of varying reliability.

A further problem was that it was sometimes difficult to make counts of the number of people worked with as individuals. For example, where outreach work was being conducted on different occasions by different workers it was difficult to track which individual men had been contacted by which workers.

Our data were collated in two main phases:

*Phase 1* covers the period from the establishment of the local sites to approximately half-way through the life of the funding (March 1990 to December 1991); the impact of the project during this period was the subject of an already published report (Prout and Deverell, 1992).

*Phase 2* covers the period between January 1992 to December 1992. Although this does not coincide with the actual date on which HEA funding for the project ended (which was March 1993), it was the last date at which it was practical to collect systematic information which could be analysed and written up.

Data from these two phases are used throughout most of this chapter but for simplicity's sake a specific comparison between them is left until the end.

The primary unit used for our analysis of impact is the project as a whole, i.e. the four local projects taken together. Where comparisons are made between the local projects, this is to show how their different combinations of opportunity and constraint have shaped their work and its outcomes.

# Whom did the project work with?

Underlying the work of the MESMAC project was an awareness of the crucial importance of the social, cultural and economic context of HIV. The result was that both the issues common to project users and the special characteristics of each group were recognised and respected.

Because MESMAC was very flexible in its modes of working and responsive to local situations, it proved successful in reaching a wide range of men who have sex with men. The range includes:

*extensive work with out gay men on the scene;

*working with less socially visible and more marginalised men.

The latter category included both younger and older men; black (Asian, Afro-Caribbean and other) men; other ethnic minorities such as South Asian and Jewish men; working class and unemployed men; married men; deaf men; men with disabilities and learning difficulties; and men selling sex.

It should not be assumed, however, that *all* the users of the project have been men. Some (a small number, which we estimate at about 200, or 2.5% of individuals contacted) were women. Some of these were contacted through work in colleges and schools, when project workers were asked to take part in social and personal education programmes involving mixed sex groups. Some outreach in clubs and pubs was in mixed sex venues and some of the work with groups (such as the formation of the theatre group Latex Productions, the work with SHAKTI and setting up 'Pink Ink') included lesbians. Similarly a small amount of the one-to-one work (for example, telephone enquiries) involved mothers whose sons were coming out.

It is also important to note that in some project work men's relationships with women partners was raised. The main example was the outreach work done by Leicester Black MESMAC; not only were many of the men whom they contacted in saunas married, but also in their gay club and pub work it was common to find black men accompanied by women partners. The work of the Married Men's Group, the Survivors' Group and Rent Boy Action also raised issues around the relationships MWHSWM (whether they identify as gay or not) may also be having with women.

The great majority (97%) of direct contacts made through the project, however, were with men.

Contrary to the fear that defining the target group as MWHSWM would lead to the neglect of gay-identified men (Scott, 1993), MESMAC worked overwhelmingly with men who identify as gay. We estimate that 80-85% of the individual men contacted have identified as gay.

The remainder (15-20%) were a mixed group of MWHSWM who do not identify as gay. They included:

(i) a large proportion contacted through scene work who identify as bisexual (see also BMRB, 1992);

(ii) a small proportion of men who sell sex to other men but who themselves identify as heterosexual;

(iii) some who were uncertain about their sexual identity (their involvement in the project may have been part of their process of deciding this, particularly in the work with young gay men and married men);

(iv) another large group were men of Asian, African and African-Caribbean origins (and other ethnic minority or cultural identities, such as Jewish) who, for various reasons, resist or reject the category gay. For some it may be a question of feeling strong family, religious and other cultural pressures not to come out; for others there is resistance to gay identity because it is seen as Western, white and/or middle-class (some have experienced racism in gay venues which seems to have reinforced this); many identify as straight, whilst others do not feel the need for a sexual identity.

Implicit in this account of the sexual identity of the men with whom the project has worked are some of the problems associated with the concept of identity, especially if it is thought of as a fixed and unitary characteristic of the individual. Whilst most men reached by the project clearly did have a relatively stable individual identity as gay, this cannot be assumed or taken for granted. In many ways what has emerged from the project is the importance of understanding sexual identity as a possibly more fluid and shifting phenomenon (see Chapters 7 and 10).

For some men their identity at a specific moment seems to have been related to the social context within which they were speaking. For example, the project workers in Leeds, who have strong and proud identities as gay men, reported that sex workers mostly identified as gay when in conversation with them. In contrast, one of the key figures in Rent Boy Action (RBA), himself a gay-identified man and an ex-rent boy, said that when working on the streets rent boys mostly claimed to be straight. The point here is not that one or the other identity must be true but just the opposite – that sexual identity may be more fluid.

The effect of social context on how identity is claimed is also illustrated by the experience of the black workers in London and Leicester. For them a major theme of MESMAC work was the difficulty of attracting other black men to events which were in some way identified as gay. Several workers pointed out that for many black men who have sex with men in a racist society there is little attraction in identifying oneself as a minority in an already oppressed minority (see Chapters 6 and 10).

# Number of direct contacts with project users

In this section we will present our findings on the number of individual users reached directly through the project. These are given in Tables 4 and 5.

As well as the diversity discussed above, the project succeeded in reaching a large number of men. Our data shows that:

> *in Phase 1 (March 1990 to December 1991) there was contact with at least 2728 individuals;

> *in Phase 2 (January 1992 to December 1992) this rose to at least 6178.

Because of inherent difficulties in collecting this data we cannot be certain how many of those counted in Phase 1 were also included in the Phase 2 figures. The possible range is, therefore, between a maximum of 8906 and a minimum of 6178. It seems unlikely that all the men in Phase 1 were recontacted in Phase 2 and our best estimate (based on a median figure) is that the project directly contacted approximately 7500 individuals. Since our data collection erred on the side of caution this is likely to be an under-estimate.

This figure is based on *direct* contact, involving an exchange or encounter (mostly face-to-face but including some telephone conversation), although these ranged from a brief conversation, through giving out a leaflet (for example during scene work) up to prolonged and intensive contact (for example during the training of peer educators).

# Levels of contact

Our figures for direct contact relate to the number of separate individuals contacted, but many of these men were contacted more than once. We therefore also collected data on the number of contacts (defined as any direct encounter with a project user, including repeat contacts). These are given in Tables 6 and 7.

Our data indicate that in Phase 1 there were 6365 separate contacts made, and in Phase 2 there were 13,162.

This gives a total for both phases of somewhat under 20,000 separate contacts with project users, indicating that each worker on average made contact with a project user on 80 occasions. Again because monitoring erred on the side of caution this is an under-estimate.

Although there were some differences between the two phases of the project (discussed below) we estimate that about 80% of users were contacted on a one-off

**Table 4.** Numbers of individuals contacted between March 1990 and December 1991 (Phase 1) by local MESMAC project, user (M) or other worker (W), and level of contact

| | MESMAC LOCAL PROJECT | | | | | | | | | |
| | Leeds | | Leicester | | London | | Tyneside | | Totals | |
| | M | W | M | W | M | W | M | W | M | W |
| Level of contact | | | | | | | | | | |
| Observation only | 22 | – | 64 | – | (100s) | – | 104 | – | 190 | – |
| One-off | 322 | 25 | 718 | 44 | 360 | 64 | 728 | 421 | 2128 | 554 |
| Occasional (2-3) | 28 | 8 | 93 | 4 | 30 | 6 | 147 | 41 | 298 | 59 |
| Regular (5+) | 10 | 6 | 131 | 19 | 30 | 8 | 62 | 17 | 233 | 50 |
| Involved in project | 45 | – | 4 | – | 18 | – | 1 | – | 68 | – |
| Employed by project | – | – | 1 | – | – | 2 | – | 1 | 1 | 3 |
| **Totals** | 427 | 39 | 1011 | 67 | 438 | 80 | 1042 | 480 | 2918 | 666 |

**Table 5.** Numbers of individuals contacted in 1992 (Phase 2) by local MESMAC project, user (M) or other worker (W), and level of contact

| | MESMAC LOCAL PROJECT | | | | | | | | | |
| | Leeds | | Leicester | | London | | Tyneside | | Totals | |
| | M | W | M | W | M | W | M | W | M | W |
| Level of contact | | | | | | | | | | |
| Observation only | 105 | – | 142 | – | – | – | 45 | – | 292 | – |
| One-off | 1954 | 525 | 428 | 380 | 1073 | 491 | 701 | 461 | 4156 | 1857 |
| Occasional (2-3) | 1059 | 122 | 133 | 37 | 51 | 46 | 190 | 118 | 1433 | 323 |
| Regular (5+) | 232 | 71 | 55 | 90 | 79 | 57 | 81 | 84 | 447 | 302 |
| Involved in project | 20 | – | 1 | – | 89 | 25 | 32 | 5 | 142 | 32 |
| Employed by project | – | – | 5 | – | – | 2 | – | – | – | 7 |
| **Totals** | 3265 | 718 | 617 | 512 | 1292 | 621 | 1004 | 668 | 6178 | 2519 |

**Table 6.** Total number of contacts (including repeat contacts) between March 1990 and December 1991 (Phase 1) by local MESMAC project and user/other worker

|  | Leeds | Leicester | London | Tyneside | Totals |
|---|---|---|---|---|---|
| Project user | 1820 | 2382 | 802 | 1361 | 6365 |
| Other worker | 34 | 151 | 170 | 694 | 1049 |

**Table 7.** Total number of contacts (including repeat contacts) in 1992 (Phase 2) by local MESMAC project and user/other worker

|  | Leeds | Leicester | London | Tyneside | Totals |
|---|---|---|---|---|---|
| Project user | 6905 | 1418 | 2379 | 2460 | 13,162 |
| Other worker | 1505 | 934 | 1249 | 1595 | 5283 |

basis (see Tables 4 and 5). Most of these one-off contacts were made through outreach work, the great bulk being accounted for by safer sex promotions (and similar work) in pubs and clubs. A smaller number were contacted through other outreach work on the streets or in locations such as saunas. The character of these encounters was typically quite short, perhaps a few minutes, and consisted of offering condoms and leaflets and inviting people to ask questions, or pointing out the presence of a safer sex display and stall. This would usually generate some in-depth conversations which might last for half-an-hour or more. A relatively small number of these one-off contacts involved one-to-one counselling, which could be very intensive, as well as helpline conversations on the telephone. Most of these forms of work could lead to further contact with individuals – often because repeat contacts were made in the same place.

The proportion of one-off contacts made by MESMAC workers was similar to that found in outreach projects in general (see Hartnoll et al, 1990: 21). In MESMAC, however, the recontact rate appears to be higher than that for outreach-only projects. In Phase 1, for example:

*600 (22%) were contacted more than once;

*302 (11%) were contacted five or more times;

Although the Phase 2 figures are harder to interpret (see below), they yield broadly similar proportions:

*2022 (32%) were contacted more than once;

*589 (9%) were contacted five or more times.

These Phase 2 figures are harder to interpret because they include contacts made during regular and large-scale safer sex promotions carried out by Leeds MESMAC during 1992. Although all the sites did club and pub outreach, the scale of the Leeds work in Phase 2 was far greater than that of the other sites. During the Leeds work over 3100 men were contacted on almost 6000 occasions – indicating that a substantial proportion of the men were recontacted. This extensive but somewhat untypical work might be thought to skew the figures. If the Leeds scene work is excluded from the calculations the proportion of recontacts in Phase 2 is adjusted to:

*797 (25%) were contacted more than once;

*589 (19%) were contacted five or more times.

Whatever figures are used, the range of recontacts was wide – between two (for example, someone encountered twice in a cruising area during outreach) and 50 times (for example, someone attending a very successful group).

This wide range is reflected in the average number of recontacts:

*in Phase 1 for those contacted more than once the average number of meetings was six;

*in Phase 2 the average number of meetings was seven (when the Leeds scene work is excluded from the calculation).

This seems to reflect the intensive character of much of the MESMAC work, especially the development of new groups where men were met very often.

A significant number of project users worked directly as volunteers for the project. In Phase 1 there were 68 such volunteers and in Phase 2 there were 142 (see Tables 4 and 5). The range of work they did was very great. Some acted as volunteers for specific, short-term activities, for example the volunteers who were recruited to help with Leeds MESMAC's scene questionnaire (see Deverell and Prout, 1992b). Others, for example in Tyneside, did outreach with the MESMAC workers in scene venues. Other work was specifically linked to setting up and running the various groups which MESMAC projects established. Some individuals would become especially involved in this work, for example by acting as a secretary or chairing meetings, or simply attending meetings on a regular basis over a prolonged period. Some men took on work that the MESMAC workers felt they could not do very easily. For example, in Leeds one black man set about building up a network of black MWHSWM and eventually formed a group of black MWHSWM. He was supported by MESMAC in doing this work but the white workers did not do it directly themselves.

Overall, we can say that whilst the proportion of one-off contacts for MESMAC was similar to outreach projects in general (see Hartnoll et al, 1990:21), the average number of recontacts appears to be higher.

At the time of writing we have found very little comparative data but an HIV outreach health education project (CLASH – Central London Action on Street Health) had an average recontact of three times (Rhodes et al, 1991:189). This difference in the average recontact rate between MESMAC and CLASH may reflect differences in the projects, for example their aims. The aim of MESMAC was to move from individual contact to collective action and we might expect that when this is successfully accomplished it leads to more intensive contact with clients than outreach alone.

## Rate of making new user contacts

In this section we examine the rate at which MESMAC workers made contact with *new* project users.

In a previous report on the impact of the MESMAC project (Prout and Deverell, 1992) we reported that during Phase 1 MESMAC recruited new contacts (i.e. not including any recontacts) at a rate of 11 per worker month. In a detailed appendix on how these figures were derived we explained that we had excluded from the calculation over 1300 men with whom project workers had had only brief contact (for example during outreach work in pubs and clubs). At the time of writing (mid-1992) this seemed a reasonable procedure. The project was still experimenting with methods of work, only one site had done mass outreach on the scene and this work seemed different to the more collective work involved in, for example, creating and building new groups. In retrospect our decision was probably wrong. As MESMAC work matured it became clear that large-scale outreach work could be an appropriate part of a CD approach and be integrated into CD strategies. On these grounds we have revised the basis of our calculations and have included in this report contacts made in all types of work.

On this basis our data show that MESMAC made *new* contacts as follows:

*during Phase 1 – 20 new contacts per worker month;

*during Phase 2 – 58 new contacts per worker month;

*taking both phases together – an average of 31 new contacts per worker month.

One difficulty in interpreting these figures is the lack of a baseline for other similar projects. Two reviews of HIV outreach available at the time of writing either do not give figures on contact rates (Rhodes et al, 1991a) or give figures which are not standardised (e.g. as a figure for each full-time equivalent worker month) (Hartnoll, 1990).

We have, however, been able to derive a comparative figure from the data provided by the evaluation of the CLASH project (Rhodes et al, 1991). This has been done by calculating standardised figures of new contacts per worker month for each project.

The MESMAC figure for new contacts per worker month is based on an assumption of 7.6 full-time equivalent workers over 17 months of work. The full-time equivalent worker figure is derived from: two in Leeds, 1.6 in London, two in Leicester and 2.5 in Tyneside (except for three months in Phase 2 when there were 3.5 workers). No allowance is made for project start-up, staff turnover or periods when projects were understaffed. The number of clients used in the calculation did not include 190 in Phase 1 and 292 in Phase 2 who were observed only. The CLASH figure assumes three full-time equivalent workers (Rhodes et al, 1991:52) reaching 741 clients over 31 months. Again no allowances are made for start-up, turnover or understaffing, although the full-time equivalent figure may be too low (Rhodes et al, 1991:100).

In these circumstances the comparison of data on contact rates must be treated with caution. Nevertheless, on this basis CLASH seems to have had a new contact rate of eight per worker month – lower than MESMAC. However, the two projects are not exactly comparable in terms of their methods of working – CLASH is a street/outreach project based in a confined area of Central London. Its geographical territory is smaller than MESMAC and it makes contact with individuals using a relatively narrow range of street-based outreach methods. This approach, although successfully making contact with a range of 'hard-to-reach' individuals, is slow and involves relatively small numbers (something MESMAC workers also reported from their own streetwork). On the other hand, MESMAC project 'patches' had larger populations than CLASH. As a CD project MESMAC had greater flexibility in its methods of working and was able to combine intensive and extensive work into an overall strategy.

The conclusion to be drawn from these factors was that MESMAC seems to have reached not only more people but was also able to engage with them at a variety of different levels, from one-off encounters to intense involvement with project initiatives. What this underlines, perhaps, is the advantage of front-line workers having flexibility over methods of working from within an overall coherent strategy.

It would be useful in future if further comparisons could be made so that a more meaningful baseline could be established for projects of this roughly similar kind. With more projects which include a CD component starting up this should become possible, and the need for these to monitor and evaluate their work is clear. Until then the contact rate figure in this report could form a starting point and could be valuable if sensitively used.

## Indirect user contacts

Although impossible to estimate, it is quite clear that the project has had effects 'cascading out' from those directly contacted. Examples include: the young men taking part in the London peer training initiative who reported talking to other friends who were not directly involved; a member of Rent Boy Action who has undertaken street outreach with sex workers independently of Leeds MESMAC workers; and the performances of the theatre group Latex Productions after it became independent of MESMAC.

Other initiatives have more deliberately adopted strategies for making indirect contact with a large number of people. A good example of this is the work done by Leicester Black MESMAC around World AIDS Day in 1992. Project members worked with the community care desk at Radio Leicester to present HIV/AIDS information on the *Six-o-Clock Show*, a programme aimed at Asian listeners.

One project initiative of this indirect type for which we have reliable information is the condom distribution scheme operated by MESMAC Tyneside. This work is the subject of a separate self-evaluation report (Miller (ed), 1993a) where the scheme, methods of working and outcomes are described in detail. In essence the scheme consisted of negotiating with the managements of a number of gay venues in Newcastle to install racks from which condoms, lubricant and leaflets could be taken by customers, and working with a volunteer who took on the job of restocking the racks each week. The type of condoms stocked were strong ones suitable for anal sex. Between August 1991 and October 1992, over 26,000 condoms (as well as a similar amount of lubricant) were distributed to men on Tyneside. In interviews with 25 of the venue customers, project workers found that 16 (84%) had taken items from the racks. Interestingly half of those asked said that they sometimes gave some of the condoms to other people (e.g. friends who were too embarrassed to take some themselves or who were from areas outside Tyneside where suitable condoms were not available). Workers also reported observing seeing more discarded condom packets (of the type distributed by the scheme and not widely available elsewhere on Tyneside) in the public sex environments in which they do outreach work. In the interview with venue customers (and other discussions with the members of a gay youth group) it was found that almost 75% of men said they thought the scheme had helped them to have safer sex and over 90% thought it had helped to make condoms more acceptable. The evaluation report concluded:

> *We believe, at the very least, that the scheme has stimulated a change in attitudes towards condoms among gay men, that it has helped others to maintain safer sex, and that it has proved to be a vital link in the multi-faceted strategy that is required if gay and bisexual men are to be empowered to look after their sexual health and avoid infection with HIV. (Miller (ed), 1993a: 55)*

Each of these examples of indirect contacts could also be looked at as instances of MESMAC helping to create better community infrastructures – something we discuss further in Chapter 9.

## Contacts with other related workers

Within a CD framework direct (or even indirect) contact with clients is an important activity but not one that excludes work and contact with other workers in statutory and voluntary organisations. In this respect all the MESMAC sites acted as a resource for, networked with and did collaborative work with other workers engaged in similar or related work. Over the whole period for which we have data on the impact of MESMAC the projects have worked with at least 3185 other workers. This work developed with the project and accelerated in Phase 2, as the following figures show (see Tables 4 and 5):

   *in Phase 1 contact was made with 666 other workers;

   *in Phase 2 contact was made with 2519 other workers.

Looking at this data in more detail shows that most of this work consisted of one-off contacts – often as a result of an enquiry or request for help and advice, or (most frequently) when MESMAC workers presented the work of their projects to groups of other professionals at conferences, workshops and other meetings.

Often, however, the contact was more prolonged. In Phase 2, for example, occasional contact was made with 323 other professionals and regular contact (defined as five or more times) with 302. Generally this work involved exchanges of information and experience and liaison around particular initiatives. It also involved lobbying other organisations, especially District and Regional Health Authorities, around work on MWHSWM.

A small number of other workers (37 in Phase 2) became more closely involved in MESMAC initiatives, working as volunteers or being employed by the project. For example, Tyneside employed facilitators for their Married Men's Group.

The aim of this sort of contact was varied but certainly involved raising the awareness of other workers on issues around HIV/AIDS and the needs of gay men and men who have sex with men. However, the most tangible outcomes of this work were at the organisational level and we will discuss these further in Chapter 9.

# Comparison of the two phases of the project

In this section we compare the patterns of contact between the two phases for which we collected data. In so doing we are able to show some differences which indicate how the work of the project changed over time.

The most striking result of the comparison is that as the work developed and the projects embedded themselves in their local context, their work both widened and deepened, i.e. the projects both contacted a greater number of individuals *and* did more intensive work. The main evidence for this from the pattern of contacts is that:

*the number of individuals reached directly through the project expanded in Phase 2 (mainly because of Leeds outreach in pubs and clubs), as did the number of indirect contacts (mainly through Tyneside's condom distribution scheme);

*at the same time the intensity of contacts, as measured by the level of repeat contacts, also increased;

*the number of new contacts per worker month increased geometrically in the second phase;

*networking with other related workers expanded greatly in the second phase.

In addition, we can point to the continued growth in new initiatives being undertaken (as well as their diversity) and the continued clarification and elaboration of needs assessment work.

Underlying each of these points is the fact that individual contact was part of a coherent CD strategy which intended to move beyond individual work and towards collective action. This is also shown in the examples of indirect contact we have given, some of which at least were part of the project workers' efforts to build up the local community infrastructure for gay men and for HIV prevention. Similarly, MESMAC went beyond making individual contact with users by networking intensively with other project workers.

Finally, our data seem to indicate that, when we compare the two phases of the project, MESMAC work generated a positive dynamic. The numbers and rate of making contact were, in the second half of the project, on an upward trend. This suggests that projects like MESMAC need at least two years (and possibly three) for the full benefits of the CD approach to become apparent. They are, however, worth waiting for.

## Summary

The flexibility permitted by the CD approach had a number of important outcomes:

*workers worked with a wide range of different groups;

*workers worked with both gay-identified and non gay-identified MWHSWM;

*insofar as comparisons are possible workers reached more men than through outreach alone and had a higher rate of making new contacts;

*workers had a similar proportion of one-off contacts to an outreach-only project;

*those men who were contacted more than once had a higher number of repeat contacts than an outreach-only project;

*MESMAC was, therefore, able to combine extensive and intensive work.

# 6 The needs of men who have sex with men

## Introduction

In the previous chapter we analysed whom the MESMAC project reached. In this chapter we look at the needs identified by the project users. As has been demonstrated already, needs assessment was integral to the MESMAC way of working and was incorporated into each area of project work. In this chapter we outline briefly the various methods that were used to identify needs, and discuss what was learnt about the needs of MWHSWM. This chapter therefore focuses on the views and experiences of the users of MESMAC. All the needs outlined here were directly reported to the workers or evaluators by men themselves, or emerged through the direct contact workers had with users in various initiatives.

We have chosen to discuss the needs of MWHSWM in two parts. First, we describe what was learnt about the needs of MWHSWM overall. Second, to balance this more general picture we discuss the different needs of more specific groups of MWHSWM. These include: married men; black men; men with learning difficulties; sex workers; men who have been abused; deaf men; and young men. The needs of these groups are highlighted because they relate to the initiatives undertaken in the project; as such these categories enable us to focus on the needs of a variety of different MWHSWM. However, readers should not consider these groups as a definitive list. For example, MESMAC also worked with working-class men and other ethnic and community groups such as Cypriot and Jewish men. In addition even more specific groups, such as older, married Asian MWHSWM were identified as having specific needs. It should also be remembered that these groups are not mutually exclusive: black, deaf gay men, for example, may have needs which cut across the categories we have created.

Whilst it is vital that the needs of specific groups are recognised and respected it is important that these do not become fixed and stereotyped. The needs presented here were identified in particular localities with particular men. Other projects should not use the experience of MESMAC, or any other project, as a short-cut to doing their own needs assessment. The findings of MESMAC are not necessarily directly translatable to other men in different localities. However, the experience of three years' work with MWHSWM should not be underestimated, and there is much that others can learn from and use as a general guide.

# Methods of needs assessment

As a CD project needs assessment was continually integrated into MESMAC work, rather than being a one-off formal exercise carried out before planning work. This view of needs assessment as something continual, integrated and dynamic meant it was seen more as a way of working than as the implementation of particular methods. However, several different approaches were used and these are described below.

The workers found that one of the simplest ways of assessing needs was through observing and talking to men. Observation often proved a good way of helping to decide where work was most needed. For example, the Leicester project undertook extensive observation of local cottages but decided not to work here as so few black men were using them. Talking to men involved, having an open, friendly approach and building up good trusting relationships was vital. As described in Chapter 4, whilst doing outreach workers would often share their own experiences and give out condoms and cards to men as a way of talking to them and discussing their needs. Opportunities to ask about needs also arose in one-to-one and group work, and workers also visited existing groups to talk to men (Deverell and Prout, 1992c). In addition to asking men directly about their needs, the workers found that men would often simply state them. For example, in the Leeds project some of the rent boys asked the workers if they could stock quelada (a lotion used to kill pubic lice) and many men asked for condoms.

Although the MESMAC workers did listen and talk to men, needs assessment was usually a more complex process than this. Often a lot of interpretive work was required to unpack what men's needs actually were. Sometimes men's 'presenting issues' were not always their major concerns; for example, an enquiry about HIV testing might in fact turn into a request for support around sexual abuse or rape; discussion on not having a regular partner and little safer sex information might in fact be related to racism. Additionally some men had such low self-esteem that they did not feel they had rights to services or information. Other men were not used to being asked what they wanted or would like, and found this way of working puzzling. This meant that discovering needs was often a slow process (see Deverell and Prout, 1992a), and a lot of work was needed to enable men to articulate their own needs. However, the effort the MESMAC workers put into getting to know men and understanding the environments they lived in paid off.

Another way of discovering men's needs was through the setting up of new groups. Through group discussions and exercises workers were able to draw out and develop their understanding of different men's needs. In order to do this building up trust was again essential, as was having a sensitive and non-judgmental approach. The fact that the workers were gay men themselves often helped to build trust and enabled them to understand and relate to the group members. Similarly, having black workers helped in working with black men (though see Chapter 4). Where workers did not feel able to run groups themselves they employed facilitators who had appropriate experience. The workers regularly talked with these facilitators about issues coming up in the group which helped to build up a picture of the needs of men they did not directly work with.

To further the opportunities for men to comment on the work of the project and express their needs, workers developed and used evaluation sheets and other feedback mechanisms. They also recorded information related to needs on their outreach monitoring forms. This material was often used as an informal needs assessment and was written up in the form of reports which were used to improve and develop the work. Collecting this information also enabled the workers to see what new needs were arising.

The most formal method of needs assessment was the use of questionnaires. These were mainly developed for use with men socialising on the gay scene (see Deverell and Prout, 1992b) and were a useful way of collecting the views of a large number of men. Such formal needs assessments often helped to widen the workers' understanding of men's needs, and helped them to prioritise what was needed. As a way of backing up the workers' more informal knowledge the results of questionnaires also proved very useful in relation to lobbying.

As can be seen above the workers drew on a combination of methods in order to assess needs. Being the basis of all their work needs assessment was something that continued throughout the project. As one worker said:

> *As far as I'm concerned once you switch off and decide that you've done all the assessing the needs then you've really given up on the project. With this sort of project, and because the way the issue of AIDS and HIV change day in and day out you have got to continually assess and evaluate where you are...and what the needs of the community are, as diverse a community as MWHSWM, that change constantly. You can't say that you've done the assessment. (21/1/91)*

All the projects were conscious of a responsibility to reach out to groups whose needs had often been forgotten or not well recognised. Where there were weaknesses or gaps in the work of particular MESMAC projects (e.g. in not effectively reaching black men) these were acknowledged and steps taken to remedy them. Although this work was often difficult it meant that the workers managed to discover a huge diversity of needs amongst MWHSWM.

## The needs of MWHSWM

As stated above the needs of MWHSWM are very diverse. Men who have sex with men come from a variety of class, ethnic and religious backgrounds, have different abilities and identities and different ideas about their sexuality. The needs of MWHSWM are therefore complex and at times contradictory (see also Davis et al, 1991).

Whilst the recognition of the diversity of needs is important, we have also been able to identify a large range of needs which are relevant to MWHSWM generally. In order to highlight these similarities we have drawn out a list of basic needs. Obviously such an overview involves making generalisations, and we recognise that not all MWHSWM will have these needs. However, our aim is not to produce a definitive list of the needs of MWHSWM but to highlight areas that deserve particular consideration.

## Homophobic society

A clear set of needs that arose throughout the work of MESMAC related to the experiences men faced through living in a homophobic and heterosexist society. It was obvious to all the workers that successful HIV work with MWHSWM had to address this wider context. As one worker said:

> *You can't divorce HIV from general gay issues – fighting HIV in gay men implies a commitment to gay men's equal rights...You can't disapprove of gay men or subscribe to the homophobia around and also attempt to be doing positive HIV work. (13/12/91)*

The lack of positive role models and validation of same sex relationships in wider society meant that many MWHSWM had needs around developing confidence and self-esteem. Even many out gay men suffered from internalised homophobia which led to their undervaluing themselves and therefore neglecting their own health needs. Many men wanted space to discuss issues relating to sexuality and also needed to have their own sexuality validated and accepted. However, this did not necessarily mean that they wanted to adopt a gay identity.

Many men had direct needs relating to combating homophobia, for example through self-defence and assertiveness training. There was also a need for support around homophobia and discrimination. In particular men needed information on their legal rights and there was a need for lobbying work to improve the rights of gay men generally.

Organisations, especially those providing services to the public, often made heterosexist assumptions. Workers found that the lack of information and service provision for MWHSWM meant that there was a tendency for MESMAC to become overloaded with referrals and requests for advice and support. It was vital that other professionals and organisations began to address and respect the needs of MWHSWM and to develop appropriate services and resources (see also Scott, 1993; Bartos, 1993; Davies, 1992). This implied a need for heterosexism and homophobia training with other professionals. As such workers felt it would be useful for those undertaking heterosexism and homophobia work to meet and share experiences and resources. Campaigning groups such as the Tyneside Police Monitoring Group could also play a role in collecting information to be used in lobbying for changes in services.

## Isolation

As a result of their marginalisation and stigmatisation, many MWHSWM found it hard to meet other men, particularly if they did not identify as gay or use the gay scene. Although these men could meet other men in public sex environments, this activity ran the risk of arrest or violence, and for many did not meet their desire for a relationship. Many MWHSWM felt socially isolated. There was a need for safe venues where men could discuss issues relating to sex and sexuality. For those men who had developed or were developing a gay identity there was also a need for opportunities to discuss issues and experiences in relation to coming out.

Many MWHSWM, including a lot of gay men, wanted opportunities to meet other men in a more social context than the commercial gay scene. They also wanted to become involved in more varied activities such as photography, sport and theatre. This was particularly the case for those men who did not like the scene, for example, because they felt marginalised there because of their age or race.

One of the main findings of the project was the importance and value men placed on simply meeting and talking to each other (see Chapter 8). There was a great need for men to have opportunities to share their experiences and get support. However, not all MWHSWM wanted only to socialise with other MWHSWM. There was, therefore, a need for existing groups to become more open to MWHSWM and for the development of some mixed groups.

## Safer sex

MWHSWM still had needs in relation to safer sex. One of the main ones was for appropriate, understandable and accurate information about safer sex, HIV and other STDs. Many men were still confused about issues such as oral sex and needed clear, updated information.

There was a need for a greater diversity of safer sex material which included a range of images and languages and was appropriate and accessible to different groups of MWHSWM, including men who were HIV+ (see also Wiseman, 1989; van Reyk, 1990). Leaflets and posters also needed to have appropriate local information and references. Material which was sex positive and validating of men's gay identity was scarce and needed to be produced. At the same time, there was a need for material which addressed men who did not identify as gay or were not certain about their sexuality.

In addition to information, MWHSWM required easily accessible, free or cheap condoms and lubricant. Men also needed information on the best type of condoms and lubricant to use and information and training in relation to proper condom usage. Many men still found buying condoms embarrassing, so ways needed to be found to make these more accessible.

As well as information and condoms, many men wanted an opportunity to discuss experiences and difficulties in relation to safer sex, for example having safer sex in long-term relationships, as well as opportunities to discuss previous risk experiences.

Work around safer sex needed to address issues such as self-esteem, empowerment, and negotiation. As such there was a need for appropriate skills and training. In some cases this involved addressing the sex men had with female partners.

A further need related to appropriate information and counselling around HIV testing. Men particularly needed to know where to go for a test, what the test meant and the possible implications of being tested.

As has been demonstrated (Rooney and Scott, 1992; King et al, 1992) there has been a lack of work with MWHSWM in relation to HIV and safer sex. As the currently most affected group in the UK in relation to HIV work with MWHSWM needs to be continued and expanded. However, it is not just the safer sex needs of MWHSWM that need addressing. For a long time the wider health needs of MWHSWM have also been neglected.

## General health

The experience of MESMAC underlined the importance of looking at health in a broad perspective (a point made by many other commentators, see for example Kjeldsen, 1991; Silin, 1987; Whitehead, 1988). Thus work with MWHSWM needed to address wider issues such as stress and drug dependency, which may directly affect men's health in relation to HIV, as well as more general health issues. Men also needed to know what services were available.

General health services also needed to be made more accessible to MWHSWM. Appropriate services needed to be developed and advertised and there was a need for heterosexism and homophobia training for doctors, nurses and other health care professionals.

There was also a need to look at men's health needs in the context of their relationships and family situations, for example by doing work around violence in relationships, or working with men's female partners.

## Resources

The experience of MESMAC showed that MWHSWM benefit greatly from being able to meet, share experiences and organise around their own needs. This meant that there was a need for resources to enable men to meet and develop appropriate initiatives. This included having access to venues as well as photocopiers, word processors, and other resources. Lesbian and gay groups have often found it hard to attract funding and this situation has been made worse with the 1988 Local Government Act which prohibits local government funding organisations which could be claimed to 'promote' homosexuality. There was clearly a need for statutory sector support and resources for lesbian and gay voluntary groups, both for general community work and more specific HIV initiatives.

## Economic needs

A further set of needs related to men's economic situation. Many men reported needs around housing, securing benefits, employment and ways out of poverty. These applied especially to working-class men and other disadvantaged men, such as some of those on the rent scene. Often these economic needs were seen to be more pressing than HIV. It was important that such needs were addressed by workers since they often had a direct bearing on men's ability to have safer sex. For example, in Leeds many of the rent boys in contact with the project talked about being paid more to have unsafe sex and several of the men contacted said that they were unable to afford condoms. Although it was hard for workers to tackle these issues directly they could be ameliorated, for example through work with housing officers and by providing free condoms and subsidised events.

Often men's economic needs were related to their sexuality so, for example, some men were made homeless through coming out or needed to be rehoused because of harassment. However, this was often not taken into account by officials. As young, single men are not a priority for rehousing this could particularly disadvantage young, gay men. There was a need for sexual orientation to be written into equal opportunities codes, and for the specific needs of MWHSWM to be taken seriously by housing officers and other officials.

This brief overview has sketched out some of the basic needs of MWHSWM. Many of these underline the fact that the lives of MWHSWM are shaped by larger social, cultural and economic forces and that sex, sexuality and HIV need to be seen within these contexts (see Chapter 7 and Homans and Aggleton, 1988; Deverell and Prout, 1992a; Connell et al, 1991; and Rodden et al, 1993). This highlights the usefulness of a CD approach which recognises the importance of addressing these influences and, where appropriate, lobbying for change.

In addition to these overall needs, the workers discovered more specific needs through their work with different groups of MWHSWM. Some of these are discussed below in order to highlight the diversity and variety of needs of MWHSWM.

# The needs of black men

The experience of the MESMAC project has shown that prevention work with black men who have sex with men often involves very different considerations from that with white men. One of the initial differences is that black MWHSWM are much less socially visible, therefore more work needs to be done to reach black men in the first place and discover their needs. It cannot be assumed that black men will be reached through general MWHSWM or gay men's work.

## Advertising and materials

One of the main findings of MESMAC work was that there was a lack of material available for work with black men. There were very few posters and leaflets which specifically addressed black MWHSWM and generic material produced for gay men was often inappropriate. Workers found that a lot of black MWHSWM were not out and were therefore often unwilling to accept information or attend events that might raise suspicions about their sexuality. Similarly, workers found that safer sex information was more likely to be widely accepted if it was designed 'for men' (rather than gay men or MWHSWM), or for black communities as a whole (see also van Duifhuizen, 1992). Raunchy, up-front gay-identified material was often inappropriate, particularly since black men were often put off by images which reinforced offensive stereotypes of black men as highly sexualised. There was a particular need for more positive images of black men in safer sex posters and literature.

In relation to HIV and safer sex information, black men needed culturally appropriate materials. It was also vital that the needs of different black communities were considered. Many different cultures and traditions are subsumed under the term 'black' and different communities may need specific targeting. For example, workers found that some Asian men assumed that black events were for African-Caribbean men only and thus it needed to be made clear that they were welcome too. Materials needed to be developed which included a range of different languages, images and references.

## Recognition of race issues

For many black men sexuality was not seen as a major issue. Living in a racist society many black men experienced a greater need for social support around race than sexuality. This was particularly the case since they were more likely to be identified and discriminated against on the basis of race. Many black MWHSWM were more likely to get involved in, and take action around, the social and political issues affecting black communities, than organise around sexuality. For example, a Leicester steering group member had to resign as he became politically active around the Gulf war and did not have enough time for the project.

The neglect of issues related to race in many existing lesbian and gay organisations meant that black men frequently found them intimidating and inaccessible. Often these organisations were predominantly staffed by white members, had white identified materials and were narrowly focused on issues of sexuality. As one of the Leicester workers said:

> *My own experience of talking to white gay men is that black gay feelings are marginalised and dismissed. [It's either] 'We're all gay, we all feel the same', or they've never thought about it...Often when you are thinking of coming out there isn't really a great deal to attract you. The whole of the gay scene as I know it isn't particularly geared towards black people. You can't think 'I'll come out because I'll have lots of support, lots of people to help me bear the pressures etc.' I'm all for making black people more comfortable [with their sexuality] rather than coming out totally isolated, or finding the only support they have is of a sexual nature. (8/5/91)*

This highlighted the need for other organisations to accept and take on board the different experiences of black MWHSWM. There was also a need for specific black initiatives. For example, the Leicester project worked with Leicester Lesbian and Gay Switchboard to set up a 'phone line service for black gays and lesbians. But although separate initiatives were important, it was also vital that the needs of black MWHSWM were integrated into existing organisations too, rather than being seen as the sole responsibility of black projects.

## Building a black gay community

Since there was not a large black gay community or culture to draw on there were few existing resources to support workers. This required a lot of initial work in relation to building community infrastructures. In London there was an out black gay scene, although it seemed to include only a small proportion of black men who have sex with men. In Leicester, and other provincial towns, the black gay scene was very small. A joke amongst Leicester MESMAC workers was that the only black gay men in Leicester were already working for the project – whilst this is not strictly true it is revealing about the realities of the situation. The Leicester project in particular found that much of its work involved thinking about and trying to create a specifically black gay culture. Events they supported, such as the SHAKTI socials and the fashion show, pointed up the need for events which had a strong but culturally appropriate flavour. This included, for example, having Asian dance music and using motifs from Asian culture in the design of tickets and publicity, as well as drawing on specifically South Asian traditions of cross-dressing. Rather than expecting black men to fit into European ideas of gay identity and culture it was important that they were able to express and explore their own.

## Family vs sexuality

A further consideration in work with black men related to their choices around coming out. Obviously for many white men coming out can be a difficult and painful process and there is often a hard choice to be made between family and sexuality, with many men leaving their families to come out. Many black men find this choice somewhat less clear cut, as for them the family is one of the few places where they can get support around racism. Additionally it is a place where they can draw on and experience their own culture and traditions, as opposed, for example, to a predominantly white, European gay scene. The Leicester workers found that many of the black MWHSWM they met were disillusioned with the scene. They had had high expectations of it as a place where they would be accepted and get support but instead had felt isolated and marginalised. As one of the workers pointed out:

> *Moving away from the family is a bigger deal. It is the only place I feel completely comfortable. I can get support, speak patois, eat Jamaican food – there are lots of other ties. (21/2/93)*

Some Asian married men reported that they received financial support from their families in return for keeping to cultural norms. This meant that coming out or making their sexuality known entailed a possible additional cost. This was particularly the case because coming out as gay could damage the marriage prospects of their brothers and sisters. Many black men felt that their identity was more bound up with their families than is the case for a lot of white men.

Because the lesbian and gay community appears to be so white and the scene is often racist and alienating, black men could feel that coming out and entering the gay community would be more difficult than staying at home and being closeted. As Peterson describes:

*Faced with anti-gay attitudes in the black community and anti-black attitudes in the gay community, black gay men experience a severe conflict between their racial identity and their sexual orientation. (1992:150)*

MESMAC workers described how many black men felt they were in limbo, stuck between two worlds, neither of which would accept them completely. Although many white men do not feel comfortable on the scene, and many white families are not accepting of homosexuality either, white men may be able to find more support amongst the lesbian and gay community. The workers found that it was important that different cultural ideas about the importance and role of the family were recognised, and that black men's experiences were respected.

## The diversity of identity

One of the important considerations in relation to work with black men was the need to address the complexity of identity and to recognise that people may choose to identify themselves in different ways. For example, some black men said there was a need for more black men to come out and identify as gay, and for there to be greater visibility of black, gay role models. However, others questioned the need for a gay identity which they saw as a white, Western one. A lot of black MWHSWM did not (and did not want to) define as gay. There was therefore a need to support black MWHSWM who did not want to take on a gay identity, as well as those who chose to identify as gay.

It was also important to recognise that some men did not identify themselves as black, or felt they had little in common with other black men. As the Leicester scene work demonstrated, some black men actually preferred to talk to white workers, because they felt threatened by an approach from someone of the same community. Because having sex with men is not culturally acceptable some black men preferred to socialise with white gay men who would accept this aspect of their identity. Some black men were also in relationships with white partners and worried about alienating them through becoming involved in a black project. There was therefore a need for workers to be sensitive to the different experiences and lifestyles of black MWHSWM and to work from the basis of men's self-identity.

Because black workers could feel rejected by users preferring to talk to white men, there was a need for black gay workers and other professionals to have appropriate support.

## Recognising HIV as an issue

As with other groups of MWHSWM black men often did not see HIV as a major priority. In some cases the racism that has surrounded the AIDS epidemic led to their distancing themselves from seeing HIV as an issue affecting black communities. Others saw HIV as a white, gay disease. There was therefore a need for work which enabled black MWHSWM to identify HIV as an issue for themselves.

Within MESMAC workers often had greater success using a more indirect approach to work around HIV and safer sex, for example through incorporating safer sex issues into 'health and beauty' workshops. Such workshops played an important role in themselves by improving men's self-image and self-esteem, damaged by the lack of positive images and role models for black gay men. Many black men on the scene told the Leicester workers that they felt unattractive compared to white men. This is also vividly described by Peterson writing about the experiences of black gay men in America:

> *White gay men express racism towards black gay men through their standards of physical beauty and the influence of good looks on social relationships...The selection of sexual partners is often made on the basis of standards of physical beauty that typically exclude characteristics likely to be found among black men. These standards emphasise aesthetic preferences for Western European attributes in skin color, hair texture, and facial features. Since black gay men are unlikely to satisfy these standards, they are less likely to be chosen as sexual partners. Therefore, these biases in choosing friends and lovers result in frequent discrimination against blacks in white gay male culture. (1992:153)*

Many black men greatly valued the opportunity to talk and share experiences with other black MWHSWM in a social setting.

The work with black men highlighted the need for a more complex understanding of the interplay of race and sexuality on people's identities. For some men their sexual identity was not always the most prominent or important identity (see Chapter 10). This situation was not unique to black men; many of the issues described above also arose in MESMAC work with South East Asian and Jewish men. It was also true of white men. For example, at times their age, class or occupation could be more important than their sexuality. Workers had to come to terms with the fact that sexuality could not be separated from other aspects of people's identities and lives. Sexuality was influenced by, and influenced many other variables.

## The needs of married men

In this section we describe the needs of married men as they were expressed in MESMAC work. We have used the term 'married men' because this was how these men were described by the workers. It may be that not all were actually married, but they were in relationships with women.

Married men are a very diverse group. Although most of the married men the project contacted were non gay-identified this was not true of all. However, most married men were not out and therefore confidentiality was of vital importance. Men needed particular reassurance that their identity would be protected and that they would not be recognised. As one worker described:

> *They feel they have a lot more to lose than other people...when I talked to this [married] guy last week he came in his car, in the daytime, and he kept checking out of the [office] window to make sure his car hadn't been stolen. Because if his car had been stolen how could he explain that to his wife, what was he doing in X on a Wednesday afternoon? That sort of thing really brings it home to you. (13/12/91)*

Meetings had to be held in venues that were non gay-identified, and where men would not be recognised. As married men often had to make excuses to their wives in order to get to meetings it was hard for them to attend groups regularly, particularly if they were held in the evening. The fact that they had to lie could also cause a lot of guilt. There was thus a need for flexibility and careful consideration about the time and length of meetings. Ways also needed to be found of contacting men outside meetings as they often could not receive calls, or mail, at home. There was also a need for non-identifying material when working with these men.

Many married men expressed a great need to discuss anxieties and feelings about their own sexuality. Their needs in relation to this were often very diverse. For example, some men feared ending their current relationship by acknowledging their sexuality, and felt isolated and guilty about having sex with men, whilst others wanted to come out and leave their wives. For many married men contacting the project was part of the process of coming out as gay; these men often wanted to know more about gay culture and the scene. However, other men did not identify as gay and wanted to find ways of meeting men to have sex with without the culture of being gay. Those men choosing to take on a gay identity required emotional support whilst they were coming out. Those who did not identify as gay and wanted to stay with their wives needed support in relation to not taking on a gay identity. For example, some men wanted to find ways of negotiating with their wives the possibility of relationships with men.

Men also wanted a chance to socialise with other men as well as discuss serious issues, to know about other STDs, and to find ways of having relationships with other men rather than just sex.

Work with married men often created a need for work with women. In particular there was a need for support and skills around negotiating safer sex with women, for example introducing condoms into an existing relationship. There was also a need to find ways of addressing the support needs of wives and female partners, for example by setting up a support group.

In addition this whole area of work could raise issues for gay-identified workers in relation to their own beliefs about the importance of acknowledging gay identity and their own tolerance of sexual difference.

# The needs of young men

The young men contacted by the project ranged in age from 16-25 and came from a variety of backgrounds. As such it is hard to generalise about their needs. However, several main themes emerged from the work as a whole and these are discussed below.

## Space to talk about sexuality and coming out

One of the most important needs for young MWHSWM was the opportunity to discuss issues relating to sex and sexuality with other men. Often young men were very isolated, many had not knowingly met a gay man before and had not been able to discuss sex and relationships with men in a detailed way with anyone. For many men there was a need to talk through confused feelings about their sexuality and to feel validated and accepted in their desire to have sex with men. Many young men also wanted support in combating homophobia. Young men also often appreciated the chance to debate wider issues relating to sex and sexuality, for example discussing the politics of 'outing', or the use of public sex environments.

For those men on the way to developing a gay or bisexual identity there was also a need to discuss their fears and experiences about coming out. Being able to draw on the experiences and support of other young gay men was particularly useful. Often this helped give men the necessary confidence to come out, either through hearing that other people's parents had not reacted too badly, or through feeling that they could get support from the group if their family rejected them.

Although meeting other young MWHSWM was often a source of relief and support, for some men it could initially be intimidating. This was particularly the case if they were not out and had not developed a gay identity, or had just come out. As one Newcastle youth group member wrote:

> *Safe sex has been mentioned frequently, but this at times can be intimidating with all the slang terms, especially if you are naive and new on the gay scene. (15/9/92)*

There was thus a need for workers to be sensitive and flexible towards the different situations of young men.

## Sex and safer sex

Although many young men had a basic knowledge about safer sex and HIV they still needed detailed information on safer sex practices and HIV transmission (for example the risks involved in oral sex). There was also a need for information on other STDs such as hepatitis B, as well as drug and alcohol use. Young men also wanted to know where they could access support and information, for example details of the local GUM (genito-urinary medicine) clinic, what type of condoms and lubricant to use and where to get them. Since young men often had limited resources, access to free condoms and lubricant was also vital.

Many young men did not have any sexual experience with men and thus felt quite anxious about negotiating the sex they wanted. In addition to having internalised feelings that sex with men was wrong, many had very little self-esteem and confidence. Thus, as with other MWHSWM, there was a need for developing skills in negotiating sex and safer sex.

There was also a need for work around sex and safer sex to be contextualised. Many young men did not perceive HIV as a major priority, for example they were more concerned about finding ways of meeting men, or sorting out housing, particularly if coming out had led to their being made homeless.

A further important issue related to men's legal rights. The current age of consent laws for homosexual acts created many difficulties for young men and for safer sex education with them. Young men needed to be aware of their legal rights and to know where to access appropriate support. As one said:

> On one instance we talked with a legal adviser who broached the subject of 'gay men and the law'. This taught us what to be on the lookout for, and there was actually someone there should we get into trouble. (15/9/92)

As well as advice relating to the age of consent men needed to know about legal issues relating to selling sex and using public sex environments.


## Appropriate and accessible materials

Many young men felt that the safer sex materials that were available were not appropriate to their needs. For example, many said they wanted images in posters and leaflets which they could relate to, rather than pictures of beautiful models in swanky flats which were far beyond their reach. Additionally some men found the language in safer sex literature intimidating and inaccessible, particularly if they were not familiar with gay slang. For those men who had not had sex, safer sex literature could also assume a level of knowledge or base of experience which they did not have. As many young men were not out they also wanted information which could be taken home without necessarily raising questions about their sexual identity.

Many young gay men did not read the gay press, go on the commercial gay scene or attend gay groups, so information needed to be made more accessible. The London project found that young men were more likely to access information from the TV, cinema, general press or youth magazines. There was therefore a need for messages for young gay men to be integrated into more generic youth materials and campaigns.

Additionally many young men did not have much money, so safer sex materials aimed at them, e.g. videos, needed to be in an affordable price range. Above all it was important that information was clear and free from value judgments.

## The scene and alternatives to it

Many young MWHSWM felt socially isolated, with limited opportunities for meeting other young MWHSWM. This was particularly the case for men who were not out, or who socialised with heterosexual friends. Although some were able to come out to their straight friends, others could not and thus felt particularly marginalised and lonely. There was therefore a great need for places for young MWHSWM to meet, talk and have the chance to participate in activities with other gay men (for example swimming, bowling and badminton). Since young men often had little money it was important that such social activities were subsidised.

Young gay men wanted the chance to build friendships with other gay men. As a Newcastle youth group member said:

> Getting the opportunity to interact with other young gay men, because otherwise the only option is to actually go out on the scene and run the risk of getting yourself into situations which you can't handle. (15/9/92)

Some young men felt that the scene was the only place where they could go to meet other gay men. However, for some it was too expensive and many felt uncomfortable and intimidated there. This underlined the need for social alternatives, especially since many young men wanted the opportunity to mix with men in a more social than sexual atmosphere, and be able to just talk to other men. Building up friendships with other young gay men meant that young men could develop support networks. Those who wanted to could then socialise on the scene together so that they did not feel so isolated and vulnerable.

## Sexuality education and safer sex information in schools

A major theme which came out of the work with young MWHSWM was the need for sex and sexuality education at school. Many men said this had to be addressed before issues relating to safer sex and HIV could be taught successfully. Several men wanted sexuality and safer sex information available at school, and others wanted homosexuality to be addressed more generally at school. Many young men felt isolated and vulnerable at school and therefore needed more support; as such there was a need for homophobia and heterosexism training for teachers.

The needs of young MWHSWM clearly highlighted the need for specific work with this group. Because of the important differences between the context of black and white work it was also important that opportunities to work specifically with black young men were created.

# The needs of deaf men

Although work with deaf men took place in all the sites, the work of London MESMAC in particular helped to highlight a major gap in service provision for deaf people. Below we highlight some of the main needs the project became aware of in relation to deaf men.

## Disseminating safer sex information

For many men in the deaf community access to information relating to HIV and safer sex was still limited. The deaf men pointed out that much generic gay safer sex material was not accessible, for example, videos without subtitles. The London site found that written information was not always useful since many deaf men had not had access to appropriate education and therefore had limited reading skills. In addition, written material frequently neglected the culture of reiteration through which many deaf men said they absorbed information. The London site found that disseminating information effectively amongst deaf MWHSWM was often best if it involved personal contact.

## Support and recognition

Because of limited access to information about HIV/AIDS there was still a lot of fear and isolation in the deaf community. Many men had little or no access to information about HIV or safer sex. For example, many of the deaf men involved with London MESMAC did not know about the need to use water-based lubricants with condoms. The men in Deaf MESMAC also told the London workers that many deaf men were dying with little support. There was thus a great need for better HIV service provision and support (including sign language interpretation) for the deaf community, as well as more resourcing for HIV and safer sex work with deaf people.

One of the main needs for deaf MWHSWM was to create a voice and lobby for their needs. Workers felt that they were often swamped by other lobbies which did not recognise the specific needs of deaf MWHSWM. This situation is beginning to be addressed through the emergence of Deaf MESMAC.

## Groupwork

Deaf men needed resources and a space to meet each other, as well as access to existing groups. Apart from sign language interpreters and written information to be provided at meetings and groups, for those men who were not out there was also a particular need for strict confidentiality in groups since the deaf community is fairly small and well networked.

From the work of the MESMAC project it is clear that the needs of deaf MWHSWM have long been neglected. Many complained that they were the last to receive information and felt marginalised within the gay community. The appearance of Deaf MESMAC is exciting in this respect since they are actively organising within the deaf community and beginning to get the issues of deaf men on the agenda of other organisations. It is important that such valuable work is adequately resourced and supported.

# The needs of sex workers

Many of the issues faced by sex workers include those covered so far, for example, access to condoms and lubricant, and skills to negotiate safer sex with both clients and partners. However, these men also had particular needs relating to their work. These included dealing with police harassment, and being clear about their legal rights. As well as being harassed by the police sex workers also reported that they faced harassment in the form of blackmail.

One of the main needs of the sex workers MESMAC worked with was for housing and money. Men also needed support around other health issues, for example, those using drugs who developed problems such as infected veins. Some of the men also needed support around mental health issues.

Many of the men wanted space to talk about sexuality. Some sex workers who did not identify as gay said that having sex with men for money could leave them feeling 'mixed up' about their sexuality. Although some men who sell sex define as gay, for others having sex with men is just a job. Therefore workers needed to be sensitive to, and work with, the different identities of sex workers.

As a stigmatised group it was important that the needs of sex workers were validated and respected, and that they were not marginalised or exoticised. In addition work with this group needed to avoid simplistic assumptions about the relationship between behaviour and identity.

## The needs of men with learning difficulties

One of the main needs for men with learning difficulties was access to appropriately presented information on safer sex. This included both spoken information as well as more visually based materials. As one of the workers wrote:

> As a worker who has learning difficulties, I am painfully aware of how inaccessible much HIV and safer sex information is...This puts people in a very vulnerable position in terms of HIV, and may in fact put them at greater risk. (Undated report)

There was also a need for developing skills around assertiveness and negotiation to enable men to make choices about the sex they had. Many men also had needs around low self-esteem.

Other needs included professionals in hostels and institutions respecting people's right to express their sexuality, and accepting that this may be with people of the same sex. This meant that there was a need to validate men's sexuality rather than seeing men desiring sex with other men as purely a result of not being able to have sex with women.

Workers felt that men with learning difficulties were a particularly marginalised group who were rarely catered for in health education initiatives (see also Wiseman, 1989). However, these men did not necessarily want separate groups, since this reinforced their isolation.

## The needs of men surviving sexual abuse

MESMAC Tyneside in particular uncovered an enormous need for support around men surviving sexual abuse. The needs of these men were not straightforward since the experience of abuse may have affected many areas of their lives. In addition, as the disclosure of abuse was often difficult, it could take time before this issue was raised.

There was a need for counselling, one-to-one work and support groups to enable men to discuss their experiences and feelings. Men also needed to explore the effects of sexual abuse on their own sexuality and their ability to negotiate sex.

One of the difficulties men who have been abused faced was the fact that their experience was often unacknowledged or denied. There needed to be more widespread acknowledgment of the existence of male sexual abuse and more sympathetic attitudes from the police and other public services (see also McMullen, 1990; Hickson, undated). This work needed proper co-ordination amongst service providers and training for the workers involved.

## Summary

In this chapter we have shown that:

*needs assessment was integrated into all MESMAC work, used various methods and sought to find out the needs of more marginalised men;

*the project found MWHSWM had some general needs, and developed a detailed understanding of the needs of different groups of MWHSWM;

*the huge diversity of needs and experiences of the different men that the project contacted reinforces that HIV and sexual health needs cannot be divorced from the broader framework of people's lives;

*work with MWHSWM requires a diversity of initiatives, materials and resources.

*the needs of MWHSWM should not be seen as fixed and stereotyped. Understanding about the complexity and diversity of the needs of MWHSWM should continue to be developed through MESMAC and other projects.

# 7 Issues in developing MESMAC work

## Introduction

In this chapter we consider some of the issues that arose in the course of the MESMAC project, expanding some of the practical issues briefly outlined in Chapter 4. Here we discuss the experience of the project in relation to issues involved in: undertaking CD work; who does the work; whom work is done with; the concepts used to describe the work; staffing structures; drawing personal and professional boundaries; implementing equal opportunities; training; support; and resources. The aim of this is to highlight some of the tensions that the work raised. Although this chapter is not focused around practical suggestions and solutions, we hope that some of what was learnt will be useful for others carrying out, or planning such work.

## Learning to do CD work

As a CD project MESMAC was based on certain principles which affected both the type of work and the way that it was done (see Chapter 1). As the project developed it was clear that this guiding theoretical framework was one of the most important dimensions of MESMAC. However, it took time for it to take root and establish itself.

Although the co-ordinators always had a clear idea about what community development involved, this was not the case for many of the workers. This meant that part of the work of MESMAC was about learning how to do CD.

At the beginning of the project many of the workers found CD theory daunting and confusing. They had the idea that it was important to start from needs, prioritise work with more marginalised men, and get people into groups, but how was all this to be done? The workers were very concerned to get things right and had many debates about how to carry out the work. As the first HIV project of its kind in Britain there was a lack of history to draw on. Sometimes the workers needed reassurance as to whether or not they were actually working in a CD way – for many it took over a year to comprehend fully what CD was.

The workers did receive some CD literature and training at the first project weekend but many felt a need for more practical and direct advice. Not all the managers were familiar with CD themselves, so in some sites CD input was not that regular. This situation improved over time, particularly as the managers and co-ordinators began to build up good working relationships and the co-ordinators became more involved in discussing and planning local work. MESMAC Tyneside also developed a closer relationship with a senior social services worker who had been involved in the Tyneside proposal and they were able to draw on her CD experience.

As the relationship with the co-ordinators improved the sites began to draw more on the co-ordinators' expertise. Some organised CD review meetings which they felt helped enormously, giving them practical tips and suggestions on how to develop the work. As one of the workers said:

> *Diagrams with arrows didn't help but later sessions where she (the co-ordinator) said 'Yes but doing that is CD' were good. (19/4/91)*

The suggestions and advice of the managers and co-ordinators in relation to actual pieces of work proved very useful to the workers. This underlines the need for detailed practical advice and support whilst workers are learning to put theory into practice.

About a year into the project a CD strategy was introduced: this proved immensely useful. Although it was based around the general principles that the project had been working with already, having these in a coherent framework enabled the workers to understand more clearly how all the elements fitted together.

A further key development in relation to the workers' confidence around CD was a national training weekend held in November 1991. This looked at the history of CD, the implications of doing CD work with MWHSWM around HIV, and the CD strategy. Through a series of exercises the projects looked at their own work in the context of the CD strategy and assessed its strengths and weaknesses. This practical focus was greatly appreciated. As one worker said:

> *I felt clearer about the CD process because of the weekend in Liverpool ...This helped to explain the processes in a practical way which could be applied to our working practice and was also a reassurance that our previous work was carried out within the CD framework. (12/12/91)*

As the project developed the workers' daily practical experience enabled them to unpack the CD terminology and understand what was involved. Although the work was complex and involved skill and sophistication, the ability to translate CD principles into practice and vice versa helped maintain a focus and legitimacy to the work and build the workers' confidence. This is illustrated by an extract from an interview with two London workers:

> *We are trying to get in touch with other agencies around London dealing with black people and black issues: Blackliners, BLGC, Let's Rap to get them to come to a meeting where we can thrash out where we can all go collectively.*

*What would (the co-ordinator) call that? Community infrastructure? Then this will lead to organisational development, and they'll lobby for better services – easy really! (15/1/92)*

Although this last quote is partly a joke about the fact that developing the work across the CD strategy is not easy, it also shows how the workers had internalised the CD strategy and were able to relate the work to this model. By the end of the project most of the workers had a good grasp of what CD involved and were very committed to the approach.

By the end of the project there were at least 14 workers trained and experienced in CD work. As one of the co-ordinators said, speaking about the lessons of MESMAC for CD work:

*One of the most striking examples is that people who are young, relatively inexperienced who don't have any formal qualifications can pick it up pretty quickly with appropriate support. That is all credit to the workers basically. It's a credit to their commitment and their grasp of it and the congruency of their own values to this type of work. (25/11/91)*

The workers' belief in the benefits of a CD approach can be evidenced in their commitment to continue working in this way when the pilot funding ceases (see MESMAC Tyneside, 1993).

The actual work undertaken by the projects is described in Chapter 4 and more detailed discussions can be found in Deverell, 1992; Deverell and Doyle, 1992; Deverell and Prout, 1992a, 1992b, 1992c; Deverell and Taylor (forthcoming), Prout and Deverell, 1992; and Miller (ed), 1993. Below we sketch out some of the general dilemmas that arose specifically in relation to doing CD work.

## How proactive should the work be?

As mentioned in the previous chapter needs assessment is integral to a CD approach. The importance of starting from established needs, rather than pre-defined ones, was taken very seriously by the workers, so much so that at the beginning some were concerned that safer sex had already been assumed as a need in the MESMAC aims and objectives. Having taken this philosophy to heart a key issue for the workers was in working out how proactive to be.

As the work developed such anxiety disappeared. There was a recognition that work had to start somewhere and that there was a need for some structure and focus. Workers learnt to view their work within an overall perspective, so, for example, rather than worrying that giving out condoms was making assumptions about people's needs, workers saw this as a way to reach men in order to discuss needs. This underlines the importance of integrating needs assessment into an overall framework.

## How directive to be?

Another key issue in relation to doing the work was how directive to be. As mentioned in Chapter 4 this was particularly the case in groupwork. As CD emphasises working with people in non-hierarchical ways there was a concern not to take over, and to encourage men to run initiatives themselves. This meant that at times some workers were anxious that they had too much control, whereas others began to feel that they were not directive enough. The London project felt they had not been directional enough at the beginning, which had been detrimental to the work (see Deverell and Taylor, forthcoming). Over time the sites began to find ways of balancing the need for some structure and focus, whilst being flexible and open. Thus they would ensure that people had control over the general direction of an initiative, rather than making them plan and participate in every decision.

## Validating own skills

A further issue the workers faced was in finding ways to validate their own skills and ideas. Being so keen to start from established needs they felt they had sometimes neglected their own knowledge and experience as gay men. As a worker said:

> It's hard because you are not meant to be directive but...we are young gay men and as long as we are not dictatorial we can be a bit more assertive about our own ideas, about the needs we intuitively know about. (15/1/92)

There was a tension between building on their own knowledge, experience and skills as gay men, and learning to be professional CD workers.

As the workers developed experience and skills, another tension arose. They began to question some of the suggestions for HIV prevention work coming from the grassroots MWHSWM with whom they worked. As one worker said:

> I do consultation, I listen to others' views, and there are people here telling me that someone with HIV should be shot, or [you should] produce scary posters. How do I deal with that? I'm bringing my own knowledge and experience to this job – I'm not a blank sheet of paper. (4/7/91)

The workers did not want to be seen as experts but needed to find ways of sharing their own knowledge and skills. They did this by getting the men they worked with to debate issues and consider different ways of working. They also began to develop initiatives which built on their own ideas but were developed through consultation with other men (see Deverell and Doyle, 1992).

## Collectivising work

As we mentioned in Chapter 4 a particular set of dilemmas arose in relation to bringing individuals together to collectivise their experiences. These issues are discussed further in the final chapter, but we outline some of the main points below.

It soon became clear that having sex with men was often not a sufficient focus around which men could organise. One of the main reasons for this was that for many men having sex with other men was something which they kept secret. For these men going to a group ran the risk of their being identified as a MWHSWM. Some did not even want to be associated with an HIV organisation, fearing this would identify them as gay (see also Bartos et al, 1993). The workers felt that it was very difficult to get people to organise around something which was secret. As such they felt that groups only really attracted men who identified as gay or bisexual, or were in the process of doing so. The projects did have some success in attracting men who did not define as gay or bisexual through the Married Men's Group, Rent Boy Action and the various black initiatives. However, this was done by focusing the group around something other than sexuality, e.g. being a sex worker or being married.

For work begun in public cruising areas a further issue was how to collectivise around activities that are illegal. Workers found that much of the sex in these environments was silent and that even trying to make contact with some of the men was impossible. Most of the men contacted here did not feel part of a community and had no desire to collectivise their experience, as often the sexual activity was all they wanted. As one of the workers explained:

> *What they do is about sex, it genuinely is about sex, it's not about wanting anything else and not being able to get it. It's not about wanting to be gay, wanting a relationship, wanting to come out etc. – those men are quite happy as they are. (24/2/92)*

The workers felt it was inappropriate to try and collectivise the work and build a community based purely on behaviour. As another worker explained:

> *I think there are some issues about fitting a CD model to MWHSWM, really – in as much as that MWHSWM is about an activity, whereas CD is about identity, in a lot of ways about society, about groups and about communities. So it feels very difficult, how to use a CD model with someone who doesn't have any social, political networks with other gay men, or other MWHSWM, and will they be artificial constructs if you try to put that together? (29/7/92)*

Collectivising work was easier with men who identified as gay since there was some sense of a shared identity to build on. However, even this was not always easy. Not all gay men were out and were still put off by the thought of being discovered. Other men were just coming out and found the prospect of going to a gay group intimidating; as one Theatre Group member said: 'Even going to a gay group is like coming out'. In addition some gay men felt that having a common identity was not a focus enough;

and some felt that there were other identities they would rather organise around; for example, as discussed earlier, for many black men organising around race was more important.

As can be seen in Chapter 4, the workers did manage to establish a lot of groups and collectivise the work successfully. However, they also accepted that sometimes group work was not appropriate or possible.

## Focus of work

Although each site had a specific brief each found it important to make further priorities. Deciding on such priorities usually evolved as a process: through talking to other people; finding out where men socialised and met; and building on the workers' own experiences, interests and skills. Because of the CD nature of the project the workers also tried to target under-resourced groups and reach more marginalised men. For example, Leicester chose initially not to work with existing groups but to try and reach men not in contact with groups or on the gay scene.

Prioritising work was a continual process. For example, some work was discontinued as workers left the project, and other work developed as new needs were discovered. In Leicester a lot of work had to be stopped because of financial difficulties which occurred part way through the project, resulting in the work which used the least resources being prioritised. In addition wider considerations also came into play. As one worker explained:

> *Steering group agreed it was not appropriate to continue working at the prison, where I was doing HIV awareness with young men in an environment where it was impossible for any of them to come out...If [you do work on the] scene the majority of men there will be having sex with men. [I'm] not sure how many of those in prison were. At some point whether [you] like it or not [you] have to engage with numbers. (19/6/91)*

The collective action philosophy of the project had an impact on the focus of the work, with stress on taking a wider focus than individual behaviour change.

As a CD project underlying all the work was a recognition of the importance of understanding the social, cultural and economic context of HIV. The workers were encouraged to take a holistic view, considering the wider social, economic and environmental influences which affected men's health. From the very beginning the workers found this approach valuable as it was clear that for many men HIV was not a priority issue. As a worker said:

> *How do you expect anybody to care about safer sex if they haven't got anywhere decent to live? I still think it's like the icing on the cake – once you get the rest of your life sorted out then you can start worrying about whether you are using a condom or not. (13/12/91)*

Contrary to some suggestions (see Scott, 1993) dealing with issues related to poverty, homophobia, housing, class and race were therefore integral to the success of the work and could not be isolated or treated as 'subsidiary factors'. As one of the unemployed men based on a housing estate in Newcastle said:

> *If you haven't got much money and you have the choice between buying condoms and a loaf of bread and a bottle of milk, what are you going to buy? (4/7/91)*

Dealing with sexuality and HIV in their wider context was, however, a challenge.

Apart from Newcastle all the projects were based in HIV organisations, and all were funded by the HEA AIDS Programme. Thus the workers experienced a tension between exploring men's perceived needs which were often not primarily, or directly, related to HIV and linking this to the project's focus on HIV/safer sex. Given the urgency of the HIV epidemic, and working in an environment where there are limited resources, it sometimes felt hard to justify more indirect work. Although the workers were keen to look at the needs of MWHSWM in a wider perspective, and to get these recognised by other organisations, they were often anxious if their work was not clearly related to HIV/safer sex. This anxiety was particularly the case since there is still a tendency for HIV work to be evaluated in relation to individual behaviour change. Not having this as an explicit aim, the workers felt that their work would be marginalised or dismissed by other HIV workers.

The fact that few general resources are specifically addressed to the health needs of MWHSWM increased this dilemma. As one worker said:

> *There is generally a need for lots of ordinary, basic work with gay men about general gay issues. I think that was always understood as part and parcel of HIV prevention work with gay men, but you do find yourself spending most of your time doing that kind of work, general gay men's support. I remember earlier thinking that wasn't right, that you can't just spend your time sitting in gay centres or wherever, but actually you have to do that. It's not that that's the easy option or what you want to do as a gay man. (13/12/91)*

In addition, because of the homophobia and heterosexism of some of the workers in other organisations, there was a need to prioritise work with them as well as MWHSWM.

# With whom should project staff be working?

As described in Chapter 1 the concept and term MWHSWM was seen as important at the beginning of the project because of its relationship to risk behaviour. Its strength was seen to lie in the fact that it could encompass all men who had sex with men, however they might identify. In the early days of the project some of the workers interpreted this as meaning that they should be prioritising work with non-identifying MWHSWM. However, this perception soon changed. As one co-ordinator noted:

> *The project was for men who have sex with men, not necessarily men, who define as gay...but in the last analysis you are going to work with gay men ...well, you are most likely to. Men who have sex with men who are not gay are not visible, or rarely visible. And all the projects seem to be starting, and I think rightly, with visibility. I mean, how can you work with what's invisible? (1/10/90)*

As time went on most of the workers began to use the terms MWHSWM and gay men interchangeably, and later even began to talk about MESMAC as gay men's work. This no doubt related to the fact that the majority of the workers identified as gay. For many of them a primary motivation for being involved in MESMAC was to do work with gay men. Indeed, by the end of the HEA funding period it was clear that the majority of MESMAC work had been with gay men. Interestingly, an earlier fear that people outside the project might be critical if all the work was done with gay men (MESMAC being a project for MWHSWM) was unfounded. Instead it seemed to be assumed that MESMAC had only worked with MWHSWM and neglected the needs of gay and bisexual men. However, despite the majority of the work being with gay men, there was a commitment to meet the needs of all MWHSWM which was reflected in the sites' continual attempts to reach more marginalised men.

Another issue that arose in relation to who was worked with was whether to work with women. Even though work with women was not the main focus of the work there were women working in the MESMAC project, many other related workers in the HIV field were women, some MESMAC work involved working with women and some clients were in relationships with women.

As an HIV prevention project it was important for the workers to take all risk behaviours into account. This meant addressing the needs MWHSWM had in relation to having sex with women. For example, the workers found that many of the men with female partners did not realise that HIV could be transmitted from women to men, or that they could transmit HIV to their female partners. It was important that work was done around this as research shows that men are more likely to have unsafe sex with their female than male partners, and women may be more at risk of getting HIV from their male partners than vice versa (Boulton and Weatherburn, 1990:11, Davis et al, 1991:19, Henderson, 1990:9). In any case the workers found that men themselves were often concerned about such issues. For example, some men having sex with women were very concerned not to place their female partners at risk; or wanted advice on how to negotiate safer sex with them; others wanted help and support to come out to their female partners.

Many of the workers found personal difficulties in working with men who did not identify as gay and did only a little work which addressed the sex these men had with women (see also Davis et al, 1991). For example, the Leeds team described how when working with Rent Boy Action, they always showed gay safer sex videos and would have felt uncomfortable with heterosexual materials, even though some of the men identified as straight or bisexual. They wondered whether this was one of the reasons why those men who stayed in the group either defined, or came to define as gay. This view was supported by a member of Rent Boy Action who said:

> *I mean our group's not specifically a gay group...and so a lot of members don't want to know about gay issues, and like MESMAC's always wanting to push gay issues, well just gay sex or gay activities. (13/2/93)*

The Leicester project did do some work with women since many of their clients were married or had female partners. However, they felt that this work was not valued or supported by other MESMAC workers.

All the sites found that it sometimes made sense to do work around sexuality as a whole rather than around gay men specifically, although at times this too was important. This meant that work with women also took place through joint work; for example, in relation to sexuality education in school, or building lesbian and gay networks. In addition, because of the project's equal opportunities framework the workers did not want to withhold valuable resources from women. They often took relevant lesbian literature to clubs when doing scene work, and undertook some initiatives which involved women. In fact working with lesbians was often part of strengthening community infrastructure. In Leicester and London the black workers found it important to work with the black lesbian and gay community as a whole since there were so few out, black gay men. Thus, although most of MESMAC work was with men, some work with women was necessary, either directly or indirectly.

## Gay, bisexual or MWHSWM?

There were continual debates within the project about the best concepts and terminology used to describe the work. The term MWHSWM and the motive for its use was interpreted in radically different ways by different project members. For some it was a useful way of recognising the fluidity of sexuality, encouraging thought about the diversity of MWHSWM, whereas for others it was a political cop out, a way of making work with gay men 'safe'.

Towards the end of the HEA funding period debates about the terminology for MESMAC type work gained wider currency and the HEA changed from using the term 'MWHSWM' to 'Gay, bisexual and other men who have sex with men' (GBO).

This caused some debate within the project. The Leicester site in particular was concerned that the term 'MWHSWM' was going to be rejected in favour of 'GBO'. Most of their work involved working with men who did not identify as gay or bisexual. They had spent time building up a structure to enable work with black MWHSWM and feared that this change in terminology would have the effect of marginalising and rendering invisible the needs of black MWHSWM. Other workers found the terminology patronising. As one said:

> *It's like a hierarchy. It's like if you are not a gay man you are 'other'...Unless you are sound about your sexuality you are somehow seen to be second rate. I prefer the term 'Mesmen' because then it, it's less of a label...People can define quite happily as a straight man and be a mesman and it's the looseness of the whole term that appeals to me. I think the whole connotations of the word 'gay men', to me it's kind of white, middle class people, kind of more privileged...well-educated types of people. (15/1/92)*

At a final Project Networking Meeting the issue of whether to use the term 'MWHSWM' or 'GBO' was discussed. Given the importance of working with as wide a range of men as possible the general consensus was that the term MWHSWM was the best option. There was a concern that workers would not make the extra effort to target MWHSWM (and thus not address the needs of many men) if future projects were set up as being for gay or bisexual men. Gay men could be targeted specifically within a MWHSWM project, and indeed the MESMAC experience showed that most of the men worked with were likely to be gay anyway (see Chapter 5). However, there was no clear-cut answer. The terminology presented a complicated set of issues, all of which had implications for the work.

# Who should work with MWHSWM?

A further issue that arose related to who should be employed to do work with MWHSWM. Initially it had been suggested that either women or men could be employed as workers but in the event only men were employed. When it came to recruiting further workers some of the sites thought about sectioning the jobs since they felt they would not employ women. One worker described why:

> *I think it needs to be a man because it's outreach work in public sex environments. I think men wouldn't react well to a woman doing that work. A lot of the men there are there because they have problems because they are married, whatever...I suppose I don't know why it should be a man, I feel that it should be, I know I haven't a rationale. I can't imagine a woman doing it. I also think it needs to be a man who has sex with men. (6/12/91)*

Generally, it was felt that it was best to employ gay men to do work with gay men. As one co-ordinator said:

*I mean you could have a gay man that wouldn't be capable of doing the work well at all. But by and large if you come from that community yourself, you have deep empathy with it, and you understand the issues, sure you're going to do a better job, aren't you? (4/11/92)*

However, there was some discussion about how dogmatic to be about this. As an HEA officer said:

*I think there is a danger, and that's part of the sort of fascism that is around at the moment, that everything for gay men or MWHSWM has to be done by MWHSWM. I think that to a certain extent is outrageous, because I think whilst you need an overwhelming proportion of gay men to work in that area, people should be entitled to have a choice, and people don't necessarily relate easily to other gay men who come from a particular standpoint about their gayness. (4/11/92)*

This was thought to be particularly the case when doing work with non gay-identified men. As a worker said:

*One of my concerns is the difficulty of having to target MWHSWM, whatever this means, who maybe have a strong heterosexual identity, as a very out, gay worker (for) someone who has no contact with the gay world apart from a bit of sex on the side. To be confronted with someone who is very out, and is coming from that point of view, may be completely alien and off putting. It's very effective when you want to go to a club, it's brilliant, but outside that environment it has a down side. (29/7/92)*

Although the project as a whole felt that a project for MWHSWM should be mainly staffed by MWHSWM, it was felt that there may be a case for employing other people too. Certainly some other projects have successfully employed women to carry out work with MWHSWM (see McKevitt and Warwick, 1993). It was felt that this may be an area worthy of further research. It was also important to think about the balance of black and white workers (see Chapter 4).

A further issue in relation to personnel was whether all the jobs in a MWHSWM project should be held by MWHSWM. Even if this was thought desirable, it was felt that it might not be practical. For example, the London project found that they could not be so selective as to only employ black gay sign language interpreters as not enough were available. Indeed several women were involved in MESMAC, as co-ordinators, administrators, evaluator or members of steering groups. Although everyone in the project recognised that there had been some tensions and difficulties having women involved, many of the workers valued the skills and expertise the women had brought and the women themselves got a lot out of being involved. However, at times the particular focus of the project made the women feel undervalued and marginalised. As two women said:

*I think all the time 'This is about men, MWHSWM, therefore what I think as a woman isn't really relevant'. You do feel as if you're a bit of a prop to them as you are forever promoting their sexuality. Sometimes I do get a bit angry and think 'Well, what about me?' (25/6/90)*

*I'm sure there's still some men involved that can't understand why there are women involved at all. I've certainly internalised that as well and said to myself 'What the hell are you doing involved in this project?' (4/11/92)*

These feelings were often fuelled by criticisms from people outside the project who questioned the place of women in a MWHSWM project. If women are employed it is important that they receive appropriate support.

In a discussion at the end of the project it was concluded that MWHSWM did not have to be employed for every job. Having the appropriate skills and sensitivity to the issues involved was seen to be sufficient, although it depended on what the work involved.

Aside from gender and sexuality it was vital to consider what skills people needed to do community development work with MWHSWM. It was felt that a wide range of skills and experiences was needed, although these did not necessarily include professional experience or academic training. Some of the main qualities and skills mentioned included:

- an awareness of and sensitivity to issues relating to gay men/MWHSWM;
- a commitment to equal opportunities;
- knowledge of HIV/AIDS;
- non-judgmental attitude;
- good communication and organisational skills;
- experience of individual and group work;
- ability to be flexible, adaptive and credible to a wide variety of groups and organisations.

## Personal/professional boundaries

One of the key issues that arose in the work was finding ways to draw personal and professional boundaries. This issue was highlighted right at the beginning of the project and was a continual theme throughout the work. In this section we discuss briefly some of the dilemmas the workers faced in drawing such boundaries.

The workers' code of conduct made explicit reference to the need for drawing professional boundaries:

> *Workers are responsible for negotiating and maintaining appropriate professional boundaries with their clients and must not use clients to meet their own social, emotional or sexual needs. It is not acceptable for workers to have sex with clients.*

The workers were involved in drawing up the code of conduct and all felt the need for, and importance of, boundaries. They felt that their work would not be taken seriously by other professionals, or the men they worked with, if it was known that they had sex with clients. As workers they were clear that they were being paid to do a job and as such had certain responsibilities:

> *My line is that if I'm working on the streets in a sense my sexuality is secondary to being a worker, and though I use my sexuality, I'm there as a worker, not necessarily as a gay man. Though I don't think I could do this work unless I was a gay man. I know that with that pay packet and with that contract comes a responsibility and that responsibility includes not having sex with those people. (17/12/92)*

The workers were concerned that if they had sex with some of the men they worked with and not others this would leave some men feeling unattractive. They also felt that it would be an abuse of their power as workers to have sex with clients, particularly where they had developed trusting relationships:

> *I still think it's bad to have a relationship with the person you've worked with. I mean, if you have an hour-long discussion with that person on child abuse...homelessness, employment, a whole lot of issues where they feel vulnerable, you've got that information. And I think that if you were to start a relationship with someone like that then I feel that would be an abuse of your position. (17/12/92)*

In this way boundaries were a way of protecting both the workers and the project. Although some have suggested that such rules are unnecessarily bureaucratic (see King, 1993b:6) the practical experience of the workers was that such boundaries were useful.

Although there were clearly important reasons for drawing boundaries this process was not always easy (see Deverell, 1993b). Some of the men, such as those with whom the workers did long-term one-to-one work, fell into the traditional professional-client relationship model, but many were members of independent groups, or were brief one-off contacts. In what sense were these individuals clients? This ambiguity around the categorisation of men was to some extent resolved informally. Workers were able to recognise qualitative differences in their relationships with different men and draw boundaries accordingly. Generally men who were group members or being counselled in one-to-one work were out of bounds in relation to sex with workers, whereas men who had only been given condoms in a club were not.

Living and working within a community meant that workers often found it impossible to have clear boundaries between work and their own personal and social lives: for example their friends would become clients, or were other HIV professionals. As one worker said:

> *You meet gay men in your work because you are working on the MESMAC project and because a lot of people, as we know, in AIDS and HIV are gay as well, so not only are they the people that you work with and spend a lot of time with in work hours, they are the sort of people you want to strike up friends with, people you are going to be mixing with anyway. Then people are saying like: 'You have to draw some sort of clear boundaries between professional and personal relationships.' What are you supposed to do, really: see all these people in work and then go home and sit in? (21/1/91)*

As such the workers' experiences were similar to those of other CD workers (see Cruikshank, 1989). However, as gay men the workers felt their situation was particularly difficult since the places where they could meet sexual partners were often also those places where they worked. Some workers tried to overcome this issue by only working in certain venues. However, for those working in small towns this was often impossible. For example, there may be only one gay club, and deciding not to socialise here because it was a place of work meant having to travel to other towns or having a very limited social life. Generally the workers decided not to use the public sex environments where they worked but most socialised on the scene, accepting the fact that the job involved some ambiguity in relation to boundaries.

Another important issue in relation to boundaries was making these clear to other people, both professionals and clients. This was particularly the case since the workers felt under pressure to establish their professional credibility and have their work valued. As a worker explained, talking about scene work:

> *It does become a problem if you are out there in your own time, you may well be out looking for someone and you do worry how other people may interpret what you are doing, because if they see you working for the rest of the week and then suddenly you are out chatting someone up... [are] they then going to say 'Look he's chatting up so and so'? That's always been a concern of mine. (24/2/92)*

Workers had to find ways of making it clear when they were working and when they were not. Communicating boundaries was especially important in outreach, since working in sexualised environments meant that the workers often had to turn people down, or stop sex happening. Through experience, workers found it was crucial to make their role clear as soon as possible. As one worker said:

> *You'd get in as early as possible that you're not looking for sex and where you're from. Other people might come up to you and say that they want to fuck you...but you have to put them off*

*and say that's not on the cards as you're there working and you immediately explain why. (17/12/92)*

As there were no real visible boundaries in outreach work, drawing boundaries could be very demanding, particularly if men were persistently asking the worker for sex. This meant that it was crucial for the workers to share experiences with each other and get support from their managers. In this situation the workers found it particularly valuable to seek support and advice from people who had actual experience of doing outreach.

A further issue in relation to boundaries arose in relation to the workers' own sexuality. They worried that sometimes they were seen as 'professional eunuchs', and did not want to be viewed as holier than thou, as this would interfere with building up relationships with their client group. The work also meant that they had to be very upfront about their own sexuality: in a sense the job meant they were permanently 'outed'. Although most of the workers could cope with this, some were concerned that it might restrict their future employment opportunities. Being so out about their sexuality did not simply have an individual impact: for some men it impacted greatly on their families and friends as well.

As well as having to consider their own boundaries workers also had to talk this issue through with people they employed, for example facilitators or signers. In some groups boundaries were built into the group guidelines. For example, it was made clear in the Newcastle Youth Group that it was not acceptable for workers to have sex with members, and they also drew up a complaints procedure for members to follow. The fact that the workers did not have sex with the men in the youth group was one of the things that the group members liked about the group.

## Staffing structures

Each of the MESMAC sites was staffed differently, with different numbers of workers being employed for different numbers of hours. All of the sites, except London, expanded during the three years, with Newcastle and Leeds employing extra workers and the Newcastle administrator increasing her hours. The Leicester site also employed a further outreach worker.

One of the main differences between the sites in relation to staffing structure was having full-time or part-time workers. These differences were most pronounced in London where all the outreach workers were part-time. This had numerous effects on the work. One of the advantages of employing part-time workers was that it increased the range of experiences and skills that could be drawn on. However, there was also a downside. Below we outline some of the main implications of having a team made up of part-time workers in order to highlight lessons for others.

## Balancing meetings with other work

Not being office-based, the London workers had fewer opportunities for relaxed, informal discussions about issues in the work, and the direction of the project, than their full-time counterparts. Therefore they had to meet more frequently to keep updated and informed.

As the work gathered pace the London team tried to cut down on meetings, particularly as these had to be held in the evenings when everyone was tired. Because so many issues had to be covered, decisions were often put off until there was time for further discussion. This, however, created problems for the administrator, who as the full-time worker needed decisions in order to get on with his daily work. As time went on team meetings therefore became more practically focused and were centred around making decisions, leaving less time for more wide-ranging discussion and debate.

## Balancing MESMAC work with other jobs

A further difficulty for the London site was the fact that all of the workers had other full-time jobs. Because of this, meetings were often held at times that suited the project members, rather than when it was necessary for the work. This affected the momentum of the work and often delayed important decisions (see Deverell and Taylor, forthcoming).

Other commitments meant that it was difficult for the workers to be flexible and responsive, so MESMAC events had to be planned well in advance. This situation was very different from that in Leeds or Newcastle, where workers had much more flexibility.

In addition the fact that none of the workers were office-based meant that the administrator had to take on more of a co-ordinating role and actually take responsibility for developing work and doing evaluation.

## Doing developmental work

Those working part-time were naturally not as immersed in the work as those involved full-time. Often it took time and effort to get back into the work and it was hard to build up a momentum and maintain continuity. This underlined the fact that CD work is very developmental, indeed, it was the developing nature of the work that made it so difficult to do with only six hours a week. As a worker said:

> *We are employed on what is basically sessional hours. It would be really different if once every week you came in and did a training session, or a few training sessions, or you spent three hours planning and doing reports. That's fine but we have evaluation, all the steering groups, committees we've had to do basically development work and you don't employ development workers on six hours a week. (15/1/92)*

## Sorting out roles

Whatever the staffing structure there was a need to work out clear roles and responsibilities and to review these. Both the Leeds and Leicester projects employed one worker as a project organiser to take responsibility for the day-to-day running of the project as well as finance and supervision. It was felt that this helped in terms of the overall management and co-ordination of the work. However, this hierarchy could create tensions between the workers. If there was no-one with a brief for overall co-ordination the workers found that it was important that each of them take specific responsibility for different areas of work.

As the projects developed all the sites found it necessary to have adequate administrative support. Both London and Newcastle employed administrators from the start, the Leicester project employed temporary, part-time administrators and Leeds negotiated administrative support with LAA.

Initially both the Newcastle and London administrators felt a little unclear as to how they fitted into the project, and it took time to work out what their responsibilities were. By the end of the project both their roles had expanded beyond the remit of administrative support. Because of the nature of the London site the London administrator's role developed into more of a co-ordinating one and by the end of the project he was undertaking training and group work. As co-ordinator he became integral to the team, keeping everyone in touch with each other.

The Tyneside administrator's role was developmental too, and expanded from administration into having responsibility for finance. As the project developed she also found herself doing more work with clients by welcoming them, answering phone enquiries and making referrals.

# Implementing equal opportunities

As a CD project equal opportunities was central to the MESMAC way of working. However, there was no overall policy relating to this. In the early stages of MESMAC the HEA did not have a policy which could be drawn on, and neither did some of the host organisations. For example, in Newcastle the host organisation's equal opportunities policy did not include explicit reference to sexuality, which had the effect of marginalising lesbians and gay men in the organisation and did not help MESMAC. The lack of specific guidelines meant that at times the workers felt there was little guidance in relation to implementing equal opportunities on a day-to-day level. However, there was a lot of commitment within the project to this way of working.

Part way through the project a new co-ordinator took on responsibility for equal opportunities; most consultation with her was through national training weekends on equal opportunities. Here the sites had a chance to look at their achievements and discuss blocks on and ways to develop their work.

In the local sites equal opportunities was taken seriously. Recruitment of the workers involved addressing issues relating to advertising, skills and experience and the make-up of the interview panel. In particular men were employed who had an orientation to CD work and appropriate experience but who did not necessarily have professional qualifications. Work was also done to enable men with learning difficulties, and those with children, to be employed, for example through providing childcare.

Once the projects were set up the workers continually worked to ensure that their initiatives were as accessible as possible. This involved: employing signers; providing money for childcare and travel expenses; having black-only groups; building positive discrimination into initiatives, such as prioritising work with black men and men with disabilities in the London small grants scheme; having subsidised and low cost events; having diverse and accessible posters and literature; and building equal opportunities policies into new groups. Through the diversity of groups established workers were able to reach a wide range of men. Part of their success in doing this was through creating safe spaces for more marginalised men to meet, and was testament to the commitment of the workers to reach as broad a range of men as possible.

Workers also tried to implement equal opportunities within groups themselves through building up the skills, confidence and self-esteem of those involved. For some members access to new information and the chance to develop skills opened up new career opportunities. The workers also conducted equal opportunities sessions in many of the new groups they established and would challenge group members where necessary, for example in relation to racism, sexism and misogyny. The workers found that it took skill to do this in a way that was taken seriously by the men without dampening the atmosphere (see Miller (ed), 1993).

As well as trying to make groups accessible, the workers aimed to ensure that all group members were able to participate. For example, in the London peer training group the deaf members were able to join in group discussions through the signer and occasionally games were developed using signs. The workers were keen to stress that people needed to be creative and adaptive. For example, although employing a signer worked well it did change the dynamics of meetings and did not solve all communication problems.

> *It is expensive having a signer. That's a price you have to be prepared to pay, and it does make sessions often quite long and laborious. Because the deaf men sign, and that has to be relayed back, and the spontaneity I think is really affected. We try and do mixed group work but if there is only one signer there is a limit to that, so people are still quite ghettoised, although integrated could be more so. In lots of ways it is quite difficult, doesn't mean is too difficult.* (15/1/92)

It was important that equal opportunities was not addressed tokenistically, for example assuming that employing a signer would solve all problems. The London workers pointed out that there was a need to find ways to communicate between meetings and to include the deaf men at all levels of the project (see Deverell and Taylor, forthcoming).

The commitment of the workers to equal opportunities ensured this remained integral to the way of working. With the help of managers and co-ordinators the workers reviewed their work and kept trying to find ways of meeting any gaps, for example finding ways of contacting more black men. For those involved in all-white projects this proved difficult but with perseverance was not impossible. Ensuring support for equal opportunities at a managerial level, for example through inviting people with particular expertise onto steering groups, also proved useful.

Nationally, discussion about equal opportunities was restricted to issues related to race for a long time. As some of the projects began to do work with deaf men and men with learning difficulties, issues relating to disability began to be addressed in national forums. This was helped by the employment of a worker with learning difficulties in Leicester who put the issues firmly on the agenda in a practical way. Similarly issues related to sex and gender, which were mentioned early on in the project, were not addressed specifically at a national level until the end of the project, when the Newcastle administrator and the evaluation fieldworker produced a paper relating to their experiences (Deverell and Bell, 1993). It seems that many of the issues relating to equal opportunities were difficult and complex and enough trust had not been developed within the project nationally for them to be addressed at an earlier stage.

# Training

There was a strong emphasis on training right from the start of MESMAC, which can be traced back to the review of safer sex workshops (see Chapter 1). The original training plan suggested that there should be three training sessions, two of which should take place before work started. Because the workers all started at different times this proved to be impossible so the training was staggered. There were seven national training weekends, which included introductory training, equal opportunities, sexuality, group work, CD, evaluation and clubwork. There was also a one-day training event on self-defence.

Reactions to the national training weekends were mixed. The main criticism from the workers was that they would have liked more practically based discussions, for example on basic counselling, or running a safer sex workshop. Several of the workers felt they had picked up groupwork skills through the participatory nature of the training, but overall most seemed disappointed with it and said they had learnt little. On the other hand most of the co-ordinators felt that the training had gone well, although some suggested that in retrospect they would do it differently.

The priorities for national training were usually decided by the group as a whole brainstorming what they would find most useful next session, thus giving the workers' input into the training programme. However, as the most frequently mentioned topics got chosen, local priorities were often displaced. One of the most successful training weekends was planned and carried out by a co-ordinator, freelance trainer and a worker. It seems the input of these different constituents created a theoretical and practical balance which the workers found useful.

Both the co-ordinators and the workers recognised that there had been a difficulty with the workers having to start work without having completed all the training.

There were several problems with the training weekends:

- The co-ordinators carried out the initial training weekends, which caused confusion among the workers as to the co-ordinators' role. In addition, the co-ordinators were initially very much perceived by the workers as an arm of the HEA which made it hard to build trust.

- A big discussion about equal opportunities on the second training weekend set up tensions within the group which affected much of the future training.

- There was an element of competition between the sites which was magnified as they began to develop strong local identities.

- For a long time the training weekends were the only places where the workers met each other. As such wider MESMAC issues would end up being explored here, taking time away from training.

- Individuals could feel marginalised, and this was particularly true for some of the black men in the project and the women.

Despite the difficulties, the workers did find the national training weekends a good place to get support and information. The opportunity to meet others doing similar work should also not be underestimated.

After the first year it was decided to have fewer national training events and to give each site money for local training. This was used for such things as counselling, typing and time management training. Other sites put on training events which they opened out to other sites, for example, Leeds did training on working with the media. Having local training helped cut down on travelling time and expenditure and allowed workers to tailor it more directly to their needs. It also enabled those sites who had appointed new workers to use this money to build up their skills in relation to basic HIV awareness, sex and sexuality, as there was not enough money to repeat the national training for them.

Although the training was of mixed success everyone was pleased that the importance of training had been recognised and that money had been made available for it. The amount of on-the-job training provided by both the managers and co-ordinators should not be underestimated. In some ways this locally tailored, specific and practical training was perhaps more useful.

## Support

Being in an innovative project meant the work was often exciting. However, it could also be difficult, frustrating and personally challenging. As such support was vital (see also van Reyk, 1990) and workers were offered a great deal of it, especially compared to many other jobs in the health and social services.

The support given to the workers varied across the projects and came from diverse sources. Most workers had support from managers and co-ordinators, as well as people in their host organisations and other HIV workers. Many also had external, non-managerial supervision. Additionally there was specific support in relation to certain areas of work, for example from the evaluators, or outside consultants. Besides this more formal support workers also drew on a range of informal networks (Miller, 1991). The support and reassurance provided by the managers and co-ordinators in relation to the work was greatly valued. The workers found it useful to have opportunities both to discuss issues generally and to receive direct advice.

Having such a wide range of people to provide support benefited the workers. However, at times it also caused confusion. There seemed to be an endless stream of people to talk to, all with different ideas and agendas.

One of the most significant problems experienced by the workers in relation to support was the fact that managers and co-ordinators all had full-time jobs. As the workers and co-ordinators built up relationships, the workers began to phone their co-ordinators more often for support and advice. Although this was very useful, at times the workers felt a lack of access to and support from them. Newcastle in particular felt quite isolated since most of those involved at a national level were based in London.

Workers received a lot of support from each other and this was helped through team-building and regular debriefing sessions. At the beginning of the project all the sites spent time team-building, which enabled them to explore ideas and feelings and to get to know each other. They all felt that it had been particularly important to discuss their own ideas and experiences in relation to sex and sexuality as part of this. As the work progressed and the workers became busier they found that they needed to structure in time to talk to each other as it did not happen informally. It was important that everyone was involved in the team-building process. The site administrators particularly could feel isolated because of their different role and needed to feel part of the team. In Newcastle this situation was compounded because the administrator was the only woman in the team but external supervision helped.

One of the important issues in relation to support was timekeeping. Because there was so much work that could be done and the work was often fragmented, the workers could easily take on too much, for example, by doing a full day's work and then several hours' outreach in the evenings. As such one of the roles of the managers and co-ordinators was to caution workers and check their workload. It was also important for the workers to monitor and record their hours.

A further consideration in relation to support concerned the managers. Some said that they would have liked more support themselves. Not all the managers went to PAG or network meetings so they did not have much opportunity to support each other. Having day-to-day responsibility for the work they felt that they would have benefited from more consultation and training. The co-ordinators' visits were usually taken up discussing issues with the workers and as such some managers felt they received little advice themselves. Where the managers and co-ordinators developed a close working relationship this was greatly valued.

## Resources, identity and materials

In order to do the work there was obviously a need for suitable resources and materials. Practical advice about this can be found in Miller (ed), 1993. In this section we consider some of the issues this work involved.

The sites quickly established that very few British materials were suitable for work with gay men/MWHSWM, particularly black MWHSWM and men with learning difficulties.

Each site was responsible for collating its own resources, although there was some sharing. It would have been useful for someone in the project to have had a role in collecting and disseminating information and resources but no one had the time to take this on. The lack of a central resource for MWHSWM material and information meant that a lot of time was spent actually getting materials. The workers felt that an organisation such as the HEA could have a useful role to play in collating and disseminating information (see also Scott, 1993).

All the sites found it necessary to produce their own materials (see Chapter 4). A key issue in relation to this was the sites' relationship to the HEA. Initially it was intended that the HEA would keep at arm's length from any materials that were developed in order to allow the sites more flexibility in terms of the style and language used. As the project progressed the HEA contract became more stringent and everything produced by the project was subject to copyright. This meant that the HEA needed to approve materials and check their factual content. About halfway through the project the HEA officers questioned the production of local materials, arguing from their broader experience of HIV work that there was a need to ensure that materials were not being duplicated. The workers and co-ordinators were very unhappy about this. As a co-ordinator wrote:

> The local sites need to produce materials arising out of their work which is relevant, accessible and produced with the involvement of local gay men. If the HEA takes a vetting role upon itself it devalues and unnecessarily constrains the work. (3/6/91)

The managers, co-ordinators and workers were concerned that they needed to be able to produce material appropriate to local needs, even if this meant producing a leaflet that had the same information as an existing one, but with local images, references and slang. They also pointed out that producing materials was often an important process of working with men. These issues were discussed at a national networking weekend where it was agreed that the sites should be able to produce such materials. The freedom and flexibility of the workers to produce their own materials proved a great asset to the project.

Developing local resources and materials also played a role in establishing each site's identity. As mentioned in Chapter 3 there was no strong sense of a national MESMAC identity at site level. This was partly related to a sense of competition between the sites, but also because they rarely met. Each site developed mainly as an independent project and spent most time establishing themselves in relation to their own locality. The priorities and experiences of the men in each locality varied and so the local project workers were unsure about the relevance of a national MESMAC identity.

Leeds MESMAC produced a poster which was liked locally, but when it appeared in a national newspaper there was criticism of the image from some of the London peer trainers, sparking a debate amongst the sites about whether they needed to consult each other when publicising projects in national forums.

One of the difficulties the workers found in creating an identity was the acronym MESMAC. They felt it would have been easier if this had reflected what the work was about. Indeed, once they started advertising their gay youth group, MESMAC Tyneside began to use the term 'Newcastle gay men's project' on their ansaphone. They felt that 'MESMAC Tyneside' sounded like a computer firm and they needed to reassure people in the first breath that the project had something to do with gay men.

The term MESMAC was equally problematic for the deaf men involved in London, as one of them signed:

> *There is a problem when I have to explain it to deaf people, have to sign and explain what each letter means. Men who have sex with men action in the community. Annoying. Not a word that means anything. (10/3/92)*

Interestingly, the deaf men who have formed Deaf MESMAC have not chosen a different acronym. This is no doubt because the term has become more well known and is now frequently used as a generic term for work with MWHSWM. The use of the term MESMAC in this way itself became an issue, and as new outreach projects began to emerge calling themselves 'MESMAC projects' the workers, managers and co-ordinators put pressure on the HEA to copyright the name. There was a concern that new projects were not all doing CD work and that MESMAC's explicit and specific focus should not be associated with general MWHSWM work.

A final dilemma for all the sites in establishing a definite identity was the fear of being ghettoised from other work. Many felt that other professionals would not undertake work with MWHSWM, seeing this as the brief of MESMAC. As such they were concerned to reinforce the need for all HIV workers to incorporate the needs of MWHSWM in their work.

There was also a fear that establishing a strong identity as a MWHSWM project would attract abuse as well as unwanted attention from the local media. At the beginning of the project everyone was quite concerned that at some point there would be a major attack on the work. Both the Newcastle and London projects attracted some press attention (see Appendix 6), but in both cases without any damaging effects on the work. In the case of Newcastle the fact that the HEA as a national body was funding and supporting the work helped in establishing its credibility. As the projects became more established and respected, and the need for work with MWHSWM was established as a major priority by the DOH (see Scott, 1993), the fear of a hostile press report which would close the projects down began to fade. This underlines how the external political contexts in which projects work can change, often quite dramatically, and underlines the value of securing organisational support for such work.

As the project developed HIV workers nationally began to promote condom use as part of HIV work. Earlier on in the epidemic, some organisations, such as THT, had encouraged people to explore alternatives to penetrative sex rather than promote condoms. By the time the workers were in post this ethic was changing. The importance of providing people with condoms and lubricant to enable them to practise safer sex was being recognised. The relative lack of availability and accessibility, particularly of strong condoms, reinforced the importance of this stance amongst the MESMAC workers. As such a large part of each site's budget was spent on condoms and lubricant. This was particularly the case with Newcastle's condom distribution scheme. In order to keep this going they successfully lobbied health authorities for money (see Chapter 9 and Miller (ed), 1993a). Although there was an initial concern that giving out condoms might be assuming needs, all the sites came to see this as an important part of their role. However, they all stressed the need to do work with men about the proper use of condoms.

## Summary

In this chapter we have shown that:

*having theory to guide work with MWHSWM is particularly useful; direct practical advice, training and support are also important;

*a range of skills is required for CD work, but workers need not necessarily have professional qualifications or academic training;

*CD work is more difficult for part-time workers;

*there is a need to do work with women, either directly or indirectly, and address the needs of men who are also having sex with women;

*a project for MWHSWM should be mainly staffed by MWHSWM;

*regular team building and support are important;

*establishing personal/professional boundaries is a useful but complex process;

*equal opportunities need to be addressed at all stages of work;

*projects need sufficient freedom to develop their own resources.

# 8 The impact of MESMAC on project users

## Introduction

As a CD project MESMAC was set up with the intention of moving beyond the individual and working for collective action and social change. Nevertheless, the various forms of data we collected from project users all indicate significant effects at the individual level. In this chapter we focus on the qualitative material that we collected to describe what the men (and women) contacted by the project gained from their involvement with MESMAC.

There were methodological and practical difficulties in producing this information (see Chapter 2). Nevertheless, we did find ways of collecting users' own evaluation of their contact with MESMAC. These fell into three main types:

(i) working directly with project users by interviewing them (individually or as groups) and asking them to complete questionnaires or evaluation sheets;

(ii) collaborating with project workers to design monitoring and evaluation methods which they could build into their work and negotiating access to project records;

(iii) interviewing project workers about their understanding of what their clients had gained through the work.

Through these methods we were able to collect a substantial amount of information and build up a good picture of individual impact. We feel it is particularly important that we obtained information directly from the project users themselves, on which this chapter is based. However, we have included the workers' observations where appropriate.

The fact that MESMAC undertook 91 diverse initiatives, all with different aims and involving different numbers and types of men, makes it almost impossible to generalise about the various impacts of the project on individuals, so we have chosen to base this chapter on case examples. These give a detailed description of what those involved in particular initiatives got from the project.

The case studies we have chosen are:

(i) The Tyneside gay men's youth group
(ii) Leicester black MESMAC's outreach in saunas
(iii) London MESMAC's peer training initiative

(iv)  Latex Productions – the Leeds-based lesbian and gay theatre group

(v)  Gay Men Tyneside – a social activities group

(vi)  Fit Together – a gay men's health group initiated by Leeds MESMAC.

These represent both the wide range of MESMAC initiatives and the different methods of collecting evaluation material appropriate to them. We hope they also convey a sense of the enthusiasm and involvement expressed by most of the individuals we spoke to directly.

As a concluding section we have provided a general overview of what those contacted by the project got from it. This brings together diverse material from across the sites and highlights the range of MESMAC's impact. We have organised this under six main headings: meeting needs; HIV and safer sex; sexuality; developing skills; confidence and self-esteem; coming out; and expanding social networks.

# Case examples of impact on project users

We have chosen to describe those initiatives for which we have the most material from men themselves. However, these were not necessarily the most successful initiatives, nor those that appeared to have the greatest impact.

## Tyneside gay men's youth group

Our first example is the youth group which was initiated by MESMAC Tyneside in October 1991 to meet the needs of young gay men in the city. The group was planned in collaboration with Newcastle Friend (a local lesbian and gay group) and a steering group composed of gay men involved in youth and lesbian and gay organisations. The steering group drew up guidelines and worked towards securing funding for paid facilitators. Funding, however, proved difficult to obtain and so the MESMAC workers offered to facilitate the group to get it off the ground. At the time of writing the group was still co-facilitated by the MESMAC workers and meeting weekly at a city centre venue.

The purposes of the group were to:

- help young MWHSWM come to terms with their sexuality;

- meet the social needs of young MWHSWM in the area;

- provide a safe and comfortable environment where young MWHSWM can meet and discuss the issues which are of relevance to them;

- provide support and advice to young MWHSWM about any aspect of their lives on a confidential basis;

- provide a safe environment where young MWHSWM can make new friends, have fun, discuss issues relevant to them and build up a network of support from people who share the experience of being gay.

The group was organised around discussions and activities which were decided in collaboration with group members. Activities included watching videos, badminton, ice skating, trips out, and there were discussions on issues such as HIV and safer sex, relationships, coming out, pornography, cottaging, religion, racism, sexism and experiences of sex. The group members were encouraged to plan and facilitate sessions themselves and also took some responsibility for welcoming new members.

There were usually 10-15 men at each meeting with eight regular men. They were aged between 16 and 26. Most of the men were white but there was contact with three Asian men. Three men with learning difficulties and one man with a mobility impairment attended the group. Most of the men identified as gay, some as bisexual and some were still unsure about their sexuality. The level of outness in the group was very varied.

Evaluation was carried out by the evaluators and the MESMAC workers through the use of group discussions (between the group and the workers, and a group interview with the evaluation fieldworker) and evaluation forms and questionnaires. All the evaluation showed that the group was highly successful. Below we highlight what the men reported on their involvement with MESMAC.

## Meeting other men

The evaluation consistently showed that most people considered meeting new people and making friends as the main benefit from the group. Many members enjoyed the opportunity to socialise with men in a supportive environment. As one man described the group:

*A safe haven in which to meet like-minded people without the pressure involved with trying to get to know people via the scene. (15/9/92)*

The supportive and social atmosphere was particularly important for those who were not out, as the group was often the only place they felt able to express themselves and get support. One man said that what he liked about the group was:

*Talking to people in confidence instead of bottling it up and bursting out. It's difficult not having anyone to talk to. (15/9/92)*

Several of the men started to meet up outside the group and some wanted the group to meet more often.

## Changes in social networks

For some men the friends that they made through the group led to changes in their social life. For example, the group usually went to a gay pub after the group; for those members who had not been to a gay bar before this acted as an introduction to the scene. The group was particularly important for those who were not out and whose social opportunities were limited to socialising with heterosexual friends. As one man said:

> It's better than going out with loads of straight friends; I can mix with my own people, make friends and talk to people, not just stand there like a lemon. (15/9/92)

Other men had visited bars or used public sex environments but not had the opportunity to develop friendships with other young men. The group enabled them to widen their friendship and social network and reduce their feelings of isolation.

The group served as a cushion to men coming out and helped them to learn about the gay scene and gay culture. Many of the men said that they had got support and confidence from the group. As one man said, in relation to what he liked about the group:

> Being able to meet in a confidential environment, support in coming out, making friends. The group is a good way to learn about the scene before actually going out to pubs and clubs. (15/9/92)

Many of the group members had had bad experiences on the scene or did not like to socialise there, saying that they found it intimidating or that they felt uncomfortable with the attentions of some older men. For many it did not offer the social and emotional support they wanted. One man contrasted his experiences in the group with those on the scene:

> It's nice talking to people without them thinking you're trying to get them into bed. That happens on the scene. (15/9/92)

Having a circle of friends to provide support helped men to socialise on the scene without feeling vulnerable and scared:

> You need friends before you go on the scene, then you can go out with a lot of people. If you walk in by yourself it can be frightening. (15/9/92)

## Coming out

The group also helped men to think through feelings about their own sexuality. The workers reported that many of the group members were now more confident about their sexuality, and several had come out to their parents since they had been in the group. This was supported by material gathered by the evaluation fieldworker. Over half of the group members who filled in questionnaires reported that the group had affected their coming out. Some of the men were already out and as such the group had not had much effect. For others the group had enabled them to come to terms with their sexuality and draw support from other young men. Sometimes this had marked effects. As one man wrote:

> It's given me the ability to deal with my sexual preference; my attitude to sex is more sensible. I haven't tried to kill myself because of being gay since I started to attend the youth group. (15/9/92)

Although some of the men were out and confident about their sexuality, many had internalised homophobia which lowered their self-esteem and made them feel anxious and distressed. Those who were uncertain about their sexuality often had feelings of loneliness and guilt. The non-judgmental attitude of the workers and the experience of being with a group of men who validated their sexuality and desires was therefore very important.

Many of the men said that hearing others talk openly and confidently about their sexuality enabled them to feel more comfortable and confident in taking on a gay identity themselves. For many of the men going to the group was the first step towards establishing a gay identity and coming out, as the following examples illustrate:

> Coming to the group was a big step for me. I came out to my parents after a while – I couldn't be bothered lying about where I was going any more. I got support from the group. (15/9/92)

> Since joining the group I've found confidence to be happy with my sexuality and to come out to all and sundry. (15/9/92)

> It has allowed me to come out to my best friend (girl) at the beginning. Another friend of mine is gay so that wasn't an issue – he actually integrated me into the group. It has, however, not helped me to come out to my parents and family and other friends. (15/9/92)

For some men their increased confidence helped when talking to other gay men and made them better able to deal with abuse from others.

Not all of the men went on to come out, or even identify as gay, some choosing to identify as bisexual. However, the group certainly played a significant role in supporting men in relation to their sexuality and helped them to feel less isolated and marginalised. Having successful, out gay, facilitators was seen by some to be important in this respect. The members felt the workers could relate to their experiences, and they served as much needed positive role models.

## Skills

Participation in the youth group enabled men to develop their awareness and skills. They learnt about safer sex, legal rights, STDs, dealing with abuse and the gay scene. They were also challenged in relation to racism and sexism and had sessions on equal opportunities.

Through contributing to, planning and facilitating sessions men also developed groupwork, communication and presentation skills. Some also helped to produce a poster and flyer for the youth group.

Members had the opportunity to share their skills and experiences, both through the running of sessions and through being consulted by other organisations in relation to particular projects. For example, the producers of the THT safer sex video for gay men talked to the group about their needs, and members were interviewed for a magazine article on young gay men. Such consultation enabled men to articulate their needs and contribute to improving service provision for young gay men.

## HIV/safer sex

Addressing HIV and safer sex was frequently addressed and always mentioned in discussions about sex. As one man said:

> *Well, there are safer sex posters everywhere. Before you get your foot though the door they are saying 'wear a condom', so you take the hint! (15/9/92)*

However, members appreciated that it was 'not rammed down your throat'. They also liked the fact that HIV information was given to them in an appropriate form, i.e., within a gay perspective on HIV.

There were several debates within the group related to HIV issues, as well as sessions on HIV testing, HIV transmission, safer sex and sex in relationships, leading to a general increase in awareness about HIV. All of the group members who filled in a questionnaire reported that they had learnt something about HIV/AIDS (33% very much, 50% a fair amount and 17% a little). Changes in specific information included the risks involved in oral sex and fucking; for example, some previously believed they were not at risk as the penetrative partner. Men were also given information about other STDs, and a nurse from the local GUM clinic gave a talk to the group.

Workers felt that the sessions on relationships, negotiating sex and safer sex had contributed to men's understanding of the social context of safer sex. This was important for men who had not yet had sex. Helping to dispel myths such as 'You are not really gay if you don't have anal sex', enabled men to feel more confident about negotiating the sex they wanted.

Members talked to each other about their experiences and would often share these with the group, for example if they had had sex for the first time, or used a condom for the first time, or had unsafe sex. The group also shared strategies for negotiating safer sex.

Workers felt that most of the group members who were sexually active were having safer sex most of the time. One of the workers felt that the norm in the group had gradually shifted from 'safer sex is boring' to 'We should be having it, it's a good thing'. He reported that some of the men would lecture others if they were not having safer sex. On occasion group members asked for safer sex sessions to be repeated, particularly if they were concerned that other group members had been having unsafe sex.

Some of the men themselves reported changes in their sexual behaviour since being in the group:

> *A big decrease in anal sex – when practised always use a condom. [I] Do not use a condom for oral sex – know the statistics and risks. Never brush your teeth before sex! (15/9/92)*

> *I would no longer consider having unsafe sex – no matter what the given circumstances were, whereas before perhaps (I) would not have been as careful. (15/9/92)*

Workers encouraged group members to use the MESMAC condoms racks on the scene and made condoms and lubricant available in the group. The men reported that it was useful having free condoms as they often could not afford them or they were embarrassing to buy.


## Confidence and self-esteem

The workers felt that changes in self-esteem were quite widespread and significant, demonstrated through their observation of marked changes in behaviour, for example very quiet men taking more interest in running groups and facilitating sessions; men talking more; and others not dominating in discussions.

The men themselves also said their confidence had increased. In the group's first evaluation session men mentioned feeling more confident in themselves as well as around their sexuality. This was also borne out through the evaluation questionnaires, with all but one of the men (who said he could not become more confident than he already was) reporting an increase in confidence. For some this increase was rated as 'very much' (33%), whereas for 50% it was a 'fair amount'.

## General support

Several of the men in the group saw the workers on a one-to-one basis. This gave them a chance to talk about issues that they felt unable to air in the group. In addition they received support around particular issues such as housing. The fact that the workers were available to offer advice and support outside the group meant that men were able to visit the MESMAC office if they had difficulties or felt distressed, rather than having to wait for the group. The interest, approachability and helpfulness of the workers was greatly appreciated. As one man said:

> They are interested in people who come to the group – it's not just a job for them. They get to know you and they want to know if everything is okay if you haven't turned up for a bit. (15/9/92)

The group provided an important and valued space for young men to socialise, receive support and information and discuss issues of common interest. It enabled many men to come to terms with their sexuality and end their feelings of isolation. In addition men were able to learn about sex, safer sex, relationships and gay culture in a supportive environment.

## Leicester black MESMAC – sauna outreach

This work consisted of MESMAC workers doing outreach work in saunas used by black (and other) men (see Deverell, 1992). The aim was to get to know men, discover their needs, and when appropriate talk to them about MESMAC, safer sex, sexuality, and STDs. Workers also gave out condoms and cards and referred men to other organisations. Because of the CD model there was a concerted effort to try and develop the work into more collective action, but this proved difficult.

Here we look at the impact the sauna work had on the men contacted. There were many methodological difficulties and precise information was difficult to obtain. The work was itself very sensitive and it was hard (if not impossible) to talk to the men outside the sauna environment. This meant, for example, that it was impractical for the evaluation fieldworker to interview men about their experiences as was done in other work. Because of the difficulty of having private conversations in the sauna, workers also found it hard to collect this information. Nevertheless they kept records on their work in the sauna and built up a detailed picture over a long period of time. In this respect the monitoring had an element of ethnography in it (Broadhead and Fox, 1990; Deverell, 1993a).

Most of the men contacted were between the ages of 22 and 50, but ranged between 17 and 65. Ethnicity varied with each sauna but there was contact with Asian, African-Caribbean and white men. The identity and outness of the men also varied but included straight, gay and bisexual men, most of whom were not out. Workers felt that most men contacted were skilled workers. There were relatively few unwaged men since it costs £3 to use the sauna.

The men responded fairly well to MESMAC, with many pleasantly surprised at the existence of a black project with information for black men. The workers gave out a large amount of verbal information. Through talking about MESMAC and safer sex, workers felt there had been changes in general awareness about HIV/AIDS amongst the men they had spoken to, although many already had a basic understanding.

Discussions with the men suggested a variety of needs. What the men wanted to know about (and what the workers were able to give information on in return) suggests some of the areas in which the men's awareness and understanding improved:

- the risks of transmission, e.g. men were particularly anxious about kissing and there was confusion about fucking, particularly in terms of the risks of being the receptive or insertive partner;

- whether hepatitis B was the same as or different from HIV;

- information about other STDs;

- where they could get an HIV test;

- varieties and availability of condoms;

- safer sex;

- sexual relationships and different sex practices.

Men also wanted reassurance about the safeness of sex that they had had previously, and many married men wanted suggestions about ways of hiding condoms from their wives. The workers discovered further specific needs, including:

- safer sex workshops in Asian languages;

- work with men selling sex, both with younger Asian men who were having paid sex with older men and with a group of men who were selling sex to pay for drugs;

- work around safer sex with women.

Workers dispelled myths, telling men:

- about the dangers of using vaseline with condoms;

- about Africa not necessarily being the origin of AIDS;
- that they were still at risk even if they didn't identify as gay.

In terms of changes in skill workers hoped men had learnt and were using safer sex techniques. In the first phase of the work condoms were rarely given out since workers did not want to make assumptions about men's needs, and because it was difficult to do this discreetly in the sauna. Later, especially in a commercial sauna, it was possible to give out condoms and show a safer sex video.

Evidence from the presence of discarded condoms suggested that they were being used. Indeed, one of the sauna attendants told the workers that there had been an increase in used condoms in the sauna. Some of the men told the workers that they had started using condoms, and several of the more regular contacts frequently asked workers for condoms. Occasionally men reported that they had told other men about safer sex.

In relation to other STDs some of the men seen regularly reported going to the GUM clinic for check-ups and hepatitis B injections. There are no figures on this as the clinic does not carry out ethnic monitoring.

This initiative proved hard to develop into collective action but was clearly a successful way of reaching more marginalised men and discovering and legitimising their needs. Many of the men contacted did not attend gay groups or visit the scene and as such had limited access to support and services. The work led to an increase in awareness about HIV/AIDS and other STDs and gave men the opportunity to discuss sex and relationships. Men also had increased access to condoms and safer sex information which was tailored to their needs as black MWHSWM.

## London MESMAC's peer training initiative

This initiative grew out of visits by the London MESMAC workers to 10 lesbian and gay youth groups in the London area (see Deverell and Prout, 1992c). The aims of the visits were:

- to assess the needs of young MWHSWM in London in relation to sexuality, safer sex, HIV/AIDS and other health needs;
- to get ideas for MESMAC work;
- to build up the team's own confidence and skills;
- to build their identity as a project.

Each youth group was visited by two workers. The sessions varied but all involved a brief talk about MESMAC and CD, followed by a discussion around safer sex,

HIV/AIDS and being gay. Six of these groups were revisited to give feedback, maintain a MESMAC profile and encourage men to get involved in the project. This work led to the setting up of two open meetings. The aims of these were: to build on ideas put forward in the youth groups, to find out needs and to produce a list of practical initiatives for MESMAC.

The men in the open meetings prioritised safer sex training as an initiative and the workers suggested using a peer training approach for this. This led to the formation of a group of men who helped to design, and then underwent, a training programme with the aim of using this knowledge to do outreach on the scene. The group met weekly for business meetings and training on issues such as HIV awareness, safer sex, negotiation and drug issues.

The initiative lasted from June 1991 to May 1992. Throughout it there was contact with 27 men on a regular basis and between five and 10 on a more casual basis. There was a core group of 10 very regular attenders. Men were aged between 17 and 25 and were mainly white English. However, there was contact with several Jewish men, one African-Caribbean man, one Turkish Cypriot man and two Swiss men. Three deaf men were involved on a long-term basis, with five or six deaf men taking part during the life-span of the work.

The peer training initiative was evaluated through two in-depth group interviews between members of the peer training group (eight at the first meeting, five at the second) and the evaluation fieldworker. Six men also returned questionnaires. The main impacts that these men highlighted are described below.

## HIV/AIDS

The workers felt that there had been changes in general HIV/AIDS awareness and this was supported by the men themselves, who reported gaining a lot of knowledge about HIV/AIDS and safer sex. For example:

*Lots of knowledge about HIV/AIDS. I thought I was well informed before! (10/3/92)*

*Before I was out too much socialising, having a drink, [I] didn't think about the future and gaining knowledge – not bothered. Getting involved and learning more information [I'm] really happy [I've] learnt lots of things [that I've] not thought much about before. It's been really useful. (10/3/92)*

In particular, men reported that they had learnt about drug awareness and the experience of drug users; had a better understanding of how HIV is transmitted, including the relative safety of oral sex; the importance of using lubrication with condoms; the role and use of service organisations for those who are HIV+; and issues relating to MWHSWM who do not identify as gay.

The men also had a greater understanding of the social and political context of AIDS, including homophobia and equal opportunities (especially, but not only, in relation to the deaf community). The men were aware of the need for confidence and support to combat homophobia, and were keen to campaign for sexuality and sex education in schools.

All of the men reported a great increase in confidence and self-esteem. In an interview with the evaluation fieldworker several men spontaneously reported an increase in their confidence, and this was reflected in the evaluation sheets. Importantly the men felt that their developing confidence enabled them to put what they had learnt to good use.

This increase in confidence helped in many areas of men's lives. For example, men felt more confident socialising on the scene as well as in their sexual encounters. As one man said:

> (It's made me) feel more confident and not scared when having sex any more. (6/92)

The workers felt that men's self-esteem had definitely increased, seeing this in their desire to take control of the group and put forward suggestions. The deaf men in particular had grown in confidence, which was shown in their keenness to raise awareness in the deaf community. Indeed, several of these men went on to get involved in Deaf MESMAC (which at the time of writing is active in campaigning for the needs of deaf MWHSWM).

## Skills

The training sessions themselves enabled men to build up their skills in relation to: presentation; communication; general HIV awareness; safer sex; negotiation and drug awareness. All of those replying to the questionnaire said they had developed skills through being involved in the project. In addition to those mentioned above men reported gaining skills in: equal opportunities practices, specifically deaf awareness; facilitating groups; expressing their own ideas; negotiating and practising safer sex.

For many men the initiative provided an opportunity to develop their existing skills and experience to support other young men. The men were keen to share what they had learnt with others. As one man said:

> I can't wait to get out there and start doing outreach. My main objective in joining MESMAC is to educate people. There is lots to do, I'm committed if others are willing. Want to go and educate people myself. (10/3/92)

The men talked to their friends about safer sex and wanted to find ways of making condoms more accessible to both young men on the scene and those who did not identify as gay, suggesting that these men may be more vulnerable.

Some of the men built on their skills and experiences and went on to get HIV-related jobs:

> *I now work in a social services HIV team. While I brought knowledge and skill from many sources what I gained from MESMAC was particularly useful. (6/92)*

The workers felt that these men may have further impact through being advocates for young gay men in the HIV field.

## Sex and safer sex

Through their involvement with the project several of the men reported that they had learnt more about safer sex and in some cases had changed their behaviour. For example:

> *Issues around HIV are no longer a cause of insecurity in my social life. I feel more able to negotiate safer sex for myself and be more experimental, knowing how to be safe. (6/92)*

> *A lot more variety of things like finger fucking and vibrators etc. I've had safe sex since I last met you all, after I had a negative HIV test (I had been unsafe previously). (6/92)*

The workers gave out almost 400 condoms and a similar amount of lubricant sachets to the men in the group. The fact that these were taken and asked for regularly suggested that they were being used. Indeed, several of the men said that they had valued access to free condoms and lubricant.

## Making friends

Many of the men had enjoyed meeting other young gay men through the initiative and had valued the opportunity to make friends. As one man said:

> *[It's] given lots of knowledge and confidence in most things I do now, and more importantly lots of genuine friends who share similar views about HIV/AIDS. (6/92)*

People in the group started socialising together and some of the men reported that they felt more community involvement. The workers said that for some of the men MESMAC had served as an introduction to other gay organisations and groups and several men went on to get involved in these.

## Future work

All of those interviewed said that they had achieved a lot through being involved in the project. Although the workers and the men were disappointed that the planned peer outreach scheme had not succeeded, the workers felt that the men would carry on as informal peer trainers. Indeed the training of this group of young men can be seen as an important new resource coming out of the project. Many men expressed a strong desire to get involved in health education for gay men.

The peer training scheme met several of the men's reasons for joining. It offered a space to meet, talk and share experiences with other MWHSWM. This should not be underestimated as for a lot of young men coming out this experience can be really valuable. Although the initiative did not actually succeed in terms of leading to peer outreach, those involved acquired knowledge and skills, leading to some men becoming involved in other gay groups or getting HIV-related jobs. The experience also informed the creation of Deaf MESMAC and the London Black MESMAC Peer Training Scheme.

## MESMAC Leeds – Latex Productions

This lesbian and gay theatre group developed through discussions between the MESMAC workers and people on the scene in Leeds (see also Deverell and Doyle, 1992). It was felt that there was a need for a form of health promotion that was fun, interesting and that people could participate in. The idea of a theatre group was put forward and one of the workers decided to develop this as he had a background in community theatre. In addition, he felt that it was an initiative in which people who felt they did not have the skills normally associated with health promotion could become involved.

The group was set up following an open meeting. It was decided that the group would be for lesbians and gay men to create a safe space where lesbians and gay men could explore personal issues, create a dynamic and vocal group within LAA and give lesbians and gay men a higher profile in the organisation. The aim of the group was to use theatre to educate, entertain and politicise. The group met weekly having workshops to share skills and aid group development and also writing and producing a safer sex review show premiered on World AIDS Day 1991. After that the group became completely independent from MESMAC; it has developed several new shows and still performs all over Britain.

During the period of MESMAC involvement the number of people involved fluctuated, but about 35 people participated at some time. Members were mainly working-class, especially the women, and aged between 20 and 45; all were white and able-bodied. The workers and the members were concerned to try and attract black members, but the fact that the group was very out, visible and white was felt to make this more difficult. Employment status was very varied, ranging from those unemployed to a deputy head and a single parent on benefits. All the members identified as lesbian or gay and were very out.

## HIV/AIDS awareness

Although the focus of the review was on lesbian and gay issues, with perhaps 30% of the material relating to HIV, the workers, and some of those interviewed, felt there had been changes in general awareness about HIV/AIDS through being involved in the group. For example, the women became more aware of HIV and safer sex as an issue for lesbians, and the men more aware of some of the issues around living with HIV, as well as becoming HIV+. Changes in specific information included: discovering what a dental dam is and what it is for; how to use condoms properly; and discovering that a woman is no more infectious during menstruation than at any other time. People also learnt about negotiating safer sex, and their rights in relation to HIV.

Members also became more politicised. In the first show there were sketches around drug companies and profiteering, and women not being diagnosed or able to get proper benefits because their presenting issues often differ from men's. Members also felt that there had been an increased understanding of the social context of safer sex, particularly why people have sex.

## Changes in social and personal situation

The theatre group had an effect on people's social and personal lives. One of the women members felt that she had only ever been seen as a mother before joining the group, whereas now she was seen as a creative person in her own right. The self-esteem and confidence of those involved also increased. This was shown by people finding it easier to read out and perform sketches in the group, and those who initially would only write gaining the confidence to perform. Members valued having the encouragement and support to express themselves and talked about greater mental well-being and a feeling of community and commonality. As one member said:

> *It's mind-blowing to be in company that you know what they're talking about, and you feel that you can contribute to. (12/91)*

There was also a change in social networks. Many of the participants valued the opportunity to meet away from the commercial gay scene and to be involved in something not focused around drinking or having sex.

## Having lesbian and gay space

People really liked the mixed nature of the group and the space to be creative and explore lesbian and gay issues. These points came up repeatedly in interviews with theatre group members, as a few examples illustrate:

*It's nice being in a room where it's more or less equally men and women and inputs and outputs are more or less equal. (12/91)*

*I really like it, I think it's great...I think you often get unfortunate segregation happening particularly in pubs and clubs. I like the opportunity to mix at this level. (12/91)*

*One thing we do have in common is a sense of being marginalised...It feels comfortable, feel I can say anything in here. (12/91)*

There is no information about whether the work affected people coming out – most members were quite out already. However, people did come out to their parents and grandparents knowing they could go back to the group and get support, and actually used these experiences for sketches.

## Skills

Members developed definite skills through their involvement in the group, as well as building on existing ones. Most people had never done any drama before and developed skills in writing and performing as well as doing voice workshops and flamenco dancing. Several completely original shows were written and produced by the group. MWHSWM were involved in producing every piece of material at every level.

Communication skills also improved. The group developed all their own publicity, in the form of press releases and a publicity sheet which they sent to universities, gay centres and clubs.

The workers felt that people had also developed skills around safer sex.

As well as providing an opportunity for members to develop new skills the group enabled people to share skills with one other. Three of the earliest workshops designed to develop the group's skills were facilitated by people in the group. The worker felt that sharing skills in this way had proved useful in making people feel needed and valued.

## Impact on audiences

As well as having an impact on those involved the theatre group itself had an impact on its audiences. Part of the group's initial role was to provide information and condoms to people in different settings. Throughout the first year of its existence MESMAC or LAA usually set up a stall giving out condoms and information at each performance. The audience had condoms thrown at them in every show and a lot of information was given out through the theatre itself.

The members clearly felt they had an educational role:

> *Being entertaining is a better way to get across [information]. Campaigns so far have been boring or dictating. We [are] presenting our impressions and knowledge in an entertaining and interesting way – so valuable. [I've] Learnt about safer sex myself. (12/91)*

The workers emphasised the theatre group's ability to tailor safer sex messages appropriately, ensuring that they had local relevance.

Latex Productions was reviewed several times in local papers, always very positively (see Appendix 6). Unfortunately, we have no direct information from members of the audience themselves. However, there were several referrals to LAA occurring as a result of its performances.

## Gay Men Tyneside

This group was one of two initiatives which developed out of a MESMAC residential weekend held in Kielder Forest. The aims of the weekend were:

- to bring together members of the various groups which already exist on Tyneside in order to share information and to network;

- to facilitate a positive group experience for gay men in a residential setting;

- to encourage by example further weekends/activities organised by the men themselves and/or their respective groups;

- to have fun.

The 17 men who went on the weekend ranged in age from early 20s to mid-50s. Two of the men were black and one man had a learning difficulty. The class and employment status of the men was very mixed and there were seven unwaged men present.

The weekend was very well received, with men giving an average rating of 8.85 (on a scale of 1 to 10) to describe their overall satisfaction. Many of the men found the weekend a confidence-boosting experience. The evaluation showed that it had given people the confidence that 'gay men could organise things for themselves and get on with each other' (Miller, 1991a). The importance of talking to and meeting other gay men was particularly highlighted, with some participants mentioning the value of meeting men they had never met before. The worker felt that men's communication skills had developed and people had learnt to listen to others and respect what they said as well as challenge prejudices.

The fact that there were representatives from all the gay groups in Newcastle on the weekend helped increase social networking, which led to the formation of a lesbian and gay networking group. This includes representatives from all the lesbian and gay groups in Tyneside (including MESMAC groups) and aims to share information, provide support and discuss ideas for joint work and funding (see Chapter 9).

The other main outcome of the weekend was the development of the social activities group. This emerged through the work of a core group of volunteers made up of men who had met on the Kielder weekend. Their aim was to plan, co-ordinate and publicise a group for future social activities for gay men. The group organised several activities as well as a further residential weekend. These, however, were not very well attended, which led to the group reviewing its organisation. The core group met with the MESMAC worker, who gave advice about evaluating the group and suggestions for improving it.

The group was relaunched in March 1992 as 'Gay Men Tyneside', with the aim of offering a meeting place and social activities for gay men of all ages. The initial meeting was very well attended and attracted a diverse group of men. The group has since met weekly for activities such as video evenings, quizzes, games evenings and sporting activities such as badminton and aerobics classes.

The group receives some financial support from MESMAC and has access to MESMAC resources, including meeting space and a photocopier. The group is run independently but has a contract with MESMAC which includes clauses relating to equal opportunities and a commitment to further a group culture which promotes safer sex. Representatives from the group meet the MESMAC worker once a month.

The group has about 30 members, with about 20 men attending each week. Members range in age from 20 to 60 and include two men with learning difficulties. Below we highlight some of the main impacts the group has had on those involved.

## Social alternatives to the scene

The remit of GMT is to provide a meeting place and social activities for gay men. It is thus not surprising that one of the main impacts on those involved has been a widening of opportunities to meet gay men and to participate in a range of activities.

A questionnaire carried out by the group with 20 members indicated that 75% of respondents attended the group regularly and nearly all valued being able to meet weekly. The majority of the men who replied to the questionnaire did use the scene and other gay groups, but some men did not use either. The group was therefore clearly helping to meet the social needs of a significant number of gay men in Tyneside.

The workers felt that GMT was the major social alternative to the scene in Newcastle and as such was a useful resource. For example, during April to December 1992 30 callers to MESMAC were referred to GMT. The workers saw it as the best place to refer men who wanted to meet more gay men and come out. The group has clearly increased opportunities for gay men to meet each other and widen their social network.

The men valued the social element of the group, with only one person giving their main reason for attending as 'to meet new talent'.

Most people said there was nothing they did not like about the group. For those who responded to this question: one person felt the evenings were badly organised; a couple did not like some of the activities; another expressed how awkward it must be for new members to feel part of the group; and another felt that people could be friendlier.

The fact that over half of the respondents to the questionnaire said they had introduced friends to the group and that three-quarters attended regularly suggests that most of the members enjoy the group. The success of the group seems to back up the MESMAC workers' consistent finding that one of the main needs of MWHSWM in Tyneside is for social alternatives to the scene.

## Safer sex

Although it was not the main aim of the group, discussions on safer sex did take place in meetings. Thirty men attended a MESMAC-run safer sex session organised by the group and members also watched the THT gay men's video.

In addition nine men from GMT attended the MESMAC 'Love Safe, Live Sexy' day. This event was designed to offer MWHSWM the chance to talk frankly and openly about being gay, sex, their feelings about HIV and safer sex and the additional pressures that AIDS has brought for the gay community. Evaluation of this event showed that it had been very enjoyable with all participants wanting more similar sessions, and nine out of 10 men saying they would recommend the session to their friends. Men particularly valued being able to talk openly in an informal atmosphere.

GMT members had access to condoms and lubricant through attendance at the group as well as a wide range of safer sex literature. The group was also the main user of the MESMAC library, which stocks gay fiction and safer sex information.

Group members were also able to access condoms and lubricant through the MESMAC condom racks on the scene. As part of the evaluation of this condom distribution scheme (see Miller (ed), 1993a) a discussion was held with 14 members of GMT who also filled in questionnaires. This showed that group members had regularly taken both condoms and lubricant from the racks. From the discussion it seemed that men used the condoms they had taken, with six men saying they used all or most of the items they took. Five said the items tended to hang around, and three said they had lost some of them. However, several of these men reported that this was because they had not had the opportunity to use them.

Most of the men said they would be able to afford condoms and lubricant if they were not free and would buy them. However, a couple said they would not. In any case, nine men said that free condoms made it easier for them to have safer sex by making condoms more accessible, reinforcing awareness, and helping to reduce embarrassment. Thirteen out of the 14 men asked thought that the scheme had made condoms more acceptable and less difficult to insist on when having safer sex. As men said:

*You don't have to ask anyone for them.*

*It's easier to accept as part of a social evening.*

*They're always around so you don't need to worry.*

*They're available and you don't have to ask potential punters if they've got any on them. (All 18/11/92)*

Some men had also taken leaflets, most taking these home and keeping them for reference, others had read them in the bars, or had taken them home and then thrown them away. One man had discussed the information in the leaflets with friends, and eight men had given condoms to others including friends or workmates. Comments about the leaflets suggested that several men found them useful and informative.

It is clear that for at least some of the men in GMT MESMAC has had an impact in raising HIV awareness and improving the availability and accessibility of appropriate condoms and leaflets.

## Running the group

One of the important outcomes of the group was that it enabled men to build on and develop their own organisational skills. The group was organised by a core group of volunteers but other members were actively encouraged to get involved. The core group organised residential weekends and a self-defence session and planned the weekly meetings. The group has produced its own publicity leaflet and each month produces a list of forthcoming activities, both of which are distributed on the scene.

The group's own evaluation showed that people were willing to get more involved in running the group, for example through fund-raising, bringing in videos and games and helping to clear up after meetings. This bodes well for the group's survival. As its questionnaire report said:

> *Perhaps the greatest challenge ahead for GMT is to have enough ideas to keep people wanting to come along, and to find what such a diverse group of gay men enjoy doing together, on a weekly basis, apart from their passion for other men is no easy task. This questionnaire does reveal that there is enough goodwill in the group to ensure the continuing success of GMT providing it remains friendly and welcoming. A good start has been made and it is heartening...that most of the people who filled in this questionnaire are more than happy a good deal of the time. (1993:11)*

The members were concerned to find ways of integrating new members and keeping the group lively and interesting. There was also a need to consider future funding. However, on the whole the group was highly successful, resulting in a positive impact on most of the men involved. It helped to decrease isolation and widen the range of social activities available to gay men. Through sending a representative to the lesbian and gay network meetings the group was also able to voice the needs and experiences of the men in the group at a community level.

## Fit Together

This group was set up as a result of a questionnaire carried out on the scene in Leeds to assess the needs of MWHSWM (Deverell and Prout, 1992b). The idea was to establish a group of gay men to produce relevant and accessible material and information relating to gay men's health. The MESMAC workers called an initial meeting which they advertised through leafleting the scene for two weeks and through adverts in the local press and the Pink Paper. This meeting attracted 18 men and led to the setting up of a group called 'Fit Together'.

Over a period of months the group drew up its own structure and defined the aims and membership of the group, with the help of a MESMAC worker. The main aim of the group was to offer relevant information and education on a range of health issues relevant to gay men and men who have sex with men. This was guided by a philosophy which was:

> *To be creative, innovative and sociable, so enabling gay men and other men who have sex with men to achieve a positive and holistic approach to health, lifestyle and self-image, encompassing social, spiritual, mental, physical and cultural issues. (6/92)*

About 15 men were involved in the group on a regular basis. Most were white and aged between 20 and 50. The group was very mixed, attracting a wide variety of gay and bisexual men, including students, sex workers, professionals and HIV workers. Three of the members were deaf.

One of the first activities that the group undertook was a residential weekend organised by the MESMAC workers. This involved sessions on issues such as eroticising safer sex, HIV/AIDS awareness and fund-raising, and was designed to provide some initial training and direction to the group. The weekend was highly successful and succeeded in bonding the group early on.

Soon after the weekend the group, with help from a MESMAC worker, set about organising a free two-day conference for gay and bisexual men. The conference was organised around a series of workshops which addressed areas such as: housing, safer sex, bisexuality, literature, Europe, HIV, drugs, deaf awareness and sex workers. The conference attracted 60 men and was highly successful. The evaluation showed that on a scale from 1 to 10 (with 1 very useful, 10 not useful) the average score given was 2.36 (n=25). Participants strongly praised the organisation and range of workshops, as these quotes illustrate:

> *Brilliantly organised – Fit Together did a wonderful job, and a good range of speakers. More please.*

> *I really enjoyed the conference. I would of [sic] liked to go into more of the workshops given time.*

> *Definitely a mixed bag of themes, workshops and attendees – refreshing change from the usual professional orientated conference. (All 5/92)*

The conference was also favourably reviewed in two local papers (see Appendix 6). One said:

> *It was refreshing to listen to people's own experiences and not just experts. Lots of the participants wanted another conference. If you think conferences are not for you, or too heavy, don't worry, go to their next one. (Northern Star, 28th May, 1992)*

The conference enabled a large number of gay and bisexual men to meet and network and helped to raise awareness of the different services in the city, for example drug agencies, the deaf awareness unit and GUM clinic. Various organisations exchanged ideas and several of the men involved in MESMAC groups gave workshops, with the session by Rent Boy Action being very highly praised. Some men felt very empowered by the conference, saying that it was difficult adjusting back to the real world afterwards. As the first Fit Together event it had a big impact on the group and much was learnt through the process. The conference also led to several new men joining the group, including the group's first black member.

After three months Fit Together became independent from MESMAC. A contract was drawn up with the group and they were given money from MESMAC. The MESMAC worker withdrew but kept in touch with the group through minutes and informal discussion.

The group successfully bid for money from Yorkshire Regional Health Authority and began to plan various initiatives and organise another conference. The group lasted for about eight months before deciding to disband. The men involved felt that their aims had been too vague and that group members had not had sufficient time to undertake the organisational work necessary for running the group, although there had been a lot of commitment. It was also suggested that perhaps MESMAC had withdrawn too soon.

Those interviewed by the evaluators were in the main positive about being involved, suggesting that they had learnt a lot through the experience of running the group and from the various discussions and activities they had had. Several of the men had made lasting friendships and many had gone on to get involved in other MESMAC groups such as Pink Ink and the Black Gay Men's Group.

Below we discuss some of the main impacts on those involved. This information was gathered through two group interviews with the evaluators (one with 14 men, the other with five), and the results of a questionnaire filled in by 12 men.

## HIV/safer sex awareness

Raising awareness about HIV/AIDS and safer sex was not the main focus of the group. The idea was to take a broader view of health, although safer sex had a place in this, as one man said:

> *Personally a lot of the attraction lies in its potential, looking at issues of health, get away from the prescribed idea that the only thing gay men are interested in is STDs. The group is setting its own agenda, (there are) new areas to look at e.g. healthy eating. (30/8/92)*

However, the great majority of those asked felt that their knowledge about HIV had increased through being involved with MESMAC. The fact that there were HIV+ people in the group, who were out about their status, also helped increase awareness about treatments and drugs.

A third of the men asked said that they had changed their sexual behaviour as a result of being in the group. It is important to note that many who had not changed said that this was because they were already having safer sex. One man said he had difficulty using condoms, even strong ones, as they often burst.

## Sexuality

Many of the men involved in the group were very out gay men. The workers also felt members were more politically active than in other MESMAC groups, and as such many of those involved were already comfortable with their own sexuality. As one man said, being in the group had not affected his coming out:

*Because I was as out as I'm going to get, I'm already a self-aware, politicised, angry, proud, gay man. (30/8/92)*

However, for other men the group had enabled them to come to terms with their sexuality, and in some cases come out. Just under half of those asked said that MESMAC had affected their coming out. For example:

*MESMAC has helped me in coming out, but I am not open to my family, but suspect my mother knows.*

*Increased self-confidence, supportive friends, increased knowledge of scene. (30/8/92)*

## Skills and confidence

Half of the men asked said that their involvement in the group had increased their skills, and 11 out of 12 men reported that their self-confidence had increased. In terms of skills men mentioned that they had improved communication, listening, facilitating, organisational and safer sex skills as well as a greater awareness of issues relating to the needs of black and deaf men.

The group helped men to develop and build on existing skills and learn new ones. For many men the group was seen as an opportunity to use their skills and experiences as gay men to help others. As one man said:

*[I] felt like doing something worthwhile, put something back into the gay community. People say the gay community doesn't exist but look at Fit Together and other groups – it does exist. We can do loads of stuff, together and individually. (30/8/92)*

The group themselves organised another residential weekend to share skills within the group. This event included sessions on healthy eating, bereavement, living wills, self-esteem, politics and health. The MESMAC workers were also invited to run a safer sex workshop.

## Broadened ideas

One of the main impacts that the group had on those involved was the experience of working with a variety of different gay and bisexual men. Several of the men said that they had learnt a lot from the diversity of experience within the group. All were very positive about the mixed nature of the group, which was felt to be very unusual.

Men learnt about issues related to deaf and black gay men, as well as rent boys and men who did not identify as gay. As one man said:

*An opportunity to meet people other than nice, white middle-class gay men. [It's] challenging looking at issues around Rent Boy Action and deaf awareness and bisexuals. As a gay man I've not been challenged to look at things I knew were there...I'm meeting so many different people, there has been a massive amount to learn and experience. There have been things that have really made me think, not just about health. (30/8/92)*

The group made a strong effort to be as inclusive as possible, which enabled men who had often felt marginalised from gay groups to be involved. As one man said:

*The fact that (they are) all so friendly and non-judgmental is fantastic. I feel very secure, which I don't in the gay community. I feel I can come here and be with gay people. (30/8/92)*

Another man who was HIV+ said he felt isolated and ostracised on the gay scene but comfortable in the group. This was echoed by the deaf and black members, who said that they felt welcome and integrated. They enjoyed being able to mix with the white, hearing men on an equal basis. As this extract from an interview shows:

*[I] feel safe and positive, feel I belong here. The fact that I'm black has nothing to do with it. In other groups being black is a problem.*

*I agree when you say 'black is not important' – being deaf is not important either when I come. (30/8/92)*

Men from more marginalised groups valued the opportunity to have their experiences heard. As one member said, in response to what he liked about the group:

*The ability to promote a very positive image of working boys in the community to other gay/bisexual men. And feeling comfortable as a person living with HIV in a group of gay men. (30/8/92)*

The black member said he had been in a lot of different groups and never felt comfortable. Fit Together, however, was different:

*I feel safe here, I'm not afraid of speaking. Want to make people aware that black people are part of the scene. It is certainly different from other groups, people are not defensive, they don't patronise me, don't get embarrassed. (30/8/92)*

The group therefore had a significant impact in enabling men who had long felt marginalised from the gay community to get their needs and experiences heard, and to be validated as gay men.

There was some concern that the group had not attracted many young people. Some suggested that as a gay men's group it put off those who were still unsure about their sexuality, or did not identify as gay. As one man said:

*It has failed to attract young people. It is not accessible, especially to those under the age of consent. Young men can be frightened to be with older gay men when (they are) confused about their sexuality. They see it as gay men, a place for gay men to meet each other only, that's true of a lot of young people I know. For young people it's very difficult. (30/8/92)*

However, overall the group was felt to have been very open, friendly, supportive and welcoming.

The group members were disappointed that the group had not survived but those that the evaluators spoke to were sure that they would go on to use what they had learnt. The men had gained a lot and were sad that they had not reached a stage of being able to do more for local MWHSWM.

Socially the group was felt to have worked well. People who had met through the group had stayed good friends and the men had really enjoyed the opportunity to make friends with men they would never have met socially. The group had challenged people's prejudices and given men an opportunity to learn new skills and put their own ideas and experiences into action. They were all very positive about the contribution of the MESMAC workers and the MESMAC project as a whole. As one man wrote on his evaluation form:

> *MESMAC is an excellent idea which has had enormous positive practical success in Leeds in many different spheres. Shortcomings are that funding was only for three years. It should be long-term and there should be many comparable projects throughout the country, including in rural areas – set up more! (30/8/92)*

## General impact on users

In this section we provide a general overview of what those contacted by the project got from their involvement with MESMAC. As previous chapters have shown, the project worked with a wide range of MWHSWM and there was a large variation in the type, length and level of involvement that men had with the project, so the impact of the project on individuals was extremely varied.

Obviously the type and length of contact men had played a large role in what they got out of MESMAC. For example, for those for whom contact with MESMAC was one-off (perhaps through receiving counselling or being in a club when MESMAC workers were conducting a safer sex promotion) the impact was mainly in terms of receiving information, advice and condoms. Those involved in short-term specific initiatives often reported developing particular skills, e.g. self-defence techniques. For others the contact was more long term and led to changes in confidence and self-esteem and enabled men to develop skills even further. In some cases this led to quite radical changes in their lives, for example through coming out or getting employment.

It should also be remembered that MESMAC worked with a large number of other professionals. This had individual impact through helping people to develop services, giving them advice and support, and through bringing professionals together (see Chapter 9).

The vast majority of people asked in evaluation exercises were extremely positive about their contact and involvement with MESMAC. Below we highlight some of the main impacts men reported. This draws on information from 640 evaluation sheets and questionnaires, interviews with users and workers and other project records.

## Meeting men's needs

MWHSWM were facilitated in getting access to services and support that they had not before. For example, men received support around issues such as coming out, dealing with homophobia, dealing with sexual abuse, finding housing, dealing with an HIV diagnosis, getting legal advice and medical treatment. The project had a significant impact, both in raising awareness about the services available to MWHSWM and in helping men to access these (for example, by accompanying men to GUM clinics or arranging meetings with housing officers). Referrals to a wide variety of other services and organisations were a routine part of the work of all the projects.

## Resourcing collective action

One of the important parts of MESMAC work was resourcing collective action. A consistent finding from the evaluation was the importance men placed on being with other MWHSWM and being able to share experiences and support each other. Through the groups and networks established or resourced by MESMAC the services and support available to MWHSWM in each locality were greatly increased. In some cases this process succeeded in building a sense of community. Men who had previously felt isolated and marginalised drew strength and support from feeling part of a wider community, and through bringing groups and organisations together MESMAC was able to strengthen community infrastructure. Through such collective work men were able to lobby organisations to get their needs met and develop new initiatives.

The project therefore played an important role in enabling men to change services to better meet their needs. For example Leeds MESMAC supported members of Rent Boy Action in lobbying the local GUM clinic. This resulted in the GUM clinic changing its HIV testing services so that men could have their results within 24-48 hours, rather than waiting a week. In addition a new appointments system was introduced so that rent boys could ring and arrange for an appointment the same day, rather than having to wait two or three days. As well as enabling the rent boys to improve existing resources, this work enabled the rent boys to find out what GUM services were available.

The projects also resourced and supported men in organising and developing new initiatives themselves. Men were able to build on their own needs and experiences and develop skills and confidence. This gave men a valued opportunity to do something for themselves and a chance to use their own creative ideas. For many gay men it was a rare opportunity to take part in group activity where their sexuality was validated. It was also an opportunity for men to do something positive, to share their skills, experience and information and help meet the needs of other MWHSWM. As one man said:

> *I think it's given me hope that people, young people, especially rent boys, would never get into the position that I'm in as somebody living with the virus... That's what I've personally achieved, that we've actually got the message of prevention out. And we've made the health authority sit up and realise there are rent boys with needs. (12/1/92)*

Some men went on to volunteer for MESMAC work and others ran MESMAC groups. Some men eventually gained employment in jobs related to HIV prevention, in part because of their contact with MESMAC. Men also learnt about other local gay groups and some started attending these. In this way individual impact took on a more collective dimension.

## HIV/safer sex

HIV and safer sex were not always the most central elements in MESMAC initiatives. However, levels of awareness about safer sex and HIV were clearly raised through most of the projects' work, even when this was not an overt aim. Four topics stand out for which all the projects have evidence of increased awareness:

- Routes of HIV transmission

- Condom use

- STDs

- Testing for HIV

Many men were more aware of the importance of safer sex as well as what it was. For example, 40% (n=50) of men surveyed on the commercial gay scene in Leeds said that MESMAC had made them think more about practising safer sex (Eades, 1993); and 51/71 of the young men London MESMAC met in youth groups gave a comment which showed an increased general HIV awareness after a MESMAC session (Deverell and Prout, 1992a).

Opportunities were created for men to discuss the difficulties they faced in adopting or maintaining safer sex. This involved discussing the social context of safer sex and issues such as power in relationships. Men were able to discuss the realities of practising safer sex, share strategies and get support. As one man said:

*Having an open discussion about HIV/AIDS brings about awareness and removes insecurities.*
*(27/9/90)*

In addition all the projects enabled the development of skills in negotiating safer sex and using condoms. Where there was regular contact with the project men themselves reported that they were more skilled in this area.

A large amount of written information and even larger amounts of verbal information about HIV and safer sex were given out. Much of this was produced by the project and often with MWHSWM themselves. This enabled information to be tailored to men's needs and in some cases helped men to feel better about their own sexuality. For example, this was particularly the case for black men in Leicester involved in creating safer sex literature with positive images of black men. Through the distribution of existing material and the production of locally relevant material men had increased access to a wide variety of leaflets and information.

In addition to information, MESMAC helped to provide the resources to enable safer sex. A total of approximately 45,000 condoms were distributed in the course of MESMAC work. A similar amount of lubricant, mostly in sachets, was also distributed. There is some evidence to suggest that some of those contacted may not have been able to afford condoms if they did not get them free (Eades, 1993; Miller (ed), 1993a). In any case, free, appropriate and accessible condoms were valued. For example, 73% (n=30) of those asked in Newcastle felt that the condom distribution scheme had made it easier for them to have safer sex (Miller, 1993a).

Even though MESMAC was not a behaviour change project we have information from some men that suggests MESMAC helped them to adopt safer sex practice. Many of the MESMAC initiatives led to a reported increase in safer sex behaviour from some of the men worked with. The changes reported on questionnaires and evaluation sheets were mainly in relation to increased condom use. Men also told the evaluators and workers that, for example, they had started using flavoured condoms for oral sex, were carrying condoms and insisting on using them and that they had learnt the importance of using lubricant with condoms. Several of the men interviewed reported that they had told other men about safer sex, or had given out condoms. There was also some evidence of a developing safe sex culture amongst some MESMAC groups.

However, as with many other projects, MESMAC found that behaviour change was inconsistent and often difficult to maintain. For example: some men started using condoms with male partners but not female ones; men used them for casual encounters but not in relationships; some men had very low self-esteem and felt they were probably infected already so did not see the point in using condoms; some did not like them; others did not want to ask partners to use condoms for fear of losing the relationship; and some men were paid more as sex workers to have unsafe sex. Through helping men to build up their negotiation skills and taking account of the wider influences that affect men's ability to have safer sex MESMAC was able to begin to address some of these issues.

## Support around sex and sexuality

For many men MESMAC provided the first opportunity they had ever had to discuss their feelings about sex and sexuality and as such was a greatly valued source of support and information. Men were able to discuss different sexual practices, relationship difficulties and their own sexual experiences in a frank way. For those men who joined groups or attended safer sex workshops there was an opportunity to discuss these issues in a supportive environment with other MWHSWM.

For many men the opportunity to share experiences and feelings with other MWHSWM was one of the most rewarding aspects of their involvement with MESMAC. As members of the Tyneside Survivor's Group said in relation to what they had got from the group:

*The relief I get from being able to talk about my abuse openly, and knowing that I can get real help and support.*

*Attending the group has made me much happier. I can offload feelings here, and talking about things gets rid of the pressures.*

*I feel stronger and more positive about my sexuality. I feel less of a 'victim' because I feel cared for and supported. (MESMAC Tyneside 1992:10)*

Having their sexuality validated and taken seriously enabled men to build up confidence and self-esteem. Men were able to support each other in relation to homophobia and to discuss having sex with men in a positive environment. This provided much needed support and helped men to feel less isolated. For example, many men experienced a sense of relief through meeting or hearing about others who had had similar experiences. Many younger men, in particular, also reported feeling less scared about sex.

## Skills

A wide range of skills, from self-defence to photography, performance to communication and assertiveness were developed in individuals with whom the projects worked. Some initiatives were specifically designed to develop particular skills. For example, the London black peer training project trained 12 men in HIV awareness and built up their skills in relation to negotiation, safer sex, listening and doing outreach. These men went on to undertake outreach work on the scene in London and used these skills to support other young black men.

For those involved in MESMAC groups participation itself led to the development of group work skills. For example, the workers in Leeds reported that the men in Rent Boy Action started to listen to each other and no longer spoke over, shouted at, or used threatening language to each other in the group. They also took more control over the group, organising and preparing the group's weekly meal, developing their own leaflet, giving out information and condoms to other rent boys, and successfully bidding for money from the Regional Health Authority.

Several of the initiatives were designed to enable men to share their skills with each other and in some cases this process led to the development of new resources such as the production of a lesbian and gay magazine (*Pink Ink*). Helping men to increase their skills, therefore, not only had an individual impact but often played a part in developing and strengthening community infrastructure.

## Confidence and self-esteem

Where projects worked regularly with individuals there was consistent evidence that levels of reported self-esteem and confidence were increased, often quite markedly. This was evidenced in self reports on evaluation sheets and in interviews, as well as workers' reports of men contributing more in groups and recognising their own needs and rights. For those in groups it was demonstrated by their taking control over meetings; facilitating sessions; running groups; and developing their own initiatives. Several men had greatly increased confidence. For example, one man in Leeds described himself as 'being at the bottom of a pit with no way out' when he first contacted the project. After a year of contact with MESMAC he had secured independent funding from Wakefield Health Authority and was conducting HIV-related talks and discussion groups in youth clubs and children's homes.

The non-judgmental stance of the workers and the opportunity to talk frankly about sex and sexuality played a large part in helping men to improve their confidence. This was particularly the case for those who were unsure of their sexual identity, or who felt isolated or marginalised from other MWHSWM. For example, one man with learning difficulties in Newcastle found that after several one-to-one sessions with a MESMAC worker his confidence increased so much that he no longer needed a social worker. He also started to go out on the scene and attend some local gay groups.

In a relatively small amount of work, for example Tyneside's work with working-class men on a housing estate, however, self-esteem and confidence-building continued to be an issue. This work showed that, despite the positive effect of the group overall, years of multiple social disadvantage and homophobia have deep effects (see Deverell and Prout, 1992a).

## Coming out

For some men contact with the project led to their developing confidence in their own sexual identity which resulted in their decision to come out. This was particularly true of young men and some married men. Often this process was helped through men being able to draw advice and support from the MESMAC workers and other MWHSWM. This enabled many men to feel less isolated and marginalised, and enabled them to learn from others' experiences.

For other men the value of the project lay in becoming involved in initiatives without having to identify as gay. This gave them increased access to information and support.

## Expanded social networks

The existence of new groups enabled men to expand their social circle and opportunities to meet people. Many group members formed new friendships through their involvement with MESMAC and reported being less isolated or lonely. Others felt less marginalised.

Men particularly enjoyed the chance to build friendships with other MWHSWM and receive social support, rather than just sexual contact with men. As one of the men in the Cruddas Park Group said:

> It's a good alternative to the scene. I feel relaxed and I've made a lot of friends too. (undated)

For some men the development of new friendships enabled them to access places such as scene venues without feeling vulnerable or marginalised. This was particularly the case for young men and black men. On the other hand, some men valued having social alternatives to the scene which they found more supportive.

# Summary

In this chapter we have shown that:

*MESMAC tailored their work to meet the needs of MWHSWM;

*the project was able to effect change in many areas of men's lives;

*the impact of the project on individuals was extremely varied;

*for many men involvement in the project led to increased personal development and for some the impact of the project led to major life changes;

*as a CD project MESMAC gave men the opportunity to design their own projects, leading to community building as well as individual impact;

*MESMAC enabled men to bring their needs to the attention of existing organisations and to lobby for change.

# 9 Community infrastructure and organisational development

## Introduction

The most usual focus of evaluation research in relation to health education (and even the wider concept of health promotion) has been the outcomes on and for individuals. The selection of this focus is linked to the continuing predominance of individual behaviour change approaches within health education as a whole. Despite a growing research literature that suggests that individual behaviour change is highly problematic (see Chapter 1), this focus persists and there are strong pressures, arising perhaps from the painful realities of epidemic and death, in the HIV field towards retaining it. As a CD project, however, MESMAC was premised on the importance of moving away from an individual focus towards seeing people in their social context. This fundamental difference required that our evaluation address this social – collective and organisational – level.

It is quite arbitrary to make a distinction between the individual and the social; in some respects Western societies are quite peculiar in both making this distinction so sharply and giving priority to the importance of the individual. As we suggested in the last chapter the direct impact of MESMAC for users of the project was created as part of a network of social circumstances and cannot be separated from these. In particular working together, for example in setting up a group or taking part in a conference, was part of the process by which individuals learnt, changed and felt validated. So whilst in the last chapter we foregrounded project users and treated the social as a context, in this chapter we do the reverse – foregrounding the collective and organisational impacts of the project and putting individuals into the background.

We have organised this chapter according to some of the basic elements of the CD strategy (as outlined in Chapter 1). This argues that a successful CD project must accomplish and link together four aspects:

*Grassroots work – working in localities directly with MWHSWM;

*Participation – involving MWHSWM in the structures and processes of the project itself and in wider decision-making;

*Community infrastructure – collectivising experience and bringing people together to act for change;

*Organisational development – changing organisations so that they are more responsive to the needs of the various communities and groups they are meant to serve.

Here we have focused our account around the last two aspects of the CD strategy - building community infrastructures and undertaking organisational development. Chapter 4 deals with the day-to-day work of local sites, the grassroots work, while Chapters 3, 5 and 6 give details of participation, i.e. how project users were involved at all levels.

# Building community infrastructure

The aim of this part of the CD strategy was to bring together groups and networks to collectivise their experience and act together in the longer term. In practice this part of the strategy can be seen as drawing on grassroots work, promoting participation and feeding into organisational development. There are consequently large overlaps and connections between this work and the other areas of the strategy.

MESMAC's work had two main groups of outcome, building links between existing groups, and initiating new groups or organisations, which are detailed below.

## Building links between existing groups

By bringing people together and creating opportunities for them to work together, MESMAC helped to increase their impact. For example, Leeds MESMAC and Fit Together held a city-wide day conference on Gay Men's Health. The meeting brought together a wide variety of different individuals and organisations who offered workshops on: bisexuality; the work of Leeds Gay Switchboard; deaf awareness; Rent Boy Action; positive attitudes (issues around HIV); the New Queer Politics; housing issues for gay/bisexual men; queer culture; the use of drugs by gay/bisexual men; counselling and support; and eroticising safer sex. In the evaluation participants rated the conference well organised, and useful, and the range of workshops good. A reviewer in the newspaper *Northern Star* commented: 'By the end of the conference, issues as well as people were fitting together, fulfilling its primary objective.'

In Leicester, MESMAC, BHAF, Leicester Black Gay and Lesbian Group and Leicester Lesbian and Gay Resources Centre did joint work towards setting up a black helpline. Their idea was to share the facilities of the existing gay and lesbian helpline but establish particular times when trained volunteers would be available for calls from black people. By working together a small amount of funding was obtained from the DHA to establish the line and the training programme for volunteers.

An example from Newcastle is the forum for gay, lesbian and bisexual organisations which MESMAC Tyneside initiated and supported. It met periodically to discuss issues of common concern. The group produced a list of gay, lesbian and other related organisations in the area. Several hundred copies were produced and circulated, including those sent to social and health service workers who are using the list to establish appropriate referrals for their clients. In 1993 a second, updated and expanded edition was produced. This was later incorporated in the commercially published 'Complete Guide to Newcastle'.

A final example comes from London MESMAC, which developed a small grants scheme. This was an initiative which offered small grants to organisations or individuals doing work with or planning provision for young gay men. The initiative was self-evaluated by the project workers and a report prepared (Taylor, Eisenstadt and Spyrou, 1993). Under-resourced groups (such as those from black and ethnic minorities, men with disabilities, and men under 21) were prioritised. The scheme was advertised, with leaflets sent to existing organisations and press releases sent to *Capital Gay* and the *Pink Paper*. After a selection process eight groups were funded: Black Experience launched an initiative to raise the profile of HIV on the club scene; Notting Hill Lesbian and Gay Group arranged an exchange visit with a similar group in Denmark; Black Men United Against AIDS trained some of their younger members in outreach work; Orientations produced promotional and safer sex materials for gay people from South-East Asia; Heinenu produced similar materials for young Jewish people; the Biosphere Project organised a day workshop on safer sex for young bisexuals; Steps in Time organised a weekend with holistic therapies for young people living with HIV; New Beginnings used the grant to pay for a venue, an information line and an answerphone; Deaf MESMAC bought a minicom and stationery as part of establishing themselves. As a result of the scheme and the positive outcomes it produced, MESMAC workers concluded that:

> *There is a definite need for people to fund the 'very voluntary' sector, particularly of lesbian, gay and bisexual groups, many of whom will not be in contact with grant-givers or particular Health Authorities.*

> *These groups are difficult to fund – communication is difficult, groups may fall apart easily etc. However, very few people are able to do it and it is a very cheap way of developing a diverse range of resources. (Taylor, Eisenstadt and Spyrou, 1993:10)*

## Initiating new groups or organisations

This has been one of the most productive and important of MESMAC's activities. Altogether MESMAC projects initiated 23 new groups (see Chapter 4). As we showed in the previous chapter the members of the various groups saw their involvement as of great personal value. Often MESMAC's work involved providing training for members who have taken their experience to other groups and ventures. Many of these groups have developed a degree of independence from MESMAC and some have become completely independent. There is every sign that many of the groups will continue to work towards meeting the needs of MWHSWM in their localities. Examples at the time of writing included:

(i)  In Leeds the theatre group 'Latex Productions' continues to develop new work and stage performances of general interest to gay and lesbian communities, often involving aspects of safer sex and HIV prevention.

(ii)  Gay Men Tyneside, which is a thriving group in Newcastle which has provided a much-needed alternative to the commercial scene. Its membership includes some of the men who formed a support group for gay men on a working-class housing estate.

(iii)  In Leicester, MESMAC and others reinvigorated the SE Asian gay and lesbian group SHAKTI. Through it they began to explore and develop a specifically Asian gay sub-culture, using symbols, music and food to develop a specific identity.

(iv)  In London Deaf MESMAC is an established group with its own meetings, events and newsletter which is having an important effect on the way safer sex is promoted and made accessible to deaf men.

The MESMAC projects themselves have become an important resource for local MWHSWM work. Three aspects of this should be highlighted:

(i)  some of the MESMAC projects filled an important gap in local provision for gay communities and are now seen as important for MWHSWM by both other relevant workers and gay communities in general;

(ii)  MESMAC produced a core of experienced and trained workers, some of whom have moved on to related jobs in other parts of the country. At the same time the projects have acted as a resource for other MWHSWM projects in many different parts of the country (see below);

(iii)  the four MESMAC projects each sought local funding to continue their work. At the time of writing three projects have won this funding and the fourth is in negotiation with local health authorities. We understand that 'Yorkshire MESMAC' (which grew out of the Leeds project) was at the time of writing the largest HIV prevention project for MWHSWM in the UK. MESMAC work will, therefore, not end with HEA funding.

In setting up new groups and helping to resource networks and forums MESMAC projects created durable outcomes to their work which will continue to be a resource for MWHSWM work in the future.

# Organisational development

## Impact on the HEA

Without HEA funding the innovative work of the MESMAC project would have been very much more difficult to establish. At the last Project Network Meeting there was recognition from members of the project that the HEA had taken a risk in supporting the work and the hope was expressed that it would continue to support innovative work. This was balanced by a concern about the HEA developing more effective consultation and feedback into policy development from the projects it supports. MESMAC formally communicated this to the HEA at the end of the project.

## Impacts on host organisations

All the local MESMAC projects have developed ways of working with and influencing their host organisation. Of course this has not been a one-way relationship and all the projects have learnt from the organisational settings within which they were located. In this section we will discuss the relationships between the MESMAC sites and their host organisations, focusing on the organisational changes the projects were able to encourage. We will point to differences in the scale, pace and direction of these influences and suggest some reasons for them.

### Leeds

LAA is a medium-sized voluntary organisation with links to the statutory sector. At the start of the project its main activities were in HIV support and counselling services, and this emphasis has remained the same. Its relationship to Leeds MESMAC, especially in the first few months of the project, was rather tense, largely because MESMAC brought both a focus on prevention and an explicit orientation to MWHSWM, including gay men. Neither of these characteristics fitted comfortably with the image LAA had developed. LAA saw itself as working with a wide range of clients and avoided an explicitly or exclusively gay identity (although in fact it works with many gay men). Although sexual practice and HIV prevention were part of its work, other issues in care and support tended to predominate.

Mutual interaction and the appointment of an ex-MESMAC worker as LAA manager gradually broke down these barriers. LAA used some of the MESMAC safer sex resources (especially their 'Love Safe, Live Sexy' campaign materials), awareness of black issues was raised (in part through MESMAC's work in supporting a black member of Fit Together) and MESMAC workers were able to refer men they met in their street outreach to the drug counselling services of LAA.

Nevertheless, the differences were never entirely resolved. In fact the outcome of the relationship has been a de facto division of labour between LAA and MESMAC; the former has kept its focus on care and support services, whilst Leeds MESMAC does prevention work with gay men. This split was deepened when LAA moved to new premises in mid-1992. Whilst this outcome would have been difficult to avoid and has advantages such as keeping the profile of work with gay men high, it does raise questions about the long-term situation: should support and prevention services be so separated; should work with MWHSWM be so separate from other HIV/AIDS work?

## Leicester

The closest (and arguably soonest achieved) working relationship between project and host organisation is found with Leicester Black MESMAC and Leicester BHAF. In fact, as the project developed the work of MESMAC became increasingly integrated with that of BHAF. Because BHAF is a small, voluntary organisation, the scope for interaction between members is large. The organisational aims of BHAF have large areas of overlap with Leicester MESMAC and this has facilitated joint work. More fundamentally, as the project developed it became clear that there were (for reasons discussed in Chapters 4 and 6) only small numbers of black gay-identified men in Leicester, and MESMAC's work had to take this into account. It was usual in talks to groups or in publicity work for MESMAC and BHAF to represent each other, and there was often joint discussion of initiatives. A more specific example might be the youth work which MESMAC did. This involved working with black youth leaders, one of whom, as a result, became a volunteer for BHAF.

The Leicester project also shows the care that has to be taken in placing a relatively well and nationally-funded project such as MESMAC with a small local voluntary organisation – as the first MESMAC Forum warned (see Chapter 1). This can create distortions and difficulties. For BHAF these were caused by the system of retrospective payment used by the HEA and exacerbated by delays in actually receiving funding. This meant that for a period of time BHAF was paying for MESMAC work out of very limited resources and this badly affected its other work. BHAF also had to use its time and resources on inducting and training staff. Leicester BHAF has, as a result of this experience, drawn up some guidelines about its future policy towards acting as a host.

## London

The relationship between London MESMAC and the THT developed steadily but more slowly. This difference suggests that it is quite misleading to lump all voluntary organisations together. Compared to BHAF, THT is large, has a more complex structure and is more diverse in its target groups. The London project manager saw three phases in London MESMAC's relationship to THT. At the start of the project MESMAC was widely viewed within THT as something quite separate. THT was developing as a widely-based HIV organisation, to some extent developing away from its earlier orientation to gay communities, but with only a limited resourcing of health education. Working with young MWHSWM was seen as rather risky within THT and some distance from it was maintained. At this time, then, the emphasis was on clarifying THT's responsibilities and role in relation to MESMAC and challenging some misconceptions about it.

The second phase began when THT set up its Health Education Team which the London MESMAC administrator became part of. MESMAC became more and more integrated into the work of THT and had a particularly important input into the Health Education Team. Issues around the neglect of gay men in prevention work now began to emerge nationally and, after challenges to THT's direction, a Gay Man's Officer was appointed. MESMAC supported and developed work with gay men. The administrator also took part in the 'phone information rota and in discussions on changing the way it worked.

In the last phase MESMAC began to impact on THT more widely. MESMAC's work with black men and deaf men made the equal opportunities rhetoric of MESMAC more concrete and its practical importance and implications for the type of work done became more visible. When a follow-up to THT's video 'The Gay Man's Guide to Safer Sex' was planned MESMAC workers lobbied to make sure that it would include black men and have subtitles and more written information to make it more accessible to deaf men. MESMAC was consulted about the images and script during production. MESMAC's experience of working with young men was also used to argue for a more sensitive treatment of issues such as coming out, self-esteem, drug use and homelessness.

MESMAC work and experience has been fed into a range of THT activities. Examples include:

(i) extensive changes to the Wellcome/THT safer sex leaflets;

(ii) lobbying within THT to change their condom distribution to include more strong types. An evaluation of the condom packs distributed at safer sex roadshows led to finance being given to the purchase of more appropriate types of condom. It was suggested that MESMAC users be consulted in focus groups discussing what was needed in the condom packs;

(iii) suggesting that a comprehensive THT resource catalogue be produced.

By the end of the project the MESMAC administrator was the longest standing member of the health education team. He had made a key contribution to THT's work and was widely respected by other THT workers. Other MESMAC workers had also been consulted on particular issues. Nevertheless, there were unresolved issues. London Black MESMAC workers felt that although they were consulted, and this was welcome, there was still a tendency to use Black MESMAC as a camouflage for a lack of systematic THT work with black communities. Even at the end of the project MESMAC still had not found a place in the existing *formal* structure of THT and remained dependent on informal networks and the workers' personal reputations.

## Tyneside

MESMAC Tyneside was the only local project based in the statutory sector (Newcastle Social Services Department). The negative side of this, especially from the MESMAC workers' point of view, was that the social services department seemed unused to working around gay men's issues. At times the workers found it an uncomfortable and homophobic environment, and questioned the commitment and understanding of individuals. Nevertheless, by the end of the project many good working relationships had been established and MESMAC had won open recognition for the quality of its work. MESMAC began to be seen as worthwhile and, as the administrator put it, 'not radical and weird any more'. Equally, MESMAC workers felt they had been able to combat heterosexism and raise awareness of the needs of men who have sex with men. MESMAC began to be used as a resource for other workers in social services when they were working with gay clients.

The positive side was that, being part of local government, the host organisation presented an existing network of committees and contacts (in Newcastle and surrounding local authorities) which the workers could enter into and begin to influence. There is now recognition in social services that HIV prevention work, including a focus on gay men, needs to be done, and a commitment to support it. A good example of MESMAC's involvement is its role in the production of the HIV Prevention Strategy for the City of Newcastle (see below).

From the project administrator's point of view the local authority administrative systems seemed slow and cumbersome, not fitting in with the faster moving priorities of an innovative project. The system was not used to dealing with an externally-funded project. She found, however, that as she formed working relationships other administrators were prepared to work more flexibly. One particular issue where some organisational change was brought about was around the administrator's need, as a woman working in a men's project (see Deverell and Bell, 1993), for some external support and supervision. At first there was resistance to this, it being said that the local authority did not accept that administrative workers (as opposed to, say, social workers) could need external supervision. In fact, in a project such as MESMAC, no easy division between administrative and other roles can be made, and after a prolonged campaign her needs were met.

Originally MESMAC was housed in the same building as the Newcastle Community Support Centre but at the end of 1991 moved to city centre offices. This move seemed to precipitate a much clearer identity for the project and it developed a local image as a centre for HIV prevention and, more broadly, a resource for gay communities and individuals in the city.

# Other organisations

All the local projects carried out a great deal of work with or in relation to other organisations in the voluntary and statutory sector. This is reflected (see Tables 4 and 5) in the number of other workers contacted during the project:

> In Phase 1: 666
> In Phase 2: 2519

As these figures indicate (and like the work with users), the pace and intensity of this work increased rapidly as the projects became established and known in their localities. Consequently in Phase 1 of the project workers were able to achieve (relative to later work) only a limited amount of organisational change. At the end of Phase 1 we pointed (Prout and Deverell, 1992) to change at different levels:

(i) Increased awareness of staff about issues related to HIV and the needs of particular groups of men. For example:
—liaison work in Leeds with the GUM clinic over the needs of rent boys;
—discussions with helpline volunteers in Leicester about the needs of black men, including those using saunas, and development work towards a black-oriented helpline;
—discussions in Newcastle with Outrage (a gay men's political group) members about the sensitivity needed when working with men who use cruising areas;
—raising awareness in Newcastle Housing Department about sexual harassment and the housing needs of gay men.
(ii) Changed policy or practice of organisations. For example:
—in Leicester, advising on the appointment by the Health Promotion Team of a MWHSWM worker;
—in Newcastle, local government policy has been influenced on HIV prevention and inter-agency work, and on the needs of young gay men.
(iii) Winning resources for MWHSWM work. For example, from Newcastle Social

Services, Newcastle Youth and Community Services, Gateshead Social Services, Gateshead District Health Authority, and the Northern Regional Health Authority.

The mix of this work varied between the projects, reflecting to some extent the opportunities which the organisational base of the project opened up in each case: most of the work in London consisted of co-operation and liaison with other voluntary organisations; in Leicester the main focus was on collaboration with other voluntary sector groups (e.g. SHAKTI) with some statutory-focused work (especially together with BHAF, e.g. in their report on black communities and HIV/AIDS, see Thakar, 1991); in Leeds the focus was on changing and influencing the statutory sector (e.g. working to improve the GUM clinic's appreciation of the needs of MWHSWM); and in Newcastle most work has been done on changing policy in the statutory sector.

At this point MESMAC's impact on organisations was mainly brought about by the project workers themselves meeting and talking to other workers and managers, writing reports and sitting on committees and working parties. Through these activities they were able to raise the profile of MWHSWM work and relay their interpretation of the needs of the different groups of men with whom they have been working.

In Phase 2 of the project this work intensified and began to produce some major organisational outcomes for the project. In part this was because the end of HEA funding was now in sight and projects began (with the help of co-ordinators and HEA officers) to seek out local sources of funding.

The striking aspect of this phase of the work is that the different elements of the CD strategy began to knit together in very effective ways. A convenient way of organising the evaluation material here is to divide the impact into that on the statutory and that on the voluntary sectors. This is not entirely satisfactory, however, since there is some overlap between the two. Where this is the case it will be made clear in the text.

## Statutory sector

Projects continued to work toward increasing the awareness of the staff of other organisations about issues related to HIV and the needs of MWHSWM, including particular groups of men. In this phase of the project, however, these efforts were much more likely to result in actual changes to the policy and practice of the organisations.

The Leeds and Tyneside projects were more strategically placed to influence the statutory sector, although there are some examples from London and Leicester. From the start Leeds MESMAC had some funding from the DHA and therefore had an entrance to formal and informal health service networks. Being located in Newcastle Social Services had similar effects for MESMAC Tyneside. These projects worked at four different levels with the health services, social services and other statutory agencies in and around their localities:

(i) direct work with service providers;
(ii) District Health Authorities and cognate service planners;
(iii) the Regional Health Authority;
(iv) a 'super-regional' level which brought together three RHAs.

## Direct work with service providers

In relation to direct service providers Leeds MESMAC worked, for example, with the health advisors and a consultant at the local GUM clinic to make its service more accessible and user-friendly for gay men and MWHSWM. It now stocks strong HT condoms, uses Leeds MESMAC 'Love Safe, Live Sexy' information, lists MESMAC as a referral point and (as a result of the work done with rent boys and their lobbying) offers a 24-hour HIV test. MESMAC workers feel the staff have become more sensitive in serving the needs of gay men; they are more aware of the type of language they use (for example, not asking a gay man if he takes 'the man or the woman's position' during sex) and of making the assumption that their clients are heterosexual. Other examples include: working to ensure that contact numbers for gay organisations are included on health promotion literature; that specifically gay events are included in World AIDS Day events. In Leicester MESMAC workers have done some joint outreach with a gay men's sexual health worker.

## District level

At the district level in Leeds most effort has gone into working with the service planning team. The Leeds MESMAC manager joined an inter-agency task group made up of 15 representatives of statutory and voluntary services in Leeds. After discussions with the group, the MESMAC manager and a representative of Leeds Health Promotion Services drafted a comprehensive Leeds HIV Prevention Strategy. This set out key five-year objectives and the means of achieving them through the various agencies concerned.

By working in this way, and taking a leading role in the task group, Leeds MESMAC was able to ensure that the needs of gay, bisexual and MWHSWM were both recognised as distinct but also integrated into the overall picture. A wide variety of groups and organisations is being consulted about the draft strategy. An interesting feature of this consultation is that it has included the groups initiated by Leeds MESMAC, some of whom are now independently functioning.

MESMAC Tyneside was involved in the production of a similar policy document ('HIV Prevention: a joint strategy for Newcastle') produced by Newcastle Health Authority and Newcastle City Council (1992). A MESMAC worker was asked to sit on the group drawing up the document, acted as a co-editor (with a member of the health promotion unit) and was responsible for introducing some of its key features: a focus on prevention (in addition to existing concerns for care and support); working a CD approach into the strategy; a section on work with gay men as a priority group; references to homophobia and combating heterosexism; and an equal opportunities perspective, especially in relation to young men and black men.

The draft document was put out for consultation, including with other MESMAC sites and other District Health Authorities.

MESMAC Tyneside has also done work with the education system. When a new worker joined MESMAC Tyneside in 1992 he had a specific brief to do work with young gay men. One of his priorities was raising awareness of HIV, sexuality and sexual orientation in the education system. By working with the LEA liaison officer for HIV he was able to raise these issues directly with other teachers and school nurses who meet for discussions in a forum on young people and sexuality. He has also worked with a Theatre in Education group and was able to modify some heterosexist assumptions in their performance (of 'Sex, Lies and Tricky Bits') as well as suggest that there should be follow-up packs of information – which are now being used. Working with a research project on young people and sexuality he was able to ensure that the research design included a focus group of young gay men.

## Regional level

At regional level the Leeds and Tyneside projects were particularly active in putting forward the need for MWHSWM's prevention work. Once again the direct work with project users proved a useful base from which to put forward these arguments and gave credibility and weight to MESMAC workers' suggestions. By using their local experience pushing forward national policy statements (e.g. in the 'Health of the Nation') they were able to raise questions about the resources going into work with MWHSWM, raise its profile in what has been funded and win commitment to maintain support for it. In particular they were able to explain the character and value of community-based work and outreach and increase understanding about the context of sexual activity. For example, Leeds street outreach and work with Rent Boy Action helped people to understand the complexity of the work and the insufficiency of responding to this with traditional health education devices such as leaflets. An important feature of this work was that MESMAC representation at regional level became formally established and was expected to continue even if particular staff changed.

In Leeds this work resulted in funding for a set of local projects linked together under the title 'Yorkshire MESMAC' (see Further funding for MESMAC work, p. 203). Leeds MESMAC has been able to act as a resource at a regional level and, for example, gave advice that ensured that one particular planned project was set up with adequate resourcing and job descriptions. For MESMAC Tyneside, too, this work resulted in funding for the continuation of the project. In this case MESMAC had already started acting as a regional resource to co-ordinate networking, information sharing and joint training and give advice and support to new or less experienced projects (for example in Durham, Cleveland and Carlisle). The meetings have discussed what is needed in setting up a project, methods of working with particular groups (such as young gay men), and employment conditions (such as having full-time or part-time workers and job descriptions). Having the MESMAC D-i-Y Guide (Miller, 1993) was useful in this work.

As evaluators we have become aware, in hearing accounts of projects that are springing up around the country, that there is a real danger that these are not properly resourced or supported because there is no understanding of what prevention work with MWHSWM really involves. There is, we believe, a continuing need for the advice and support role which the MESMAC projects and others have begun to play.

## Super-regional level

Leeds and Tyneside's work at regional level was taken forward when three RHAs combined resources to draw up purchaser service specifications for MWHSWM work. In the new NHS internal market, purchasers are often unsure what they should be asking service providers of MWHSWM work to do. MESMAC projects in Leeds and Tyneside were able to feed their knowledge and experience into these discussions and the results will be disseminated to other regions.

The London project also developed links with the statutory services and successfully negotiated for funding with four Regional Health Authorities for the continuation of its work after the end of the HEA funding (see below). For the first time, all four regions jointly funded an HIV project.

# Being a resource for other workers

All the projects acted as a resource for other workers and projects. Whilst Leeds and Tyneside also did a great deal of policy development work with statutory organisations, in London and Leicester more emphasis was put on direct contact with other projects and workers. To a large extent this difference is explained by the opportunities available to the different projects.

In lobbying local organisations about the needs of black MWHSWM, Leicester workers have faced a double barrier. Not only do they have to overcome institutionalised homophobia but also racism. For example, when BHAF tried to find statistics on STDs in Leicester analysed by ethnic group, they found that these were not compiled. They were unable, therefore, to track changes and use local epidemiological information as part of the evaluation, planning and prioritising of work. Consequently MESMAC and BHAF have lobbied the DHA to begin ethnic monitoring on hepatitis B. Clearly this has to be done with many safeguards but without it work with black communities faces another obstacle.

Leicester MESMAC also found that its national HEA funding meant that it was not seen as 'a local project'. This made it more difficult to enter into local networks and make links with local funding sources.

However, where direct contact with other projects has occurred, it has been very productive. For example, Leicester MESMAC was consulted by the district health authority and the Leicester Lesbian and Gay Resource Centre about the appointment of a men's sexual health worker. It helped to plan the project and took part in the appointment in July 1992. Since then MESMAC attended the steering group of the project and was able to bring its experience and perspective to the development of his work. In particular it has been able to contribute to discussions on:

(i) The differences between HIV prevention work with white gay men and black men. These discussions have led to some joint outreach work in Leicester scene venues. The support provided here has been two-way. For MESMAC workers it has meant that their particular interest in working with black men can be presented as part of more general HIV prevention work (see also Chapter 6).

(ii) Working conditions and practices in outreach. Here they have been able to feed in the MESMAC experience on issues such as support, hours, the impact of outreach on the workers' own social life, and the importance of limits and boundaries around work. The MESMAC National Code of Conduct has been an important resource here.

(iii) Local needs. This input came directly from Leicester MESMAC's own experience. They have been able to identify areas where work is needed but has not been done by MESMAC, for example cottaging and cruising areas mainly used by white men. The collaborative outreach has also enabled them to offer black men a choice in whether they talk to a black or white worker.

Leicester has also contributed to work with deaf people. One of the MESMAC workers had some sign language training. Together with a Leicester AIDS Support Services worker he obtained funding from Leicester City Council to run a course in signing for HIV workers. The project's commitment to equal opportunities led to four places on the course being set aside for black workers. There was also an emphasis on signing drug and sexuality concepts. Leicester also did related work with the Deaf Centre by providing basic safer sex education for deaf people and this has led onto further work with one of the Centre workers.

Leicester also did work on a safer sex pack for men with learning difficulties, which has good potential as a resource for workers with this client group. A MESMAC worker developed a pack of visual information and an accompanying audio-tape with a graphic designer. He consulted a wide range of other practitioners (e.g. social workers, counsellors and doctors at the GUM clinic). Feedback was obtained from social services and the DHA and it was intended to do further work modifying and widening the scope of the pack.

In London, as discussed above, there are four RHAs and, for a project with only one full-time worker, resources were not concentrated enough to manage this complexity. Also, because of the size of THT and its existing national recognition, the main opportunities for policy development with other agencies for a project in London MESMAC's position tend to come by working *through* the structure of its host organisation. This, however, takes time to develop.

The bulk of London MESMAC's work in relation to other workers has, therefore, involved responding to enquiries (for example, MWHSWM projects in Folkestone and Worcester). In one case (the Crescent Project in St Albans) the work arose when THT was asked to do an audit with the project workers. The MESMAC administrator was asked to be involved and the report produced led to changes in the structure of the project, facilitated outreach work and validated the work that had already been done.

The MESMAC administrator also had a substantial input into the planning of the Stop AIDS London Project, drawing on the MESMAC experience to do so. At an early stage of its development this was an outreach project but his suggestions introduced new elements aimed at bringing groups together, doing more needs assessment, and taking on an equal opportunities dimension, particularly in relation to black men, bisexuals and non gay-identified men.

London MESMAC has also contributed to an important new project, London Deaf MESMAC, for HIV prevention work with deaf gay men. It grew from an AIDS Ahead invitation for MESMAC to contribute to an open day for deaf gay men. Two deaf men who had been part of MESMAC's peer education project also became involved in setting up Deaf MESMAC. At the time of writing two issues of a newsletter had been produced and a residential training weekend held. MESMAC workers have contributed to and supported this work, including winning funding from Haringey

Council. Deaf MESMAC has also received funds from the London MESMAC Small Grants Scheme (see above).

A rather different way of resourcing other workers was undertaken by the workers on London Black MESMAC when they initiated the Black Action on AIDS Project. This work once again shows how the different elements of a CD strategy can begin to knit together. Although work with young black MWHSWM had long been an aim of the project the impetus grew when only a few became involved in the London peer training initiative. The project workers decided that specific events for black men would have to be held and started, in late 1991, with a party for black men. This was very successful and was the starting point for a number of initiatives that became known as London Black MESMAC. BAAP was one of these and was aimed at bringing together black workers in HIV, gay and lesbian organisations. Although establishing the group has been difficult, representatives from nine different organisations have come together and agreed its terms of reference. These include: developing strategies for HIV prevention outreach with black lesbians and gay men; providing support for members; identifying needs and feeding back and/or lobbying provider organisations; exchanging information about resources and activities.

An evaluation questionnaire was sent both to those who have been attending meetings and those invited but who have not attended. The responses show that BAAP has identified some of the needs that black workers in London feel they have. It was striking that the replies from non-attenders of BAAP to a question about their needs as black HIV workers in London mirror the points identified by BAAP. For example:

*Regular updates so that workers feel informed, confident and supported.*

*Support by other black staff. Networking. Skill sharing. Help with access to appropriate resources.*

Most of those who attended, although critical of the organisation of the meetings which they thought needed to be more focused, feel they have benefited from going. For example:

*I think BAAP has achieved work on an individual basis i.e. the group has provided support to members, also provided a space where many workers/people interested in HIV prevention can come together.*

*BAAP has helped me in terms of support.*

*It has enabled me to have contact with a range of black people who ordinarily don't have contact with the organisation I work with.*

# Working with voluntary sector organisations

For reasons essentially the same as those which produced Leicester and London's emphasis on working directly with other projects and workers, these two projects also developed a focus on working with voluntary organisations.

In Leicester, the project worked with SHAKTI, a social group for South Asian gay and lesbian people, throughout the life of the project. Up until 1992 this consisted mainly of supporting and promoting the social gatherings it organised (which people from all over the UK attend). MESMAC (and BHAF) organised a stall with safer sex literature and information (some in Asian languages and Swahili) for these events. In 1992 MESMAC took the initiative to restart SHAKTI after organisational problems led to a decline in the number of events organised. A more structured membership group was organised and the group decided to have a political as well as social function. Through this work MESMAC has begun to strengthen its ideas about helping to build gay sub-cultures with specific ethnic identities. For example, events might have different food and music and publicity could draw on design motifs from Asian and other cultures.

In London the small grants scheme proved an important way of supporting new and existing voluntary sector activities.

# Further funding for MESMAC work

At the time of writing all four sites have prepared funding bids to continue their work in some form. Leeds, London and Tyneside have received funding commitments.

MESMAC Tyneside will continue and expand its work with joint funding from the Regional Health Authority and Newcastle Social Services. Two more part-time workers will be recruited specifically to do outreach work in clubs and pubs. As explained above, MESMAC Tyneside's regional funding is in part to support its role as a co-ordinator and resource for other MWHSWM projects in the region. The funding is for three years.

In Leeds a funding package from Regional and District Health Authorities has been put together to support the creation of a network of linked projects which will be known as 'Yorkshire MESMAC'. The projects comprise: Leeds MESMAC, which has one year of funding to employ two community outreach workers; Wakefield and Pontefract MESMAC, which will employ community outreach workers and make a contribution to peripatetic outreach in the region; Bradford

MESMAC will be set up in the same way; and Hull MESMAC, which will draw on Yorkshire MESMAC resources for part-time outreach work. Negotiations for work to be started in Harrogate, York and Northallerton are also underway. Drawing on their experience of the last three years Leeds MESMAC workers will play a key role in training, supporting and supervising this work. The work done is planned in two stages: the first will concentrate on building up community infrastructure (continuing Leeds MESMAC's approach) and doing grassroots work (especially outreach); as local bases are established and experience gained, the projects will link together to pool skills and support each other. An important feature of the planned work is the participation strategy being built into the management structure of both the local projects and Yorkshire MESMAC as a whole.

London MESMAC has received funding from four London RHAs for three-year funding to employ two full-time workers, some sessional workers and to provide administrative support. They will continue the community development health education work of the last three years but will have two specific aims: to work with young men and black men. Additionally London MESMAC has raised funds for a part-time worker to research, publish and disseminate a report on the health education needs of black MWHSWM in relation to HIV/AIDS education and prevention.

## Summary

In this chapter we have shown that:

*MESMAC's community development approach successfully linked up grassroots work and the participation of local MWHSWM with the building of community infrastructure and organisational development;

*host organisations were helped to develop and change through their involvement with MESMAC;

*MESMAC worked at all levels with a range of organisations in both the statutory and voluntary sectors;

*MESMAC projects became an important source of experience and advice to other MWHSWM projects;

*MESMAC projects won new resources for initiating and continuing work with MWHSWM.

# 10 Community, diversity and alliances: a concluding discussion

## Introduction

At the beginning of this book we suggested that as a CD project for MWHSWM working within the context of HIV, MESMAC was involved in a complex exploration of the relationship between community, identity and behaviour. We believe that the strength of the project lay in its ability and commitment to work both with building community and working with diversity.

In the preceding chapters we have summarised the main learning points from the project, which we shall not repeat here. Instead we provide a further discussion of the main issues with which MESMAC work is continually engaged: community, identity and diversity. Through this we bring together what was learnt through the work as a whole.

One of the crucial factors which enabled the project to combine the benefits of community-based work with the importance of recognising diversity was the CD strategy and theoretical principles which guided the work. This enabled the sites to work with a large diversity of MWHSWM in numerous ways, and to link areas of work by finding ways to work at an individual, collective and organisational level. We believe that the work involved in articulating such different levels of work together was crucial to the success of the project. In the final section of this chapter we discuss CD as a strategy for building alliances between the many different constituencies necessary for effective HIV and health promotion for MWHSWM.

First, however, we shall address the concept of community in some depth. Until this point we have avoided theoretical discussion. In this last chapter, however, we feel that some theoretical understanding of the concept of community will be useful in understanding the tensions and successes involved in MESMAC's work.

## The concept of 'community'

As we pointed out in the introduction to this book the term 'community' presents an interesting dilemma. It is a term deployed by many different people in relation to a huge range of phenomena, from 'community policing' to 'community arts'. 'Community' is continually referred to, organised around and appealed to in part because the term has a rhetorical power to imply an intrinsic value. However, the very flexibility of the term makes its meaning difficult to pin down, and on closer inspection it can seem to have a rather hollow ring.

In recent years the concept of community has been revisited by some social scientists who, by reworking theory, have reconstituted it as a useful analytical term. One such writer is the social anthropologist Anthony Cohen (1985). Below we outline his ideas about community because we feel that these are potentially very useful in understanding some of the processes that CD work entails. Although many of his points about community are not new, his ideas may provide a useful framework through which to begin to understand some of the issues related to working with community, identity and diversity.

Cohen criticises previous theoretical approaches to understanding community, suggesting that by seeing community as an objective 'thing out there' and trying to define and describe it objectively, the most useful questions have not been asked. He writes (1985:19-29) that in his view community is best not:

> ...approached as a morphology, as a structure capable of objective definition and description. Instead...(he suggests we should try to)...understand 'community' by seeking to capture members' experience of it. Instead of asking 'what does it look like to us?',...we ask 'what does it appear to mean to its members?'. Rather than describing analytically the form of the structure from an external vantage point, we are attempting to penetrate the structure, to look outwards from its core.

He suggests that when people use the term community they are often implying two related ideas: that the members of a group of people have something in common with each other; and that this thing in common distinguishes them in a significant way from members of other groups:

> The word thus expresses a relational idea: the opposition of one community to others or to other social entities...the use of the word is only occasioned by the desire or need to express such a distinction...(it is appropriate therefore)...to focus...on the element which embodies this sense of discrimination, namely, the boundary. (Cohen: 1985:12)

Cohen argues that the most important boundaries that are used to delineate communities are symbolic ones. Since symbols are highly flexible in the way they can be interpreted they may be seen in very different ways – not only by people who place themselves on opposite sides of the boundary but also by people on the same side. From the outside communities typically look homogenous; but from the inside the differences between members can look enormous. Sometimes members will want to emphasise what they have in common but at other times they will de-emphasise, or even deny, this commonality. Which way events move is highly contingent and difficult to predict.

Equally important is the recognition that communities are social and cultural constructions rather than objective entities. Ultimately all communities are communities of meaning. In particular, the symbolic boundaries of a community are created and maintained by its members – and they can be recreated or changed as well. The symbolic boundaries of community are thus always in flux. By the same token, however, some members of a community may identify most strongly with the community when they sense that the boundaries are under threat or being breached.

Importantly Cohen points out that the symbolic boundaries of communities are constructed both by those within the community and those without. In this way the different definitions and constructions interplay with each other.

Finally, individuals may identify as members of different communities at different times and in different circumstances to different degrees. Because community is about meaning (beliefs and ideas) there is nothing automatic about the process of coming to share a sense of identity with others. Because an individual looks, from the outside, as if they should identify as a member of a community, does not mean that they necessarily will, or will do in all circumstances. On the contrary, when individuals stand on the boundary between communities they may have to make difficult choices about where they want to belong.

Although Cohen does not discuss gay communities (concentrating his analysis mainly on the ways people symbolically mark their sense of belonging to a place) many of the points he makes can be seen as relevant. As Weeks (1986) has argued, British gay sub-cultures are an historically specific phenomenon that rest on a particular set of circumstances that emerged in Europe in the 19th and 20th centuries. In the first place was the Victorian construction of a medical category, 'homosexuality', that saw particular types of sexual activity (thought of as 'deviations') as attached to a certain 'type' of person. In the 20th century, as urbanisation took place, the conditions for gayness as a way of life were constructed (see D'Emilio, 1983, for an account of the US experience). Where medical discourse had seen 'deviation', gay communities put celebration and identity. As gay communities were constructed a key part of the work involved the production of symbols that marked membership, for example clothing and other forms of bodily appearance; specific forms of speech, especially slang terms; places and spaces to meet others; political organisations and media. Being a member was and remains, in large degree, about sharing an understanding of these symbols.

Cohen's point about communities looking homogenous from the outside but diverse from within is also relevant here. Although the gay community is often portrayed in very stereotyped and simplistic ways from without, from within there is a huge diversity. For example, the outside (straight) view of gay men as a totality may from within be divided into clones, leather queens, drag queens, scene queens, political activists, SM gays, closeted men, bisexual men, queers; or young men, middle-class men, working-class men and black men; or in many other different and diverse ways. However, as Cohen again suggests, at times these different groups of men may also assert their commonality through uniting behind the idea of the gay community, for example for the purposes of political action or celebration.

The importance of this excursion into Cohen's reworking of the concept of community is that it may help us to understand some of the issues that arose within the MESMAC project, specifically those relating to diversity, community and identity. In the next section we draw together some of what was learnt through three years' experience of working around these issues. In doing this we have utilised Cohen's work to try and illuminate some of the issues that arose.

## Building on and building up community

One of the key principles that informed the development of MESMAC was that it should draw on and recognise the existing grassroots work which had taken place within gay communities around HIV and safer sex. This idea was put into practice very early on through the initial forum to develop and discuss the MESMAC project proposal, and was carried through into the writing of site proposals. This ethic of consultation and participation was continued throughout the project. All the workers spent time establishing what was already taking place within their local community in order to consult and find out needs, and to build on, learn from and integrate MESMAC initiatives with existing work. Contrary to some suggestions (see, for example, Scott, 1993) the term MWHSWM did not seem to alienate the voluntary sector – all the sites worked successfully with a large number of lesbian gay and bisexual groups. This took the form of needs assessment; joint work; resourcing existing gay groups; providing resources to develop new groups; providing training and support; and networking.

In this respect, however, the experience of Leicester MESMAC as a black project was somewhat different. It found that there were no well established black community groups in Leicester formed around a specific sexual identity. In consequence there were few existing resources to draw on. Indeed the MESMAC experience in all the sites (but especially for Leicester and the work with black men in London) shows that specific efforts are needed to contact black MWHSWM. It cannot be assumed that black men will be reached through general MWHSWM or gay men's work. In fact the Leicester project found that much of its work involved thinking about and trying to create a specifically black gay culture rather than expecting black men to fit into

European ideas of gay identity and culture. However, they did work with existing groups, both through supporting and networking with other black groups (including black community organisations) and through working to have the needs of black MWHSWM incorporated into existing lesbian and gay organisations.

One of the advantages of working with gay communities was the ability to target existing networks of gay and bisexual men through community organisations, networks and meeting places. For example, one of the important focuses for all the sites was the local gay scene, which proved to be a good place to reach large numbers of white gay men. The projects also used the gay press and other community networks to advertise MESMAC initiatives and feed back information. Where such local networks were not well developed MESMAC helped build them up (see Chapter 9). Such work enabled projects to build up their image as part of the local gay community and contributed to building community infrastructure.

Through working with existing community organisations the workers were also able to draw on local experiences of lesbian and gay organising. Many existing organisations had a history of using shared experience and support as an organising base, both in relation to political action and service provision. This was something the workers were able to learn from and develop through building on gay men's sense of community and finding ways to relate this to safer sex and HIV.

Working with existing networks of gay and bisexual men also had the advantage of informing workers about other networks. Combined with their own knowledge of local communities the workers were able to use this information to target other places where men met, for example local public sex environments. In Cohen's terms we can understand all this work with existing networks, organisations and places as working with the shared symbols members of a community may have. By using these workers were able to tailor their work effectively to those who shared this identity. The work Leicester MESMAC did in trying to develop a black gay culture, for example by using Asian motifs on posters and flyers, shows how important having a shared set of symbols can be.

Although using existing networks and organisations was crucial, particularly in contacting gay and bisexual men, it also had limitations. For example, the workers found that many young gay men do not read the gay press, use scene venues, or take part in gay cultural or political movements. This was also true of many black men. As many gay-identified men were not linked into gay community organisations, other work was needed to target them. Often this involved setting up new initiatives to meet their needs.

Another group not reached through gay-identified networks was non gay-identifying men who have sex with men. Contact with these men in other settings confirmed that many of them felt isolated from the gay community, and indeed many had no desire for such contact (see also Bartos et al, 1993). Thus it was important to find other ways to meet them. The workers found that outreach, one-to-one work, phone work, encouraging referrals from other organisations, advertising in the general press, specific group work, and non gay-identified leaflets were all good ways to reach non-identifying MWHSWM. Working with other organisations to incorporate the needs of MWHSWM into generic work and to undertake specific targeted work was also important.

## Who is in the community?

One of the issues in working from a basis of existing community organisation related to who was defined as belonging to the community. Not all gay-identified men were seen to be part of the community and some felt excluded from it. For example, some of the gay-identified rent boys said that many gay men looked down upon them, or made it clear that they did not want rent boys to be associated with the gay community. Organising work around identity and community could have the disadvantage of reproducing existing inequalities related to race, ability, class, occupation, age and other social divisions. This issue has been pointed out by other commentators in relation to earlier grassroots work around safer sex (Patton, 1990; Dada, 1990) and is supported by MESMAC's experience. For example, deaf gay men and black men contacted by the project have argued very strongly that they have missed out on previous information and support, or that available services, information and support have been inappropriate or inaccessible. Specific initiatives such as London Deaf MESMAC have begun to address these shortcomings.

The importance of equal opportunities within the CD approach meant that the projects had a commitment to make their initiatives as accessible as possible. They did this through such things as providing signers, childcare, subsidising events, having black-only events, free food, and through challenging racism and sexism within groups. Through this the projects were particularly successful in attracting men who had previously felt isolated or marginalised from gay communities, and enabled them to feel more a part of a community. In addition many of those involved in MESMAC initiatives said that they had valued the opportunity to meet men they would never have met socially, and to have been made to think about issues relating to black men, deaf men and sex workers.

This underlines the diversity of experience that exists amongst men who identify as gay and bisexual and the need for workers to consider who is included, and who left out, in the existing communities they choose to work with. This means exploring the boundaries of communities and mapping out where different communities overlap.

# Identity, community and collective action

One of the early experiences of the project was that it was easier to work collectively with men who had open and confident gay identities (also reported by Davis et al, 1991, in an Australian context). Workers found it particularly hard to collectivise work with men who did not positively identify as gay or bisexual, or who wanted to keep their identity secret. It is instructive in this respect that Patton, describing the work of D'Emilio, Weeks and Bronski in relation to the development of modern gay identities and communities, notes that:

> *Each views the development of a public* [our emphasis] *sexual identification as a key stage in the process of identity and community formation.* (1985:123)

Indeed MESMAC workers found that it was much easier to develop collective action with those men who were willing to be out about their identity. This underlines an important difference with much other CD work which is organised around identities, issues or communities that are public, or that people are happy to be associated with (for example their place of residence). Many MWHSWM do not have a public sexual identity, or indeed do not want an identity based around their sexual practice. This makes immediate collective action more difficult as work usually has to proceed in ways that will not publicly identify men, obviously limiting the kind of activities that can be undertaken.

The workers found that many MWHSWM who did not identify as gay were resistant to the forms of collective action they attempted, and were only interested in accessing resources, support and information. One of the main reasons for this was that for many men having sex with other men was something that they kept secret. For these men the prospect of working collectively ran the risk of their being identified as a MWHSWM or involved being open about their activities in a way that was totally unacceptable and unrealistic. In any case for many men having sex with other men was all that they wanted, they did not see themselves as part of a community and felt they had little in common with others they had sex with. It was important that this was respected and that it was not assumed that all MWHSWM wanted to come out and adopt a gay identity (see also Bartos et al, 1993; Prestage and Hood, 1993). For example many of the black men whom the Leicester project met in saunas made a distinction between themselves as MWHSWM (MESMEN), and gay men whom they did not identify with. As a worker said:

> *Mesmen will often distinguish between what they do, that is, have sex with men and what gay men do, which is love men, be camp, live together etc. (10/3/92)*

For these men the value of MESMAC lay in the opportunity to access resources and support without having to identify as gay or bisexual.

However, it did prove possible, if done sensitively, to form groups for (or including) non gay-identified men by focusing around other issues, for example the Married Men's Group and Rent Boy Action. This involved building up trust in order to find out men's needs and building groups around these needs, the use of non gay-identifying venues and strict confidentiality. Workers also encouraged individual men to get involved in particular groups of interest to them.

Although it was recognised that collective action was not always appropriate in relation to non-identifying MWHSWM (outreach, phone work and one-to-one work being preferable), for some men this was important. For those who wanted it the opportunity to meet, talk with and get support from other men in a similar situation was very valuable, particularly in reducing isolation and reassuring men that others were in a similar situation. For other men there was a desire to organise around other issues they had in common, despite differences in their sexual identity, or lack of sexual identity. Rent Boy Action in Leeds, for example, focused around legal rights and dealing with harassment. Although only a few men may get involved, collective work with non-identifying MWHSWM should not be ruled out. The important point is to work from the basis of men's own needs and be responsive to these.

For those men who had a sexual identity and who were open about it, collective work was significantly easier. MESMAC found that working from a basis of existing community organisation and shared identity was very helpful in collectivising work with gay and bisexual men. This was often the case as many gay-identified men became involved as a way of supporting other gay men or sharing their experiences with others (see Chapter 7). The process of sharing experiences and working collectively, of being put in touch with other groups and organisations, of making new friends and being able to develop their own initiatives was of great importance. It helped many of those who became involved to feel a strengthened sense of community. For some men such contact with the project led to a greater certainty and confidence in their own sexual identity which led to a decision to come out.

This way of working also showed evidence of men adopting and maintaining safe sex, through promoting self-esteem and strengthening attachment to the gay community and gay identity (see also Kippax et al, 1990; King 1993a). Men also valued the opportunity to discuss sex and sexuality in a friendly and supportive environment and to receive appropriate information and advice. As Derek Jarman (1992:29) has recently written:

> It's important for us to talk about sex, to define ourselves in a world which has never talked about us or even let us talk about ourselves...When you start to talk, it confirms you are living.

However, it should be noted that not all gay men wanted to attend groups and those who were not out, or just coming out, could find the prospect of going to a gay group intimidating.

Although MESMAC has shown that it is much easier to attract men to groups if they share something in common, this 'thing' may be additional to their sexuality. Often sexual identity is not enough, or rather other differences can be more important than a shared sexual identity. Some of the longest-running MESMAC groups were those based on specific activities which were additional to gay identity and provided an organising focus. An example was the lesbian and gay theatre group 'Latex Productions'. This does not mean that sexual identity is not important, but on its own it is not always sufficient as a focus for organisation. Other differences and experiences such as class, race or political views can fracture any unity based on shared sexual identity.

# Multiplicity of identity

One of the important practical experiences in the work was the need to consider how men identified and to recognise that they may have more than one identity, and attachment to various communities. In particular the work with black men highlighted the need for a more complex understanding of the interplay of race and sexuality on people's identities. For example, in a racist society many black men may experience more need for social support around race than sexuality. This is particularly the case since black men are more likely to be identified and discriminated against on the basis of race. This means that many black MWHSWM are more likely to get involved in, and take action around the social and political issues affecting black communities, than organise around sexuality. Therefore work with black MWHSWM has to recognise the importance of issues and experiences related to race (see Chapter 6).

The importance of considering the multiplicity of identity should, however, not be seen in a simplistic way. As Avtar Brah has written:

> *Structures of class, racism, gender and sexuality cannot be treated as 'independent variables' because the oppression of each is inscribed within the other – is constituted by and is constitutive of the other. (1992:137)*

Thus it is not simply a case of thinking about race and about sexuality and trying to fit these issues together, but considering how race and sexuality interact and affect each other, for example the way ideas about race construct black men's sexuality as exotic and animalistic (Manuel et al, 1989; see also Brake, 1976 on gender and sexuality).

MESMAC has shown that people have different identities which are more or less important in relation to different situations, times and people (see also Gatter, 1991; Gatter, 1993; and Weeks, 1990). For some men their sexuality is not always the most important or prominent identity. It is important that this fluidity of identity is taken into account. Identities are not fixed and unitary but multiple, historical and circumstantial. Workers have to be flexible and acknowledge that men may choose to identify, or are identified, in different ways at different times.

The multiplicity of identity underlines another important point, that gay men themselves have different understandings of the notion of a gay identity and do not attach equal importance to it (Plummer, 1975; Watney, 1993). For example, some men, though identifying as gay do not feel that they have much in common with other gay men. Mobilising around identity and community involves emphasising the symbolic boundary of commonality which in turn marks out difference. In this way it may serve to exclude those who choose not to define in this way, or indeed define themselves in opposition to gay men. As Bartos et al note:

> ...the self-conscious construction of personal identity in terms of sexual object choice applies to only a highly politicised part of the (behaviourally defined) population of men who have sex with men. (1993:20)

Work which appeals only to gay identity and community, though important, will not reach many other men who have sex with men.

## Identity or behaviour concepts?

At the time the project was set up the use of the term MWHSWM was in vogue, its importance being seen to lie in the fact that it recognised that there is no necessary link between identity and behaviour. However, as MESMAC developed, the term came under criticism (Watney, 1993). One of the criticisms stated that:

> Conceptualisation of the work based on MWHSWM models tends to lead to an emphasis upon targeting men on the margins at the expense of men at the core of the gay and bisexual communities. (Scott, 1993: Appendix 1)

At first sight such a reading of the term may seem convincing, and indeed in the very early days of the project some of the workers thought they should prioritise work with non gay-identified men (see Chapter 7). However, this perception soon changed and often project members would describe the project as gay men's work. This no doubt reflects the fact that the vast majority (80-85%) of those reached by MESMAC were gay-identified men. One of the important findings of MESMAC was that having a brief related to working with MWHSWM did *not* mean that the needs of gay and bisexual men were neglected. However, it *did* mean that there was a commitment to meet the needs of all MWHSWM. Ways were found to reach more marginalised men, including more isolated gay men as well as non-identifying MWHSWM. The fact that the CD strategy emphasised the importance of working around the basis of expressed need gave the workers particular flexibility in this area, because it legitimised the development of specific initiatives for men who identified in different ways.

The experience of MESMAC reinforces the view that MWHSWM is a diverse group, and that there is no clear relationship between sexual identity and practice. For example, some men were very out and identified as gay or bisexual; others identified as gay or bisexual but were not out. Others did not have a definite sexual identity. Many of the married men and some of the rent boys expressed feeling confused about their sexuality. Some of these men went on to define as gay or bisexual, whilst others did not. Still others felt the identities available to them were not culturally appropriate, or did not feel a need to have a sexual identity.

This lack of need for an identity based on sexual practice is also reported in an Australian context by Bartos, McLeod and Nott (1993:iv). They state that for many non-identifying MWHSWM (msm) sexual identity is largely irrelevant:

> *Sexual identity is not a major issue for msm...Sexuality is not a key part of their sense of personal identity, which is based instead on other personal relationships (e.g. family, career etc.).*

However, even when men contacted by MESMAC did have a clear sexual identity, this was not always revealing about sexual behaviour. For example, men identifying as gay might be having sex with women, and men who identified as straight might be having sex with men. This complex situation reinforced the lack of necessary commensurability between identity and practice which is well documented in sexuality and sex research literature, and has been raised by other MWHSWM projects (Boulton and Weatherburn, 1990; Davies, 1990; Davis et al, 1991; Weatherburn et al, 1992; BMRB, 1992; Murray, 1992; Siegel and Bauman, 1986; Bartos et al, 1993; Prestage and Hood; 1993, Rodden et al, 1993). Within MESMAC recognition of this diversity and complexity highlighted the limitations of using categories based on identity.

Debates about the best concepts and terms to use continued throughout the life of MESMAC. 'MWHSWM' was seen to be useful because it recognised the diversity and fluidity of sexuality and encouraged workers to think about non gay-identified men. On the other hand, it was felt by some to deny the history and culture of gay men, and to neglect gay men's attachment to identity. Politically workers also wanted to highlight work with gay men and win resources for it.

Given the importance of working with as wide a range of men as possible MWHSWM was felt to be the best option. There was a concern that people would not make the extra effort to target non-identifying men if projects were defined in terms of gay and bisexual men. This was particularly important in relation to black men, as MESMAC found that most black MWHSWM do not relate to HIV prevention if it is organised around gay identity. Indeed, the Leicester project in particular stressed the usefulness of the term MWHSWM because so few of the black men they worked with accepted the identity gay. However, it was recognised that there were no clear-cut answers. Both concepts had benefits and drawbacks; the terms gay and bisexual attract some men but alienate others.

## Who should do MESMAC work?

Most of the workers in the project were gay-identified men and this proved to be a great asset in the development of the work, with many gay-identified users commenting that it helped to build trust as well as provide a feeling of empathy and understanding.

Although it was felt best to have gay men work with other gay men it was important to recognise that being gay did not necessarily mean that workers would have had similar experiences with users. Sometimes other differences such as class meant that they had very different life experiences and lifestyles (see Deverell and Prout, 1992a).

MESMAC also raised the issue of whether gay workers were best in relation to work with non gay-identified men. For example, because of their own strong gay identity, a difficulty for some of the workers was in accepting that not all MWHSWM wanted to identify as gay. Many of the workers wanted to support men coming out and validate their gay identity (see also Davis, 1991). However, as the work progressed they realised that the situation was more complex. Many of the MWHSWM did not see themselves as gay, or did not want to take on this identity. The workers felt that as very out gay men they may alienate some men who have sex with men. This was of particular concern in outreach, where it was clear that some MWHSWM shied away from contact with gay-identified men.

There was much debate as to whether all jobs, including administration and support roles, needed to be held by MWHSWM. The project's experience was that given appropriate skills and sensitivity they need not be, but that workers who are not MWHSWM need appropriate support. If future projects were to employ women it was felt that this entailed a recognition at management level of potential issues in relation to gender and sexuality, good managerial support for women workers, the provision of some external supervision, team-building from the outset and regular team discussions (Deverell and Bell, 1993).

For workers, being part of the community they worked with brought some benefits. For example, they became known and trusted and were often able to build up informal links which were useful in their work. However, a difficulty in this respect was that living and working in the same community and having a code of conduct which stressed the importance of sexual boundaries meant that the work could have a negative impact on the workers' own social/sexual life (see Chapter 7). Indeed the workers' feelings of empathy with project users meant that sometimes they did not feel a great distinction between themselves and those with whom they worked. As gay men the workers were themselves part of the client group and many had an emotional and political motivation for doing the job. At times their identity as a professional was therefore less strong than their identity as a gay man. Indeed some of the workers suggested that one of the reasons why boundary-making was hard was that 'professional culture' and 'gay culture' constructed very different ideas about sex and sexual boundaries (Deverell, 1993). In Cohen's terms we can see that the workers were at times pulled between the different communities to which they belonged. Having to retain credibility both amongst other professionals and other MWHSWM, whilst still maintaining their own sense of integrity and political commitment, could be stressful. This underlined the importance of appropriate support and the need for organisational recognition and understanding of such issues.

Another related issue arose for black workers. Some of the black workers found that some users did not identify themselves as black, or felt they had little in common with other black men and therefore actually preferred to talk to white workers. This was also the case for those black men who feared being identified as a MWHSWM and therefore felt threatened by the approach of someone from the same community. This experience underlines the importance of not making assumptions about how people choose to identify themselves, or who they will feel most comfortable with. As Cohen notes, because an individual looks from the outside as if they should identify as a member of a community, it does not mean that they will. Workers, therefore, need to build reflection and evaluation into their work cycle and review their strategies in light of practical experience and local circumstances.

## Work with women

Orientating work around gay identity and community obviously had benefits but it could have the effect of silencing certain issues or making them difficult to address, for example through marginalising women and men's relationships with women. In MESMAC many of the gay workers found it difficult to address needs in relation to the sex men were having with women, and that at times the women working in the project felt marginalised, or found it hard to raise issues relating to gender (see Deverell and Bell, 1993).

If we understand not having sex with women as one of the symbols used to define gay men (both within the gay community and outside it) then we can see that discussing such an issue is bound to be difficult or uncomfortable. It could be seen as threatening the community (and therefore the identity) boundary. This may explain why bisexually identified men and women have found it so hard to be accepted within both gay and straight communities. By having sex with both men and women they are very clearly straddling a boundary traditionally used to distinguish gay men from heterosexuals and vice versa. Indeed Boulton and Weatherburn suggest that the development of a distinct gay identity in the West has served to strengthen the distinction between homosexuality and heterosexuality which militates against bisexuality (1990:18).

It is not surprising that the women members of MESMAC experienced a feeling that talking about MWHSWM having sex with women, or indeed female sexuality, was socially taboo amongst gay men. By raising issues relating to sex with women, particularly gay men having sex with women, the notion of a gay identity as it is currently constructed (in opposition to heterosexuality) was symbolically threatened.

This problem of boundary also had implications for work with men. For those MWHSWM who were having sex with women, organising work around gay communities and identities had the effect of only addressing part of their sexuality. For example, many of the men with female partners did not know about HIV transmission routes between men and women, and having information which only addressed sex with men did not help this situation. As an HIV project it was important that such issues were addressed, particularly as these were often of major concern to the men themselves, who wanted help in negotiating safer sex with female partners or in getting support to come out to them, or just wanted to talk about their relationships. It proved important not to assume that such issues only applied to men who identified as straight or bisexual as gay-identified men may also be having sex with women (see for example Weatherburn et al, 1992; BMRB, 1992:6), a point which some commentators seem to overlook (Scott, 1993).

In relation to equal opportunities it was also important to think about the effects of only working with men. The vital work of addressing the support and resource needs of MWHSWM and building their skills and self-esteem could have a damaging effect on their women partners. By doing work which only empowered men in relation to safer sex there was a danger of reproducing existing inequalities. Those workers who worked closely with married men, for example, came to see the need for work which met the support and resource needs of their women partners. It was important that such work was considered, even if it was best done by other projects or workers.

The experience of MESMAC shows that some work with women is important, even in a men's project. This may be through joint lobbying and support work with women (particularly lesbians) around issues relating to sexuality and service provision, as well as work around sex that men may be having with women. In this respect thinking about the boundaries that are worked within is important. Men may be having sex with partners who are seen to belong to different communities, or having sex which in the current orthodoxy would seem to place them in different communities.

# Varying needs

As Cohen points out, behind the symbolic boundary of a community (which emphasises its commonalities) there is often a high degree of division and difference. It was clear from the start of the project that men may have different needs, not just through having different identities but because of class, race or other factors. The benefit of the CD strategy in this respect was its stress on working from a basis of established need. Work was organised around discovering what men actually wanted rather than making assumptions about their needs. Needs assessment in MESMAC was, therefore, integral to the whole approach and not adopted as a one-off exercise (see Chapter 6). We consider the work of the project in identifying both the common needs of MWHSWM and the differences between different individuals and groups to be of great importance to future HIV prevention work with MWHSWM.

By monitoring, discussing and reviewing their work the sites continually developed their understanding of the needs of those with whom they were working. Key to this process were: a great deal of direct contact with MWHSWM; the flexibility of front-line workers to respond to the emerging and changing picture of needs, and the autonomy to translate these directly into new initiatives; the skills and sensitivity of the workers, including their own experience and involvement as gay men/MWHSWM; and the support and experience of managers and co-ordinators.

Identifying needs was a complex and interpretive process, not a simple and mechanical one. The workers had to listen and learn and have flexibility to be responsive to both individual and local variation.

Men who have sex with men were found to have many needs in common. These included: numerous needs related to living in a homophobic and heterosexist society; dealing with and overcoming isolation; resources and support around safer sex; needs relating to general health issues; access to resources; and economic needs. However, MESMAC also showed that the needs of MWHSWM were very diverse. Men who have sex with men come from a variety of class, ethnic and religious backgrounds, have different abilities and identities and different ideas about their sexuality. Because of different social and economic circumstances not all men have the same choices or means to realise their choices. For example, MESMAC found that young men, married men, sex workers, men with learning difficulties, men who have been sexually abused and deaf men all have particular and different needs (see also Davis et al, 1991; Connell et al, 1991). Because the needs of MWHSWM are complex and at times contradictory there is no one right way of working – work with MWHSWM needs to start from men's felt needs and requires a diversity of initiatives materials and resources (see also Bartos et al, 1993, Wiseman, 1989, Scott, 1993).

One of the recurring findings of the various needs assessments was that for many men HIV is not their main priority (see also McKevitt and Warwick, 1993; Kjeldsen, 1991). In this respect the advantage of the CD approach was that it focused work on the issues of importance to men themselves, and therefore legitimised work which directly addressed these wider concerns. This meant that MESMAC work involved meeting needs related to issues such as coming out, dealing with homophobia, finding housing, in establishing social alternatives to the commercial scene and in getting legal advice and medical treatment.

MESMAC did not reduce the needs of MWHSWM to those solely concerned with HIV and other STDs. This in itself was important as by working closely with and from within communities, and seeing the world from their point of view, MESMAC confirmed that HIV prevention cannot be separated from wider social, cultural and economic issues. For example, men may not be able to afford condoms, men may be made homeless through coming out, or may have low self-esteem caused by homophobia which affects their choices and skills in relation to safer sex. Rather than seeing such issues as merely a context for HIV or sexuality issues it was important to see how HIV and sexual health needs were integrated in complex ways into the broader framework of people's lives (see also Bartos et al, 1993:59).

One of the tensions raised by taking a more holistic approach to health promotion was how to keep a balance between direct work on HIV and wider issues (such as dealing with homophobia or housing problems). This took time to achieve but all the projects found ways of both keeping HIV on the agenda when working in indirect ways and responding to wider issues when working directly around HIV.

The experience of MESMAC is similar to that of Cindy Patton, who writes:

> *To those outside AIDS organising AIDS continues to be viewed primarily as a single issue. To those inside, the range and complexity of issues tapped seems almost impossible to combat. (1985:17)*

This supports the need to move away from HIV prevention which maintains a narrow behaviour change focus. In the second decade of the epidemic it is important that prevention work begins to consolidate and learn from past experience. The experience of MESMAC is that there is a lot to learn from wider health initiatives and health promotion theory which stresses the importance of addressing wider issues and inequalities.

Working within a CD strategy, MESMAC had the ability and commitment to combine both the benefits of community-based work with the importance of recognising and addressing diversity. By organising work around sexual identity and community the projects worked successfully with existing community organisations and networks of gay and bisexual men. Building on this basis of shared experience and support proved particularly useful in collectivising work. However, the work also discovered a diversity of need and experience amongst MWHSWM, both within gay and bisexual communities, as well as amongst men who did not identify in this way. This highlighted how an emphasis on community and commonality can also hide diversity. The experience of MESMAC is that there is a need to look beyond the boundaries of existing communities in order to reach MWHSWM who do not identify as gay or who feel marginalised from gay communities, because of their age, race or differing commitment to a gay identity. In this case successful collective work often involves organising around something other than sexuality, and recognising the diversity of men's identities.

MESMAC has shown that *both* work based on sexual identity and work based on sexual behaviour are needed, each has advantages and disadvantages; each approach can exclude some men; the full range of MWHSWM will only be reached if both approaches are used. The experience of the project is that a CD strategy provides both the flexibility and the autonomy to work successfully with this diversity.

# Community development as a space for building alliances

We argued in Chapter 1 that MESMAC brought together many different constituencies and interests, including: a government agency, freelance professionals, evaluation researchers, statutory and voluntary sector organisations in different localities, front-line workers and a diverse range of MWHSWM. Despite the tensions that are inevitable in such an enterprise, MESMAC did lead to a successful collaboration. In part this was because of the important contribution that each of these different constituencies was able to make. Beyond this, however, is an equally significant point: that MESMAC was constituted as a space *between* these constituencies. Each had something to contribute but none could entirely dominate it. It was built by a process of negotiation and alliance-making in which everyone had to lose something in order to gain more.

The CD strategy was of major importance in this process. By stressing the need to work at different levels, it involved the project in building alliances and bringing together different groups. This work was often difficult and involved working with a number of tensions. However, ultimately such a process enabled the integration of grassroots work, community infrastructure, organisational development and participation.

One of the important points about grassroots work in MESMAC is that it started from the needs and experiences of men themselves and actually involved them in the process of designing, developing and running their own initiatives. Men were able to tailor initiatives to their own needs. The CD approach meant that projects tried to find ways to feed their grassroots work into building community infrastructure and organisational development. By finding ways to enable men to participate in this work the workers often helped men to develop their self-esteem and a belief in the importance of their own needs and rights. This often had direct practical effects; for example, improving services at a GUM clinic or securing housing.

The projects felt a responsibility to network and be accountable and responsive to the local community and developed ways to consult the communities, groups and individuals with whom they worked. Much of this work was integrated with the direct, practical work and overlapped with MESMAC's ongoing needs assessment, evaluation and review. This also involved finding ways for people to participate in MESMAC itself. Such participation was harder to achieve and it seems that few men wanted this involvement, preferring to volunteer for direct work on HIV prevention or become involved in running a specific group. The workers were successful in finding ways to enable men to facilitate and run the groups they set up, and indeed several of these groups went on to become independent. MESMAC also found ways to enable men to participate in other organisations through lobbying, advisory work or attending networks.

By working collectively, bringing together groups and networks, local community infrastructure was enhanced. People were brought together and resources shared (for example, through conferences, networks, training and joint work). In addition MESMAC projects developed new initiatives, often in conjunction with other groups. An important part of building community infrastructure involved supporting and resourcing existing groups (for example, through small grants, training, providing meeting space or resources). Because lesbian and gay groups face difficulties in attracting funding such support was often vital, as was lobbying to improve this situation. It was found that even a small input of resources or funding could have a big impact. All this work was vital in helping to build up a stronger sense of community and in expanding the range of services and support available.

In some cases MESMAC enabled the local lesbian and gay community to expand and develop. Thus some of the MESMAC projects have filled an important gap in local provision and were seen as important for MWHSWM by both other relevant workers and gay communities. The continued funding of three of the sites and the independent groups they have initiated should mean that they will continue to be an important resource in their locality.

The CD strategy funnelled the fruits of grassroots work, participation and community building into organisational development. Workers were encouraged and validated in the process of representing the needs of MWHSWM around HIV and other health issues on the agendas of other organisations, especially those in the statutory sector. Therefore, as well as working directly with MWHSWM, MESMAC worked with service providers and other organisations to make them more responsive to the needs of MWHSWM.

Where possible workers fed back their findings and encouraged organisations to change and develop new services. Through this lobbying process MWHSWM were facilitated in gaining access to services they had not previously used and in improving the services available. This involved such things as homophobia and heterosexism training; sexuality work in schools; policy work; raising awareness about the needs of different groups of men including black men, men with learning difficulties and deaf men; and helping to start particular new initiatives. Referrals to a wide variety of other services and organisations were also a routine part of the work of all the projects. Good relationships were formed between MESMAC and these other agencies that allowed the development of more appropriate inter-agency referrals.

Organisational work was also necessary to get the needs of MWHSWM recognised and thus to build bridges between gay community organisations and the statutory sector. Through this experience MESMAC demonstrated the importance of working at an organisational as well as a grassroots level. Engaging with other organisations enabled more lasting change and widened out the responsibility for addressing the health needs of MWHSWM to statutory and voluntary organisations, rather than overburdening existing HIV and gay organisations. Given that many MWHSWM do not identify as gay or are unwilling or uninterested in participating in gay and HIV organisations such generic work is vital (see also Bartos, 1993). It is also crucial that the needs of gay and bisexual men are validated and met by existing organisations (see also Scott, 1993), and that they receive appropriate targeted initiatives developed to meet their self-defined needs.

MESMAC has shown that organisational work can lead to the engagement and representation of MWHSWM in policy work as well as service provision. This work is vitally important. Indeed the push by others for the recognition at a policy level of the needs of gay men in relation to HIV can be seen to have had an impact in the number of new MWHSWM projects that have been set up (Scott, 1993). Although institutional and policy recognition is only one element in any campaigning and lobbying work, and ways still need to be found to put this into practice successfully and appropriately, it can provide useful political leverage (Altman, 1993:6). Indeed it is only by tackling issues at this organisational level that many of the structural changes necessary for effective grassroots work will occur.

For gay-identified men such collaboration with government agencies has clear risks. There is an understandable fear and caution around working with organisations which have neglected and pathologised gay men, and a resistance to others outside the community doing work with gay men. This tension is encapsulated in Cindy Patton's point that:

> *Identity is visibility...the condition of both community and annihilation. (1990:129)*

The fear is that by becoming more visible, and asserting the rights, needs and experiences of MWHSWM, this will lead to greater social control. There is also a fear of co-option which can dilute the agendas of communities and grassroots workers, or cause them to lose credibility amongst their own constituencies (Altman, 1988:311; King, 1993b). These fears underline the importance of building in participation mechanisms to ensure that alliance-building is continually informed by grassroots work. MESMAC shows that it is vital that workers maintain their base in grassroots work and do not become isolated from the changing needs of communities. There is therefore a challenge to workers to maintain their flexibility and responsiveness.

A further danger is that by building on existing gay communities inequalities within those communities will be reproduced and reinforced. This is particularly so in relation to race (Altman, 1988; Dada, 1990). Indeed the MESMAC workers involved in policy and planning work often found a need to highlight the need for work which specifically addressed the needs of black MWHSWM, as well as specifying the need for work with MWHSWM (including black and gay men) in generic work, e.g. youth work. This underlines the importance of maintaining an equal opportunities approach at all levels of work.

Whilst recognising the real dangers of visibility it should be remembered that there is a positive side. As Altman has pointed out increased visibility can also lead to a recognition of the legitimacy of different communities (1988:307). The experience of MESMAC suggests that there is much to be gained from engaging with the current political rhetoric of needs and rights and using this as a way to legitimise access to services and resources. As Tony Whitehead has argued, reflecting on his involvement in the HIV voluntary sector:

> *Instead of behaving like so many good little Florence Nightingales, developing our own educational and support services within the gay community, we AIDS activists should have fought for such services within the statutory sector...We have been forced to resort to a kind of gay freemasonry in order to get action on vital issues such as housing, which should be a fundamental right. (1989:107-9)*

This comment underlines the point that as well as specifically targeted and community work there is a need for gay men (and MWHSWM generally) to be seen as part of the body politic, what is referred to as 'the general population', rather than, as Simon Watney has pointed out, being seen as 'entirely disposable' (1989, 1990). Organisations have to become more accountable to those whom they are supposed to serve, which includes MWHSWM. MESMAC has shown that working with organisations to win recognition for the needs of MWHSWM can be done.

Obviously rights newly won can easily be lost. The process of legitimation and recognition can be fragile – and is related to wider political questions about the meaning of citizenship (see Watney, 1990). However, by building on gains made so far through gay community and HIV politics there is a possibility that the needs and rights of MWHSWM will be further legitimated. As Weeks has argued, there is a need to think through the relationship between professionals and various communities as a democratic, rather than inevitably a bureaucratic, relationship (1989:132).

Government agencies and organisations also take risks in trying to build alliances with communities. Successful CD work means that workers need flexibility, autonomy and resources, and organisations have to be willing to support them in these, give up some direct control and see through the consequences of opening themselves up to the needs and innovative ideas from the grassroots. This often involves challenges to the status quo which can be threatening. MESMAC shows that this process, whilst difficult and requiring patience, can lead to a strengthening of organisations (see also Scott, 1993). As a representative of NE Thames Regional Health Authority was recently quoted as saying:

> *Health authorities have to accept that working in the HIV prevention area does entail some risk. We must be prepared to support community groups which are undertaking this much needed work. (Pink Paper, 9/7/93)*

An important part of CD work involves articulating different agendas. This can prove difficult, frustrating and slow and often involves trying to balance the interests and needs coming from grassroots work with those of professionals and organisations. However, when successful such work may lead to more lasting change and achieve greater impact than simply working at a grassroots or organisational level. MESMAC experience was that such alliances can be built.

A community development approach is practical, realistic and relevant to HIV prevention work with men who have sex with men. By creating a space between the different constituencies and interests involved it can build alliances and foster collaboration. It is particularly effective at exploring the diversity and range of needs amongst MWHSWM and through combining different levels of work to meet those needs produces durable results. MESMAC has been an important initiative with many implications for future HIV prevention and its experience is an important resource. We strongly recommend that this example of innovative work should be followed and developed. As one of the users of MESMAC said to us:

'Set up more!'

# References

Aggleton, P. (1989) 'Evaluating Health Education About AIDS', in Aggleton, P. *et al* (eds), *AIDS: Social Representations, Social Practices*, Lewes: Falmer Press.

Aggleton, P. and Moody, D. (1992) 'Monitoring and Evaluating HIV/AIDS Health Education and Health Promotion', in Aggleton, P. *et al, Does It Work? Perspectives on the evaluation of HIV/AIDS health promotion*, London: Health Education Authority.

Altman, D. (1986) *AIDS and the new Puritanism*, London: Pluto Press.

Altman, D. (1988) 'Legitimation through Disaster: AIDS and the Gay Movement' in Fee, E. and Fox, D. (ed), *AIDS The Burdens of History*, London: University of California Press.

Altman, D. (1993) 'Expertise, legitimacy and the centrality of community' in Aggleton, P. *et al AIDS: facing the second decade*, London: Falmer.

Bailey, L. and Calder, J. (eds) (1990) *Baseline Review of Community Development and Health Education (CDH)*, Milton Keynes: Open University, commissioned by the Health Education Authority.

Baker, J. and Craig, M. (1990) 'Management Committees as One Model of Local Accountability: the lessons we can learn from our experience.' Milton Keynes: Open University: Paper given to 'Roots and Branches: a Winter School on Community Development and Health', March 1990 (mimeo).

Bardill, P. (1993) 'Developing HIV prevention work with Black and minority ethnic communities-issues for DHPCs as purchasers', in *Healthy alliances in HIV prevention*, Evans, E., Sandberg, S. and Watson, S., (eds) London: Health Education Authority.

Bartos, M. (1993) *Community Versus Population: The Case of Men Who Have Sex With Men*, Paper given at the Seventh Conference on Social Aspects of AIDS, London.

Bartos, M., McLeod, J. and Nott, P. (1993) *Meanings of sex between men*. No place of publication: a study conducted by the Australian Federation of AIDS Organisations for the Commonwealth Department of Health, Housing, Local Government and Community Services.

Beattie, A. (1991) 'Knowledge and Control in Health Promotion: a test case for social policy and social theory', in Gabe, J. *et al, The Sociology of the Health Service*, London: Routledge.

Bell, C. and Newby, H. (1971) *Community Studies*, London: Allen and Unwin.

Berridge, V. (1992) 'AIDS: History and Contemporary History' in Herdt, G. and Lindenbaum, S. (eds), *The Time of AIDS: Social Analysis, Theory and Method*, London: Sage.

Boulton, M. and Weatherburn, P. (1990) *Literature Review on Bisexuality and HIV Transmission*, London: Academic Department of Public Health, St. Mary's Medical School (mimeo).

Brah, A. (1992) 'Difference, Diversity and Differentiation', in Donald, J. and Rattansi, A. (eds), *'Race', Culture and Difference*, London: Sage.

Brake, M. (1976) 'I May Be a Queer, But At Least I am a Man: Male hegemony and ascribed versus achieved gender', in Barker, D. and Allen, S. (eds), *Sexual Divisions and Society: Process and Change*, London: Tavistock.

British Market Research Bureau Ltd. (1992) *Gay Pubs and Clubs 1992: Report on a quantitative Survey*, London: BMRB (mimeo).

Broadhead, R. and Fox, K. (1990) 'Takin' it to the streets. AIDS outreach as ethnography', Journal of Contemporary Ethnography, 19, 3:322-48.

Burgess, R.G. (1984) *In the Field: An Introduction to Field Research*, London: George Allen and Unwin.

Carter, E. and Watney, S. (eds) (1989) *Taking Liberties AIDS and Cultural Politics*, London: Serpent's Tail.

Cohen, A. (1985) *The symbolic construction of community*, London: Routledge.

Connell, R.W. *et al* (1991) 'Social Class, Gay Men and AIDS Prevention', *Australian J. of Public Health*, 15, 3: 178-89.

Crawford, R. (1977) 'You are dangerous to your health: the ideology and politics of victim-blaming', *International Journal of Health Services*, 7: 663-80.

Cruikshank, J. (1989) 'Burnout: an Issue among Canadian Community Development Workers', *Community Development Journal*, 24, 1: 40-54.

Dada, M. (1990) 'Race and the AIDS agenda', in Boffin, T. and Gupta, S. (eds), *Ecstatic Antibodies: revisiting the AIDS mythology*, London: Rivers Oram Press.

Davies, P.M. (1990) *Some Problems in Defining and Sampling Non-heterosexual Males*, Project SIGMA Working Paper No. 3., London: South Bank Polytechnic.

Davies, P. (1992) 'Men Who Have Sex with Men', in Curtis, H. (ed), *Promoting Sexual Health*, London: British Medical Association Foundation for AIDS.

Davis, M.D., Klemmer, U. and Dowsett, G.W. (1991) *Bisexually Active Men and Beats: Theoretical and Educational Implications*, Sydney: AIDS Council for New South Wales and Macquarie University AIDS Research Unit.

D'Emilio, J. (1983) *Sexual Politics, Sexual Communities*, Chicago: University of Chicago Press.

Deverell, K. (1992) *Outreach Work in Saunas: The Experience of Leicester Black MESMAC*, MESMAC Evaluation Working Paper No. 4, Keele University: Department of Sociology and Social Anthropology (mimeo).

Deverell, K. (1993a) 'Using Participant Observation in Sauna Outreach', *Practicing Anthropology*, Fall, 1993.

Deverell, K. (1993b) *Out of Bounds – Constructing sexual boundaries at work*, Paper presented at ASA Conference July 1993, Keele University: Department of Sociology and Social Anthropology (mimeo).

Deverell, K. and Bell, J. (1993) *Some thoughts on being straight women in a men who have sex with men project*, Keele University: Department of Sociology and Social Anthropology (mimeo).

Deverell, K. and Doyle, T. (1992) *MESMAC Leeds: An Evaluation of the Establishment of a Lesbian and Gay Theatre Group*, MESMAC Evaluation Working Paper No. 6, Keele University: Department of Sociology and Social Anthropology (mimeo).

Deverell, K. and Prout, A. (1992a) *MESMAC Tyneside: Working with Men on a Housing Estate*, MESMAC Evaluation Working Paper No. 1, Keele University: Department of Sociology and Social Anthropology (mimeo).

Deverell, K. and Prout, A. (1992b) *Using a Questionnaire to Start Work on the Scene: The Experience of Leeds MESMAC*, MESMAC Evaluation Working Paper No. 2, Keele University: Department of Sociology and Social Anthropology (mimeo).

Deverell, K. with Prout, A. (1992c) *Community Development with Youth Groups: Some Practical Lessons from London MESMAC*, MESMAC Evaluation Working Paper No. 3, Keele University: Department of Sociology and Social Anthropology (mimeo).

Deverell, K. and Taylor, J. (forthcoming), *An Evaluation Of A Young Gay Men's Peer Education Initiative*, MESMAC Evaluation Working Paper No. 7, Keele University: Department of Sociology and Social Anthropology (mimeo).

Douglas, M. (1970) *Purity and Danger: an Analysis of Concepts of Pollution and Taboo*, Harmondsworth: Penguin.

Eades, S. (1993) *An Evaluation of the Love Safe, Live Sexy Campaign*, Leeds: Leeds MESMAC (mimeo).

Engel, E. (1978) 'Health Education in Schools: a philosophical dilemma', *Health Education Journal*, 37: 231-3.

Evans, B. *et al* (1993) *Healthy Alliances in HIV Prevention*, London: Health Education Authority.

Feek, W. (1988) *Working Effectively*, London: Bedford Square Press (with the National Council for Voluntary Organisations).

Finch, J. (1986) 'Community Care and the Invisible Welfare State', *Radical Community Medicine*, Summer: 15-22.

Fitzpatrick, R., Boulton, M. and Hart, G. (1989) 'Gay Men's Sexual Behaviour in Response to AIDS – Insights and Problems', in Aggleton, P., Hart, G., and Davies, P. (eds), *AIDS: Social Representations, Social Practices*, London: Falmer Press.

French, J. and Adams, L. (1986) From Analysis to Synthesis Theories of Health Education, *Health Education Journal*, 1986, 45, 2.

Fullan, M. (1982) *The Meaning of Educational Change*, New York: Teachers College Press.

Gatherer, A. *et al* (1979) *Is Health Education Effective?* London: Health Education Council Monograph Number Two.

Gatter, P. (1991) *On Neutral Ground? The culture of HIV/AIDS voluntary organisations in London*, London: South Bank Polytechnic (mimeo).

Gatter, P. (1993) 'Anthropology and the culture of HIV/AIDS voluntary organisations' in Aggleton, P. *et al AIDS: facing the second decade*, London: Falmer.

Gay Men Tyneside (1993) *Report On Questionnaire: November 1992*, Newcastle Upon Tyne (mimeo).

George, S. *et al* (forthcoming) *Bisexuality and HIV prevention: A report on an initial assessment of the needs of and provision for bisexual people with regard to HIV prevention*, London: Health Education Authority (mimeo).

Gordon, P. (1988) *Safer Sex Workshops for Gay and Bisexual Men: a Review*, London: Health Education Authority (mimeo).

Green, J. and Chapman, A. (1992) 'The British Community Development Project – Lessons for Today' *Community Development Journal*, 27, 3: 242-258.

Hamilton, D. *et al* (eds) (1977) *Beyond the Numbers Game: A Reader in Educational Evaluation*, London: MacMillan.

Hammersley, M. and Atkinson, P. (1983) *Ethnography: Principles in Practice*, London: Tavistock.

Harris, E. M. (1992) 'Accessing Community Development Research Methodologies', *Canadian Journal of Public Health*, 83, 51: 62-66.

Hartnoll, R. *et al* (1990) *A Survey of HIV Outreach Intervention in the United Kingdom*, London: Birkbeck College Drug Indicators Project (mimeo).

Health Education Authority (1988) *AIDS Division Statement of Objectives*, London: Health Education Authority.

Henderson, S. (1990) *Women, HIV, Drugs: Practical Issues*, London: Institute for the Study of Drug Dependence.

Henriksson, B. and Mansson (1992) 'Sexual negotiations, An Ethnographical study of men who have sex with men', Paper given at AIDS and Anthropology Group, Culture, Sex behaviour and AIDS, Amsterdam.

Hickson, F. (undated) *Gay Men As Victims Of Non-Consensual Sex*, Project SIGMA Working Paper, 34. London, Project SIGMA (mimeo).

Homans, H. and Aggleton, P. (1988) 'Health Education, HIV Infection and AIDS', in Aggleton, P. and Homans, H. (eds), *Social Aspects of AIDS*, London: Falmer Press.

Hopkins, D. (1989) *Evaluation for School Development*, Milton Keynes: Open University Press.

Jarman, D. (1992) *At Your Own Risk, A Saint's Testament*, London: Vintage.

Johnson, T. (1972) *Professions and Power*, London: Macmillan.

King, E., Rooney, M. and Scott, P. (1992) *HIV Prevention for Gay Men: A survey of Initiatives in the UK*, London: North West Thames Regional Health Authority.

King, E. (1993a) *Safety in numbers: safer sex and gay men*, London: Cassell.

King, E. (1993b) 'Stop AIDS London!' *The Pink Paper*, 14th March, 1993 London: Gay Community Press Ltd.

Kippax, S. *et al* (1990) *The Importance of Gay Community in the Prevention of HIV Transmission*, Social Aspects of the Prevention of AIDS Study A, Report No. 7, Sydney: Macquarie University.

Kjeldsen, M. (1991) *Streetwise Youth Report*, London: Streetwise Youth Project.

Kotarba, J. and Lang, N. (1986) 'Gay Lifestyle Change and AIDS: Preventative Health Care', in Feldman, D. and Johnson, T. (eds), *The Social Dimensions of AIDS*, London: Praeger.

Lees, R. and Smith, G. (1975) *Action-research in Community Development*, London: Routledge and Kegan Paul.

Lishman, J. (ed) (1984) *Evaluation: Research Highlights in Social Work 8*, London: Jessica Kingsley.

Locker, D. (1991) 'Social Causes of Disease', in Scambler, G., *Sociology as Applied to Medicine*, London: Bailliiere Tindall.

Manuel, P., Fani-Koyode, R. and Gupta, S. (1989) 'Imaging Black Sexuality', in Reeves, M. and Hammond, J. (eds), *Looking Beyond the Frame: Racism, Representation and Resistance*, Links 34, Oxford: Third World First.

Martin, R. (1990) *Definitions of Community Work*, London: Federation of Community Work Training Groups.

MacDonald, B. and Walker, R. (1976) *Changing the Curriculum*, London: Open Books.

McCormick, R. *et al* (eds), (1982) *Calling Education to Account*, Milton Keynes: Open University Press.

McKevitt, C. (1993) *Solidarity, empowerment, AIDS and anthropology*, Paper given at BASAP Conference on Anthropology and HIV, London: Health and Education Research Unit, Institute of Education (mimeo).

McKevitt, C. and Warwick, I. (1993) *Health Education Authority Men Who Have Sex with Men Project: Examples of Good Practice in HIV/AIDS Health Promotion. Interim Report*, London, Department of Policy Studies, Institute of Education, (mimeo).

McMullen, R. (1990) *Male Rape: Breaking the Silence on the Last Taboo*, London: Gay Men's Press.

McNaught, A. (1988) *Race and Health Policy*. London: Croom Helm.

MESMAC (1990) *First Report*, London: Health Education Authority.

MESMAC (1991) *Second Report*, London: Health Education Authority.

MESMAC (1992) *Third Report*, London: Health Education Authority.

MESMAC Tyneside (1993) *Annual Report 1992/3*, Newcastle-upon-Tyne: MESMAC Tyneside (mimeo).

Miller, D. (1991) 'Workshop on support and referral', in Aggleton, P. et al, *Outreach work with men who have sex with men*, Bristol: Southmead Health Authority.

Miller, D. (1991a) 'Report on the Kielder Forest Weekend', Newcastle-upon-Tyne: MESMAC Tyneside.

Miller, D. (ed) (1993) *MESMAC DIY Guide, A Practical Guide to Community-Based HIV Prevention With Men Who Have Sex With Men*, London: Health Education Authority.

Miller, D. (ed) (1993a) *A Report on the Distribution of Free Condoms and Lubricant in Gay Bars in Newcastle-upon-Tyne*, Newcastle-upon-Tyne: MESMAC Tyneside (mimeo).

Murray, S. (1992) 'Components of Gay Community in San Francisco', in Herdt, G. (ed), *Gay Culture in America: Essays from the Field*, Boston: Beacon Press.

Newcastle District Health Authority and Newcastle City Council (1992) *HIV Prevention: a Joint Strategy for Newcastle*, Newcastle: NDHA and NCC.

O'Brien, R. (1993) in *Health Chief Wavers over 'Obscene Card'*, The Pink Paper, 9 July 1993, 285, 3, London: Gay Community Press Ltd.

Patton, C. (1985) *Sex and Germs – The Politics of AIDS*, Boston: South End Press.

Patton, C. (1990) *Inventing Aids*, London: Routledge.

Peterson, J.L. (1992) 'Black Men and their Same-Sex Desires and Behaviors', in Herdt, G. *Gay Culture in America: Essays from the Field*, Boston: Beacon Press.

Plummer, K. (1975) *Sexual Stigma: An Interactive Account*, London: Routledge and Kegan Paul.

Plummer, K. (1988) 'Organizing AIDS', in Aggleton, P. and Homans, H. (eds), *Social Aspects Of AIDS*, London: Falmer Press.

Prestage, G. and Hood, D. (1993) *Targeting Non-Gay Attached Men Who Have Sex With Men: New*

*Data, Outreach and Cultural Issues*, Paper given at the Seventh Social Aspects of AIDS Conference, London.

Prior, L. (1989) 'Evaluation Research and Quality Assurance', in Gubrium, J.F. and Silverman, D. (eds), *The Politics of Field Research: Sociology Beyond Enlightenment*, London: Sage.

Prout, A. (1992) 'Illumination, Collaboration, Facilitation, Negotiation: Evaluating the MESMAC Project', in Aggleton, P. *et al*, *Does It Work? Perspectives on the evaluation of HIV/AIDS health promotion*, London: Health Education Authority.

Prout, A. and Deverell, K. (1992) *The Impact of the MESMAC project: an Interim Review*, MESMAC Evaluation Working Paper No. 5, Keele University: Department of Sociology and Social Anthropology (mimeo).

Quadland, M. et al (1987) 'The 800 Men Study: A systematic evaluation of AIDS prevention programs', New York: GMHC Inc.

Rhodes, T., Holland, J. and Hartnoll, R. (1991) *Hard to Reach or Out of Reach? An Evaluation of an Innovative Model of HIV Outreach Health Education*, London: Tuffnell Press.

Rhodes, T. *et al* (1991a) *Out of the Agency and on to the Streets: A Review of HIV Outreach Education in Europe and the United States*, London: Institute for the Study of Drug Dependence (mimeo).

Rodden, P., Kippax, S. and Crawford, J. (1993) 'Project Male-Call: Class Differences in Sexual Partners', London: Paper given to the Seventh Conference of Social Aspects of AIDS, Southbank University, July, 1993.

Rooney, M. and Scott, P. (1992) *Working Where the Risks Are: Health Promotion Interventions for Gay Men and other Men Who Have Sex with Men in the Second Decade of the HIV Epidemic*, London: Health Education Authority (mimeo).

Rossi, P.H. *et al* (1979) *Evaluation: a Systematic Account*, Beverly Hills: Sage.

Rutherford, J. 'A Place Called Home: Identity and the Cultural Politics of Difference', in Rutherford, J. (ed), *Identity Community, Culture, Difference*, London: Lawrence and Wishart.

Scott, P. (1993) 'Beginning HIV Prevention Work with Gay and Bisexual Men' in *Healthy alliances in HIV prevention*, Evans, B., Sandberg, S. and Watson, S. (eds), London: Health Education Authority.

Shaffir, W. and Stebbins, R. (eds) (1991) *Experiencing Fieldwork, An inside View of Qualitative Research*, London: Sage.

Sheffield Health Authority (1992) *Community Development Strategy*, Sheffield: Healthy Sheffield Support Team.

Sheffield Health Authority (1993) *Community Deveopment and Health: The Way Forward in Sheffield*, Sheffield: Healthy Sheffield Support Team.

Siegal, K. and Bauman, L. (1986) 'Methodological Issues in AIDS-Related Research', in Feldman, D. and Johnson, T. *The Social Dimensions of AIDS, Method and Theory*, London: Praeger.

Silin, J. (1987) 'The Language of AIDS: Public Fears, Pedagogical Responsibilities', Teacher's College, Record, 89, 1.

Smith, G. and Cantley, C. (1985) *Assessing Health Care*, Milton Keynes: Open University Press.

Smithies, J. (1991) *Organisation and Community Development*, Unpublished Thesis, Sheffield Business School.

Smithies, J. and Adams, L. (1990) *Community Development and Health Education*, London: Health Education Authority.

Smithies, J., Adams, L., Webster, G. and Beattie, A. (1990) *Community Participation in Health Promotion*, London: Health Education Authority.

Stake, R.E. (1967) 'The Countenance of Educational Evaluation', *Teacher's College Record*, 68, 523-44.

Stenhouse, L. (1975) *An Introduction to Curriculum Research and Development*, London: Heinemann.

Stufflebeam, D.L. (1985) 'Stufflebeam's Improvement Oriented Evaluation', in Stufflebeam, D.L. and Shinkfield, A.J. *Systematic Evaluation: A Self-instructional Guide to Theory and Practice*, Dordrecht: Kluwer-Nijhoff.

Taylor, J., Eisenstadt, K. and Spyrou, S. (1993) *London MESMAC Small Grants Scheme, Self Evaluation Report*, London (mimeo).

Thakar, K. (1991) *Leicester Black Communities HIV/AIDS Research Project Report*, Leicester: Black HIV/AIDS Forum.

Townsend, P. and Davidson, N. (1982) *Inequalities in Health*, Harmondsworth: Penguin.

Van Duifhuizen, R. (1992) 'Minority Ethnic People' in Curtis, H. (ed), *Promoting Sexual Health*, London: British Medical Association.

Van Reyk, P. (1990) *On The Beat: A Report On An Outreach Program Of AIDS Preventative Education For Men Who Have Sex With Men*, Darlinghurst: AIDS Council of New South Wales.

Watney, S. (1987) 'People's perceptions of the risk of AIDS and the role of the mass media', *Health Education Journal*, 46, 2:62-5.

Watney, S. (1988) 'Visual AIDS – Advertising Ignorance' in Aggleton, P. and Homans, H. (eds), *Social Aspects of AIDS*, London: Falmer Press.

Watney, S. (1989) 'Taking Liberties: An Introduction', in Carter, E. and Watney, S. (eds), *Taking Liberties, AIDS and Cultural Politics*, London: Serpent's Tail.

Watney, S. (1990) 'Practices of Freedom: 'Citizenship' and the Politics of Identity in the Age of AIDS', in Rutherford, J. (ed), *Identity, Community, Culture, Difference*, London: Lawrence and Wishart.

Watney, S. (1993) 'Emergent sexual identities and HIV/AIDS' in Aggleton, P. *et al*, *AIDS: facing the second decade*, London: Falmer.

Weatherburn, P. *et al* (1992) *The Sexual Lifestyles of Gay and Bisexual Men in England and Wales*, London: Department of Health.

Webster, G. (1989) 'Community Development and Health Promotion – Links between Theory and Practice', London: Paper for the Public Health Alliance Symposium on 'Health for Who?', December, 1989.

Webster, G. and Smithies, J. (1991) *A Community Development Strategy*, part of work for Healthy Sheffield Community Action Plan, Sheffield: Healthy Sheffield 2000, Community Development Strategy.

Weeks, J. (1986) *Sexuality*, London: Tavistock.

Weeks, J. (1989) 'AIDS, Altruism, and the New Right', in Carter, E. and Watney, S, *Taking Liberties AIDS and Cultural Politics*, London: Serpent's Tail.

Weeks, J. (1990) 'The Value of Difference', in Rutherford, J. (ed), *Identity Community, Culture, Difference*, London: Lawrence and Wisehart.

Whitehead, T. (1988) 'Prostitutes, HIV and oral sex', Capital Gay, 366, 28th October.

Whitehead, T. (1989) 'The Voluntary Sector: Five Years On', in Carter, E. and Watney, S. (eds), *Taking Liberties AIDS and Cultural Politics*, London: Serpent's Tail.

Wiseman, T. (1989) 'Marginalised Groups and Health Education', in Aggleton, P., Hart, G. and Davies, P. (eds), *AIDS: Social Representations, Social Practices*, London: Falmer Press.

# Appendix 1: MESMAC project members

| | |
|---|---|
| Lee Adams | (Co-ordinator) |
| Paul Bagnall | (MESMAC Tyneside Project Manager) |
| Anthony Bains | (Leeds MESMAC Project Worker) |
| Pat Bardill | (Co-ordinator) |
| Chris Barrett | (MESMAC Tyneside Project Worker) |
| James Barrett | (PAG Member) |
| Simon Bartlett | (MESMAC Tyneside Project Worker) |
| Jan Bell | (MESMAC Tyneside Administrator) |
| Ismail Bingor | (MESMAC London Project Worker) |
| Derek Bodell | (HEA Officer) |
| Guy Brain | (PAG Member) |
| David Burkle | (PAG Member) |
| Ajay Chotai | (Leicester MESMAC Project Worker) |
| Elsie Cresswell | (MESMAC Administrator) |
| Katie Deverell | (Evaluation Fieldworker) |
| Tom Doyle | (Leeds MESMAC Project Worker, Organiser) |
| Kevin Eisenstadt | (London MESMAC Project Worker) |
| Julian Faisal | (London MESMAC Project Worker) |
| Ray Gaston | (Leeds MESMAC Project Manager) |
| Clint George | (Leicester MESMAC Project Worker) |
| Peter Gordon | (Co-ordinator) |
| Anthony Hillin | (Consultant to London MESMAC) |
| Monica Hingorani | (PAG Member) |
| Terry Joe | (London MESMAC Project Worker) |
| Frankie Lynch | (London MESMAC Project Manager) |
| Mark Maguire | (PAG Member) |
| Mary Mantell | (PAG Member) |
| Irene McArdle | (MESMAC Administrator) |
| David Miller | (MESMAC Tyneside Project Worker) |
| Shaun O'Leary | (Leeds MESMAC Project Organiser) |
| Ayo Oyebade | (Black Sub-group Member) |

| | |
|---|---|
| Nagina Parwez | (Leicester MESMAC Administrator) |
| Patrick Price | (MESMAC Tyneside Worker) |
| Alan Prout | (Evaluator) |
| Sukhjinder Sandhu | (Leicester MESMAC Worker) |
| Jef Sawyerr | (PAG and Black Sub-group Member) |
| Hazel Slavin | (Co-ordinator) |
| Tyrone Smith | (Leicester MESMAC Worker, then Manager) |
| Kyriacos Spyrou | (London MESMAC Worker) |
| Hong Tan | (London consultant, PAG and BSG Member) |
| Jamie Taylor | (London MESMAC Administrator) |
| Karun Thakar | (Leicester MESMAC Manager, Consultant) |
| Matthew Toresen | (Leeds MESMAC Worker) |
| Warren Weisner | (PAG Member) |
| David Wiseman | (HEA Officer) |
| Denise Worme | (Black Sub-group Member) |

(This list does not contain steering group members, or those who were only involved in the project for a very short time.)

# Appendix 2: Participants in first planning forums

## Forum participants

Lee Adams
Phil Bain
Colin Bell
Marc Brittain
David Burkle
Graham Calvert
Len Clarke
David Critchard
Dominic Davies
Alistair Gault
Peter Gordon
Paul Heritage
Anthony Hillin

Keith Houghton
George Leach
Nigel Leach
Frankie Lynch
Will Mallinson
Mark McGuire
Alan Prout
Mike Rhodes
Hazel Slavin
Jan Smithies
Warren Weisner
David Wiseman

## Black and ethnic minority forum participants

Barrie Brandon
Norman Goldner
Arnold Gordon
Frankie Lynch
Anthony Kwok
James Monteith

Vernal Scott
Tyrone Smith
Jan Smithies
Hong Tan
Karun Thakar
Dave Wiseman

# Appendix 3: The data-set at the end of the project

This book is based on the following data.

## Site visits

We made the following number of visits to each site:

Leeds – 13
London – 28
Leicester – 14
Newcastle – 13

Usually site visits were for one whole day. In the case of Newcastle long travelling distances meant visits usually lasted two days. There were more visits to London as meetings were usually shorter because part-time workers could only attend meetings in the evening. There were also more meetings with specific workers to talk about their particular areas of work. In London more of the co-ordination of the evaluation was done by the project administrator.

Usually the site visits were taken up by extensive interviews with project members and gathering project records and documents. On some occasions they involved planning specific evaluation activities with the project members: three meetings in Leicester; five in London; three in Leeds; one in Newcastle. Much additional work was done over the phone.

We also had meetings with HEA officers and the co-ordinators to discuss aspects of the work: seven with the HEA and six with the co-ordinators.

## Formal interviews

Excluding informal conversations (which were countless) we conducted:

4 with HEA officers
6 with co-ordinators
2 with black sub-group members
7 with managers
1 with PAG member
1 with steering group member
13 with Newcastle project workers

11 with Leicester project workers
12 with London project workers
10 with Leeds project workers

## Documents

Where possible we collected full sets of the following:

- minutes of the PAG and PNMs
- MESMAC reports
- site reports

We had copies of many of the local projects' own records. These included:

- minutes of project steering groups
- 91 impact review sheets
- phone logs
- monitoring forms
- evaluation sheets
- workers' notes and reports
- interviews carried out by project workers
- project reviews and plans
- project diaries
- transcripts of debriefing sessions
- plans for particular activities
- small grant application forms
- questionnaire results
- self-evaluation and other project evaluation reports

## Participant observation

We did participant observation and kept fieldwork notes at:

- 9 training weekends
- 6 co-ordinators meetings

- 10 local project steering groups
- 7 project advisory group meetings
- 4 project network meetings
- 1 volunteer briefing session

## Evaluation material from clients/users

This included:

- 7 group interviews
- 640 questionnaires and evaluation sheets

Other important material included: MESMAC-initiated groups' own documentation and evaluation records (questionnaires; evaluation sheets; terms of reference, minutes and a theatre group script).

## Miscellaneous

This included:

- copies of MESMAC leaflets and posters
- examples of MESMAC materials (such as condom packs, mugs, T-shirts and a learning difficulties resource pack)
- local project briefing papers
- newspaper reviews and articles about MESMAC events

# Appendix 4: Self-evaluation guidelines

This involves asking questions about:

- why you are evaluating
- what you want to evaluate
- how you are going to do it
- who is going to take on which tasks

The following questions may help to focus your thoughts.

## 1. What are the goals of the evaluation?

What is the primary purpose? In the self-evaluation approach, *improving* or *developing* work is the starting point. The goal of self-evaluation is to review work systematically and make judgements about whether the aimed for improvements and developments have been achieved. This is done by planning the collection of information on work (monitoring) and identifying the criteria of success.

There may be secondary goals.

## 2. What is the focus of the evaluation?

What particular aspects of the work are to be evaluated?

You might think about context, process and outcomes. Remain vigilant for unintended outcomes.

## 3. What methods of evaluation will be used?

What information is needed to decide how successful the work has been? Do you need to review criteria of success?

What information already exists or is already collected?

What information needs to be specially collected?

How will you collect it? (Project diaries? Evaluation sheets? Questionnaires? Debriefings? Minutes of meetings? Observation? Interviews? etc.)

How will you record the information?

## 4. What criteria will you use?

How will judgements about the work be made?

How will you review whether your criteria are realistic?

How will you recognise and value unintended outcomes of the work?

## 5. How will you organise the evaluation?

Who will do what? How will the evaluation work be divided up?

Who is good at what? Who wants to develop new skills and/or knowledge?

What resources are needed?

What support is needed? Who will provide it?

Who will moderate the evaluation (i.e. give an 'outsider's' view)?

## 6. How will you apply what is learnt through the evaluation?

How will you feed back the evaluation into decision-making?

When are your reviews and planning sessions?

## 7. How will you disseminate the results of the evaluation?

Who are the findings for? Who will see them? Are there different audiences?

How will you write up the findings?

# Appendix 5: Example of a MESMAC group contract

## Contract between Leeds MESMAC and Fit Together

1. This is a contract between Leeds Mesmac Project and Fit Together, Gay's Men's Health Group.

2. For the purpose of this contract, the Leeds Mesmac Project will be known as the Project.

3. For the purpose of this contract, Fit Together will be known as the Group.

4. The Project will supply the Group with seeding money of £5,000 less any costs already incurred.

5. Seeding money is a one-off payment used for maintenance and development of the Group. Any further monies the Group may require from the Project will be subject to a grant-giving process at present being developed by the Project.

6. The Project has no control over the activities and educational campaigns of the Group, though the Project reserves the right to correct any misinformation about HIV transmission.

7. The seeding money is granted on the understanding that the Group works in a non-oppressive and anti-discriminatory way, and abides by its agreed philosophy stated on the 30th June 1992. The Project reserves the right to review its financial support if the philosophy of the Group changes.

8. In the event of the Group ceasing to exist, all remaining money will be returned to the Project or its nominated organisation.

9. The nominated organisation is the Health Education Authority.

10. The Group will keep proper and correct financial records at all times and will provide the Project with a detailed breakdown of how the monies have been spent within fourteen days of a request being made.

Signed.................................................
On behalf of MESMAC

Date.................................................

Signed.................................................
On behalf of Fit Together

Date.................................................